Annotated Teacher's Edition
Laboratory Manual A

Prentice Hall

Biology

PEARSON
Prentice
Hall

Upper Saddle River, New Jersey
Boston, Massachusetts

CONTENTS

Pearson Prentice Hall™ is a trademark of Pearson Education, Inc.
Pearson® is a registered trademark of Pearson plc.
Prentice Hall® is a registered trademark of Pearson Education, Inc.

ISBN 0-13-115295-5

9 10 11 12 13 14 15 16   11 10 09 08 07

Introduction to the Teacher

Biology is an exciting area of study for the high school student. And many recent developments that have been extensively reported in the news media—the cloning of animals, AIDS epidemic, and genetic fingerprinting, to name a few—have made biology perhaps even more exciting and relevant today than ever before.

Laboratory Manual A is designed to capture the excitement of biology through a variety of interesting and informative activities. In addition to reinforcing key concepts and scientific terms, these activities help students understand and appreciate the processes involved in scientific experimentation.

Laboratory Manual A contains 40 Laboratory Investigations directly related to the information presented in Prentice Hall *Biology* by Miller and Levine. It also contains 8 Laboratory Skills activities that give students an opportunity to practice and master specific laboratory skills, which include making metric measurements, applying the scientific method, using a microscope, and using graphing skills. *Laboratory Manual A* is intended for the use of average and above-average students. *Laboratory Manual B* is meant for use by less-able students.

This Annotated Teacher's Edition provides the information you will need to perform the investigations and activities with your students. It includes answers to all investigations and activities, guidelines for laboratory safety and the use of animals in the classroom, comprehensive lists of laboratory equipment and materials, notes on the care and maintenance of live organisms, instructions on the preparation of specific chemical solutions, and a number of annotations that will help you organize and stock your biology laboratory and facilitate your teaching.

Laboratory Investigation Format

The investigations and activities in *Laboratory Manual A* are designed to strengthen students' laboratory, critical thinking, and science process skills and to provide a practical application of material presented in the student textbook. The easy-to-follow format of each Laboratory Investigation allows students to complete the investigations on their own, perhaps after an overview and brief explanation from you. This gives you an opportunity to provide the necessary help to those individuals or groups of students who require teacher assistance.

Each Laboratory Investigation has the following format:

Title A brief title presents the topic explored in the investigation. To the right of the title are teacher annotations regarding the time required for the investigation and the textbook pages in Prentice Hall *Biology* by Miller and Levine that correspond to the laboratory investigation.

Introduction The Introduction provides background information that the student will need to complete the investigation, develops relevant concepts, or relates the Laboratory Investigation to specific concepts discussed in the student textbook. In a few cases, this section may also provide new concepts and terms specific to the investigation.

Problem Each Laboratory Investigation challenges the student by introducing a problem in the form of a question or series of questions. Students should be able to solve the problem(s) upon successful completion of the Laboratory Investigation.

Pre-Lab Discussion Asking them to identify the role of certain materials or the reasons for specific steps in the Procedure, questions in this section prepare students for the active understanding needed to take full advantage of the Laboratory Investigation. Questions in this section may also highlight safety procedures to which students should pay careful attention.

Materials This section lists all materials required to conduct the investigation. The quantity of material for each investigation is indicated for individual students, pairs of students, or groups of students. Teacher annotations on how to prepare materials specific to the investigation are found in or near the Materials section. The necessary equipment and materials for all of the Laboratory Investigations are listed alphabetically and by category on pages T8 to T16.

Safety If a Laboratory Investigation requires specific safety precautions, students are alerted to that fact in the special Safety section as well as in the Procedure. The Safety section is intended to make students aware of potential hazards before the investigation is begun, thereby decreasing the risk of accidents.

Procedure This section provides a detailed step-by-step outline of the Laboratory Investigation procedure. Diagrams are included where necessary to further explain a technique or illustrate an experimental setup.

The Procedure contains a number of symbols and instructions that guide students as the lab is performed. Safety symbols, which appear next to certain steps in the Procedure, signal students to begin following specific safety precautions for an indicated step in the procedure and all following steps. **CAUTION** statements within the steps of the

Procedure warn students of possible hazards and indicate how accidents can be avoided. **Notes** in the Procedure direct students' attention to special directions or techniques. At the end of some steps in the Procedure, students may be instructed to record data or answer questions.

In keeping with the traditional scientific method, observations are recorded in each investigation. Observations are often recorded by filling in data tables, graphing data, labeling diagrams, and drawing observed structures, as well as answering general questions.

In the Annotated Teacher's Edition, annotations to the questions in Procedure and Analysis and Conclusions are printed in red on the pages corresponding to the student pages. These annotations include answers to objective questions, sample drawings and diagrams, and anticipated student data when these can be predicted.

Analysis and Conclusions Questions in this section are designed to assist students in answering the investigation's Problem, relating the investigation to concepts learned in the textbook, and drawing conclusions about the results of their investigation. Using data gathered during the investigation and knowledge gained from the textbook and Introduction, students are asked to analyze and interpret their experimental results. Many questions emphasize possible applications of the experiment and allow students to relate the investigation to real-life situations.

Going Further Each Laboratory Investigation concludes with a section entitled Going Further. This section suggests additional activities that may be used to enrich or supplement the investigation. The Going Further activities may also be used as alternatives to the Laboratory Investigation. Complete instructions are included so that individual students can perform the Going Further activities without additional teacher help.

Design an Experiment Labs One Laboratory Investigation in each unit (except Unit 1) asks students to develop their own experiments. In these activities, the Pre-Lab Discussion helps guide students in planning their experiments. A list of **Suggested Materials** follows. In place of a set Procedure, a section titled **Design Your Experiment** leads students through the planning and performance of their own experiments.

Modifying the Laboratory Investigations

School schedules often do not permit extended laboratory periods. *Laboratory Manual A* provides a number of options to help you circumvent the difficulties associated with having limited laboratory time. First, most investigations require only 30 to 40 minutes and thus can be completed within a single class period. Second, the investigations are often divided into two or more parts. This provides flexibility by allowing you to select the parts of the investigation that best suit your needs, objectives, and laboratory situation. In addition, you can often schedule the parts of an investigation to be performed during different class periods, as your schedule permits. Finally, a number of the investigations have annotations that suggest specific ways in which the investigation may be modified for a shorter laboratory period.

Correlation Between Textbook Chapters and Laboratory Investigations

Laboratory Manual A is designed to accompany Prentice Hall *Biology* by Miller and Levine in the presentation of a comprehensive biology program for high school students. When used in conjunction with the textbook, *Laboratory Manual A* reinforces, expands, and enhances the student's experiences of reading the textbook and participating in classroom discussions. Although the investigations are numbered to correspond to chapters in Prentice Hall *Biology*, they can be used with any high school biology program.

Guidelines for Laboratory Safety

Safety should be an integral part of the planning, preparation, and implementation of a laboratory program. Both the biology teacher and the student are responsible for creating and maintaining an enjoyable, instructional, and safe environment in the biology laboratory.

A number of general safety concerns are discussed. You should also refer to pages 7 through 11 in the Student Edition of *Laboratory Manual A* for a detailed discussion of safety rules and procedures. You may want to expand or modify the safety guidelines, procedures, and rules suggested here according to local and state government regulations and policies, as well as school regulations and policies. The school administration should be able to provide you with specifics on local safety requirements.

General Safety Considerations

Emphasis on proper safety precautions for each laboratory investigation is an essential part of any pre-laboratory discussion. Prior to each investigation, demonstrate the proper use of the required equipment. Demonstrate any potentially hazardous procedure used in that investigation. Always wear the required safety protective devices during the demonstrations and the investigations. If students are required to wear safety goggles, you and any visitors to the class must also wear them.

During an investigation, move about the laboratory to keep constant watch for potentially dangerous situations. Behavior that is inappropriate to a laboratory situation should be curtailed immediately. Wild play and practical jokes are forbidden in the laboratory. Once students realize that the practice of safety is a required part of the course, they will accept a serious approach to laboratory work.

Any laboratory investigation a student performs should have your prior approval. Students should never work in the laboratory without adult supervision. At the conclusion of the lab investigation, cleanup should follow authorized guidelines for waste disposal. The laboratory should be restored to a safe condition for the next class.

Classroom Organization

Furniture and equipment in the laboratory should be arranged to minimize accidents. Assign students to laboratory stations. Each station should be equipped with a flat-topped table and laboratory bench. Do not use desks with slanted tops. Provide several locations where students can obtain needed supplies. Control traffic flow in the room to prevent collisions between students who are carrying or handling equipment. Tell students to leave their personal property in a designated location, away from the laboratory stations. Do not use the floor and benches for storage area. Stress that good housekeeping is important in maintaining safe laboratory conditions. Students should keep all laboratory work areas clean. Unnecessary papers, books, and equipment should be removed from working areas.

Be sure that water faucets, hot plates, gas outlets, and alcohol or Bunsen burners are turned off when not in use.

Safety Equipment

Any classroom where laboratory investigations are done should contain at least one each of the following pieces of safety equipment: (1) fire extinguisher, (2) emergency blanket, (3) fire alarm, (4) phone or intercom to the office, (5) eyewash station, (6) emergency shower, (7) fume hood, and (8) first-aid kit. If any of these basic pieces of safety equipment is not available, you may need to modify your laboratory program until the situation is remedied.

Make sure students know the location and proper use of all safety equipment. Where appropriate and practical, have students handle or operate the equipment so that they become familiar with it. Make sure all safety equipment is in good working order. All malfunctions should be promptly reported in writing to the proper school or district administrator.

Fire and Emergency Equipment At the beginning of the school year, you may wish to give each student the opportunity to actually operate a fire extinguisher, as the sound and action of a CO_2 fire extinguisher can be quite alarming to those who never used one. You may also want to have students practice smothering imaginary flames on one another with the emergency blanket.

Eyewash Station The eyewash station should be used if chemicals are splashed onto the face or eyes. The exposed area should be left in the running water for 15 minutes.

Emergency Shower The shower is used when chemicals have been spilled on a student's body or clothing. The student should stand under the shower for a minimum of 15 minutes and remove contaminated clothing. Have a bathrobe or some other type of replacement clothing handy in case a student's clothing must be removed.

You may want to set up one or two spill kits in your laboratory. The contents of a spill kit are used to neutralize chemicals such as acids and bases so that they can be cleaned up more easily. Baking soda (sodium bicarbonate) can be used to neutralize acids. Vinegar (acetic acid) can be used to neutralize bases. Commercial spill kits for acids, bases, and a number of other chemicals are available from supply houses. Consult Materials Safety Data Sheets (MSDS) for instructions about first aid and proper disposal of chemicals.

Fume Hood Use a fume hood whenever students are working with volatile or noxious chemicals. Make sure that the room is well-ventilated when students are using any kind of chemicals or are working with preserved specimens. Warn students of the flammability and toxicity of various chemicals.

First-Aid Kit A typical first-aid kit contains an assortment of antiseptics, bandages, gauze pads, and scissors. Most also contain simple instructions for use. Be sure to read the instructions if you are not familiar with basic first-aid procedures. A first-aid kit should be taken on all field trips. For field trips, you may wish to add such items as a bee-sting kit, meat tenderizer, tweezers, and calamine lotion. Do not dispense medication (including aspirin).

Cleanup

Before beginning an investigation, instruct students in the proper cleanup procedures. Mark certain containers for the disposal of wastes and the collection of soiled glassware and equipment. Have students dispose of broken glassware in a separate trash container. Before the end of the laboratory period, have students unplug microscopes and other pieces of equipment and put them away in their proper location. Have students wash glassware, wipe up spills, and do whatever else is necessary to clean up their work area. At the conclusion of the laboratory investigation, the room should be restored to a clean and safe condition for the next class. You may wish to institute a policy of not dismissing the class until the laboratory area meets with your approval.

Preparations and the Storage Room

Reagents stored in the biology stockroom should be clearly labeled and stored safely. Take inventory of reagents frequently and keep up-to-date records of their use. Check local and state regulations for maximum permissable amounts of reagents allowed in school. In case of fire or vandalism, inform the authorities of possible hazards to the community. Keep all chemicals in a locked storage area that is accessible only to you or individuals under your direct supervision.

Some chemicals are incompatible and should be stored separately. Check local and state laws for regulations on storage of flammable liquids. The National Fire Protection Association recommends that flammable liquids be stored in vented, flame-resistant cabinets. Store large containers near floor level. Make sure that storage shelves have a raised lip at the front to prevent containers from sliding forward.

Hazardous Materials

Some reagents can be explosive and should not be on the premises. If found, they should be removed by trained fire or police bomb squads or by other qualified officials.

Known carcinogens and probable carcinogens have frequently been found in biology stockrooms and should be removed by health authorities or a licensed commercial company. If you have doubts about the hazards of any reagent in the stockroom, contact an appropriate agency (NIOSH or a local health agency) and read the information in the MSDS.

Known carcinogens commonly found in school science laboratories include the following:

arsenic powder	formaldehyde
arsenic trichloride	lead arsenate
arsenic pentoxide	benzene
arsenic trioxide	chromium powder
asbestos	sodium arsenate
benzidine	

Probable carcinogens include the following:

acrylonitrile	cadmium powder
cadmium chloride	cadmium sulfate
carbon tetrachloride	chloroform
ethylene oxide	nickel powder

Exercise great care in using refrigerators. Never store flammable liquids in a refrigerator unless it is explosion-proof. Do not store food where microbial cultures are stored. Clean refrigerators frequently and safely discard old material.

Laboratory Glassware

Probably the most common school laboratory accidents involve cuts from chipped or broken glassware and burns from hot glassware. Discard any glassware that has a crack or chip. Use only borosilicate glassware. Fire-polish the ends of glass tubing. Allow hot glassware to cool on a hot pad for several minutes before picking it up. Never hand hot glassware to another person. If an accident should happen, first aid for minor cuts and burns is immersion in cool running water. For cuts that are bleeding heavily, apply pressure with folded toweling or gauze. Call a health professional immediately.

To insert glass tubing into a stopper, lubricate the stopper hole and the tubing. Wrap the tubing in several layers of toweling and gently work the tubing into the stopper, using a twisting motion and keeping the hands as close together as possible. Wear heavy gloves. Remove the tubing in the same manner as soon as possible. Tubing that is stuck is nearly impossible to remove without cutting the stopper.

To avoid unwanted cultures, clean glassware frequently by using laboratory detergent. Most deposits can be removed with dilute hydrochloric acid or sodium hydroxide solution. Do not permit students to eat or drink from laboratory glassware.

Measuring small amounts of liquids with pipettes is common in investigations. But never pipette by mouth. Use rubber suction bulbs designed for use with pipettes or pipette fillers.

Safety Procedures With Microbial Cultures

Never culture pathogenic bacteria. However, treat all bacterial cultures as if they are pathogenic. Firmly seal with clear tape any bacterial plates that are used for student inspection. For sterilization, use a high-temperature gas flame rather than an alcohol burner or candle flame.

Cultures should be killed before disposal. Autoclave all cultures and contaminated glassware at 15 pounds pressure per square inch (103.4 Pa) for 20 minutes. Disposable plates should be incinerated.

Safety Procedures With Microscopes

Never use direct sunlight as a light source for the microscope. The lenses may concentrate the light and cause permanent retinal damage. With a soft cloth dipped in isopropyl alcohol, clean the eyepiece of each microscope between viewers. Make sure any electrical cords are out of the main traffic pattern of the classroom.

Safety Procedures With Dissections

Handle sharp and pointed instruments with care. Make sure the specimen is firmly secured on a dissection tray or cutting board. Caution students never to dissect a hand-held specimen. Make sure that the scalpels and scissors are sharp and adequate for the job. If razor blades are used for cutting tissues for slide mounts, use only single-edge non-injectable blades. Dissecting instruments should not be removed from the laboratory and should be stored in a locked cabinet. Inventory materials before students leave the room.

Formaldehyde has been identified as a carcinogen and mutagen. Any formaldehyde-preserved specimens in the stockroom or classroom should be removed from the school site by qualified health authorities or a licensed commercial company. Specimens are now sold in alternate preservatives. Follow the instructions on the package for preparing specimens for dissection. Most should be rinsed in running water before use. Some may need to be soaked in water overnight if the preservative is particularly strong-smelling. Specimens that have not been preserved should be used sparingly and only for a short time. Use only healthy specimens. Instruct students to wear masks and gloves to guard against infection. After dissection, specimens should be discarded in separate containers that can be transported to an incineration site.

Field Studies

Before taking the students on a field study, examine the area for possible safety hazards. Look for terrain or water hazards and poisonous plants and animals. Obtain the necessary written permission from parents and school authorities. Instruct students on proper dress and behavior. Make sure that students are thoroughly familiar with the investigations they are to conduct. If students are to form small groups, decide in advance when and where they will reassemble. Do not allow any student to travel alone.

Identify any students who have special health problems, especially allergies. Alert these students to potential hazards. Be sure they are adequately prepared to deal with emergencies.

Laboratory Skills Materials and Equipment

Note: Safety equipment has not been listed. It is recommended that a laboratory apron, safety goggles, and heat-resistant gloves be worn when required.

Item	Quantity per Group	Laboratory Investigation
Balance, triple-beam	1	3, 7
Beaker		
50-mL	1	3
100-mL	2	7
250-mL	2	6
Bunsen burner	1	6
Cloth, soft	1	5
Coin	1	3
Coverslip	1	5
Dissecting probe	1	5
Filter paper	1	7
Flint striker (or matches)	1	6
Food coloring, red	10 mL	7
Funnel	1	7
Graduated cylinder		
10-mL	1	7
100-mL	1	3, 6, 7
Iron ring	1	6, 7
Knife	1	4
Lens paper	1 package per class	5
Meter stick	1	3
Metric ruler	1	3, 6
Microscope, compound light	1	5
Newspaper	1 page per class	5
Paper towels	2	4
Pipette, dropper	1	5
Plastic bags with twist ties	2	4
Potato, medium-sized	1	4
Ring stand	1	6, 7
Rubber stopper	1	3
Safety equipment	See Laboratory Skills 1.	1
Scissors	1	5
Scoop	1	7
Slide		
microscope	1	5
prepared	1	5
Sodium chloride	5 g	7
Test tube, small	1	3
Tongs, beaker	1	6
Weighing paper (filter paper or a piece of paper towel)	1	7
Wire gauze	1	6

Laboratory Investigations Materials and Equipment

Note: Safety equipment has not been listed. A laboratory apron, safety goggles, and plastic or heat-resistant gloves should be worn when required.

Item	Quantity per Group	Laboratory Investigation
Acid		
acetic, 10%	dropper bottle	38
hydrochloric, 20%	100 mL	36
hydrochloric, 1%	dropper bottle	17
Agar, sterile nutrient agar plate	2	19
	1	40
Alcohol, ethyl, 95%	70 mL	23
Animal maze	1	34
Anole		
live	1	31
preserved	1	31
Antibiotic disks: aureomycin, chloromycetin, penicillin, streptomycin, tetracycline, terramycin	any 3	19
Apple (or potato)	1	28
Apple juice, unsweetened, 50%	20 mL	2
Bacteriophage culture, T-4	1 culture per class	40
unknown	1	40
Balance, triple-beam	1	1, 4, 7, 36
Balloon, round	1 per student	37
Beaker	1	25
50-mL	1	23
150-mL	1	1, 23
250-mL	2	1, 7, 8, 12, 36
400-mL	1	38
500-mL	2	9
600-mL	1	2
Beans		
pink (pinto)	120	16
red	60	16
white	60	16
Benedict's solution	dropper bottle	2, 38
Bird specimens or illustrations	10	15
Biuret reagent	dropper bottle	2
Blepharisma culture	1 culture per class	20
Block or other regular object	1	1
Bone, uncooked pork or beef	1	36
	2	33
Bottle, 2-L soft drink	1	24
Bowl, large shallow	1	22
Box (or large container)	1	34
Brassica rapa seeds	10	24
Bread	2 loaves per class	21
Bromthymol blue solution	25 mL	3, 8
dropper bottle	3	
Brown alga, *Fucus*	1	22
Bunsen burner	1	2, 19, 38, 40

Item	Quantity per Group	Laboratory Investigation
Butter, melted	20 mL	2
Cabbage, purple	1 per class	9
Cage, small animal	1	34
Carrot	1	23
Cheese, cheddar	2 large chunks per class	21
Cheesecloth	40 cm²	12
Chlorine bleach solution concentrated	dropper bottle	26
Clock (or watch with second hand)	1	34
Coin	3	11
Cookie sheet (or cooking tray, large metal)	1 per class	36
Corn oil	20 mL	2
Cotton ball	1	9
Cotton swabs, sterile	1	40
	2	19
Coverslip	1	22, 26, 27
	1 per student	17
	3	10
	5	20
	6	12
Culture tube with top	4	3
Didinium culture	1 culture per class	20
Direct current power source	1	13
Disinfectants: chlorine bleach, household cleaner, household disinfectant, phenol	any 3	19
Dissecting pin	1	27
	12–18	30
Dissecting probe	1	10, 27, 30
Dissecting tray	1	22, 23, 27, 30, 31
DNA samples	See Investigation	13
Egg	3 per class	2
decalcified	2	7
Escherichia coli B culture	1 culture per class	19, 40
Ethanol, 95%	30 mL	12
Euglena culture	1 culture per class	20
Evergreen sprig	4	8
Eye patch (or eye cover)	1	35
Field guide		
birds	1	15
plants, woody and nonwoody	1	5
Filter paper (approximately 8 cm diameter)	2	24
	4	25
disks, sterile	4	19
Floodlight	1	8
Flower pot, clay	1	34
Forceps	1	9, 10, 19, 22, 23, 24, 27, 30
Frog, preserved	1	30
Fruit, citrus	1 piece	21
Funnel	1	25

Item	Quantity per Group	Laboratory Investigation
Gel electrophoresis apparatus	1	13
Gelatin solution, 1%	20 mL	2
	6 mL	17
Gloves		
heat-resistant	1 pair	36
nitrile	1 pair per student	36
plastic	1 pair per student	3, 4, 6, 19, 22, 23, 26, 27, 28, 30, 38, 40
protective work	1 pair	5
thick	1 pair	34
Glue or transparent tape	1	14
Graduated cylinder		
10-mL	1	2, 17, 38
25-mL	1	12
100-mL	1	1, 36
Grantia, preserved whole specimen	1	26
Gum arabic solution, 1%	4 mL	17
Hand lens	1	21, 22, 24, 26, 27, 28
or dissecting microscope	1	22, 23
Honey solution, 4%	20 mL	2
Horticultural vermiculite or perlite	1 large bag per class	4
Hot plate	1	9, 38
Ice	10 cubes	1
Incubator	1	40
Index card	2	20
Inoculating loop	1	40
Iodine solution	dropper bottle	2
Irregular object	1	1
Lamp, fluorescent plant	1 per class	3, 4
	1	24
Legume seeds	8	4
Lettuce	leaf	10
macerated	1 leaf	2
Liver, fresh beef or pork	2-cm cube	12
Marker,		
felt tip	1	7, 36
permanent	1	21, 30
Matches	1 book	19, 38
Mealworms, egg, larva, pupa, adult stages	1 colony per class	28
Meter stick	1	1, 5, 8, 35, 37
Methyl cellulose	1 dropper bottle	20
Methylene blue stain	1 dropper bottle	12, 23
Microscope slide	1 per student	17
	1	12, 22, 23, 26, 27
	3	10
	4	6
	5	20
	6	12
Microscope		
compound light	1	6, 10, 12, 17, 20, 22, 23, 26, 27, 29, 36, 39
dissecting	1	22

Item	Quantity per Group	Laboratory Investigation
Mortar and pestle	1	12, 25
Moss, *Polytrichum*	1 small clump	22
Nitrogen-free nutrients	2 L	4
Notepad	1	5
Nutrient broth, sterile	12 mL (1 mL per test tube)	40
Oatmeal	2 large boxes per class	28
Oven	1 per class	36
Pad, heat-resistant	1	36
Paper bag	1	16
brown	1	2
Paper towels	2 large rolls per class	1, 2, 7, 8, 21, 30 31, 36
Paper, construction:		
green, yellow, brown, red, black, white	1 sheet of each	31
white, unlined	one sheet	27
Parafilm (or glass plate)	1	36
Paramecium caudatum culture	1 culture per class	20
Pebble, small	1	1
Pen light	1	35
Pencil		
colored	2	24
glass-marking	1	2, 6, 19, 20, 24, 32, 38, 40
Petri dish	1	24
	4	6, 25
Petroleum jelly	1 jar per class	6
pH test paper	1 vial per class	6, 17
Pipette		
dropper	1	8, 10, 12, 20, 23, 27
	2	17, 26
	3	2, 6
1-mL with safety pipetting bulb	1	12
transfer	1	13
Plastic bag		
clear	10	21
food	1	30
Plastic containers with loose-fitting lids	4	28
Plastic pot, 5-inch (sterile)	4	4
Plastic spoon	2	7
Plastic wrap	1 roll per class	25
Potato, macerated	20 mL	2
Prepared slide		
cat ovary, transverse cross section	1	39
compact bone with Haversian system	1	36
Cnidarian (*Hydra*)	1	29
earthworm (*Lumbricus terrestris*)	1	29
flatworm (*Dugesia*)	1	29
Helianthus root	1	23
Helianthus stem	1	23
hydra, whole mount	1	26
moss antheridia and archegonia	1	22
moss protonema	1	22
rat epididymis, transverse cross section	1	39

Item	Quantity per Group	Laboratory Investigation
rat testis, longitudinal cross section	1	39
roundworm (*Ascaris lumbricoides*)	1	29
3 types of human tissues	1	10
Zea root	1	23
Zea stem	1	23
Protractor	1	32
Radish seedling	10	9
2-week-old	1	23
Rhizobium bacteria	1 packet	4
Rodent	1	34
Rodent food	1 bag per class	34
Rubber mallet	1	5
Ruler	1	4
metric (30 cm)	1	1, 19, 20, 24, 27, 31, 32, 37
Salt (NaCl)		
solution, 0.9%	10 mL	12
Scale, bathroom	1 per class	37
Scalpel	1	5, 8, 12, 14, 22, 23, 26, 27, 30
Scissors	1	5, 6, 20, 22
SDS solution, 10%, (sodium dodecylsulfate)	5 mL	12
Silver nitrate solution	dropper bottle	38
Snail	2	3
Spoon, large slotted	1	9
Squid	1 per pair of students	27
Stakes, wooden	16	5
Stirring rod, glass	1	6, 12, 17
Stopper (for large test tube)	1	9
(for medium test tube)	1	17
	3	6
Strainer	1	25
String	large ball	5
Sudan III stain	dropper bottle	2
Syrup	200 mL	7
Tape		
masking	1 large roll per class	2, 3, 36
transparent	1 roll per class	19
Test tube		
medium	1	17
	3	6
	10	2
	12	38
large	2	9
	8	8
Test-tube holder	1	2, 38
Test-tube rack	1	2, 3, 19, 38, 40
	4	8
Textbook	3	11
Thermometer, Celsius	1	1
Tomato (two different varieties)	1 of each	25
Tongs	1	36

Item	Quantity per Group	Laboratory Investigation
Tongue depressor	1 box per class	6
Toothpick	1 box per class	26
Triangle, right (measuring tool)	1	5
Twist tie	10	21
Urine samples, simulated (See investigation)	1 L of each per class	38
Water plant	4 cuttings	3
	leaf	10
Water sample (See investigation)	3	6
Water, distilled or deionized		
	20 mL	2
	200 mL	7, 8
	250 mL	9
	1 L per class	19
	4 L	4
pond	2 L	3
sea	250 mL	22
Weighing container	1	7

Materials Inventory

Equipment

Animal maze

Balance, triple-beam
Block or other regular object
Bowl, large shallow
Box (or large container)
Bunsen burner

Cage, small animal
Clock (or watch with
  second hand)
Coin
Cookie sheet (or cooking tray,
  large metal)

Direct current power source
Dissecting pan
Dissecting pins
Dissecting probe
Dissecting tray

Eye patch

Field guides
  birds
  woody and nonwoody plants
Floodlight
Flower pot, clay
Forceps
Funnel

Gel electrophoresis apparatus
Gloves
  heat-resistant
  nitrile
  protective work
  thick

Hand lens or
  dissecting microscope
Hot plate

Incubator
Inoculating loop
Irregular object

Lamp, fluorescent plant

Marker
  felt tip
  permanent
Meterstick
Microscope
  compound light
  dissecting
Mortar and pestle

Oven

Pad, heat-resistant
Pebble, small
Pen light
Pencil
  colored
  glass-marking
Plastic containers
  with loose fitting lids

Plastic pots, 5-inch (sterile)
Protractor

Rubber mallet
Ruler
  metric (30 cm)

Scale, bathroom
Scalpel
Scissors
Spoon, large slotted
Stakes, wooden
Stoppers
  for large test tubes
  for medium test tubes
Strainer
String

Test-tube holder
Test-tube rack
Textbooks
Tongs
Triangle, right (measuring tool)

Glassware

Beaker
  50-mL
  150-mL
  250-mL
  400-mL
  500-mL
  600-mL

Coverslips
Culture tubes with caps

Graduated cylinder
  10-mL
  25-mL
  100-mL

Microscope slides

Parafilm (or glass plate)
Petri dishes
Pipettes
  dropper

1-mL with safety pipetting bulb
  transfer
Slides, microscope
Stirring rods

Test tubes
  medium
  large
Thermometer, Celsius

Living Organisms

Anole

Blepharisma culture
Brassica rapa seeds
Brown alga, *Fucus*

Didinium culture

Escherichia coli culture

Euglena culture

Legume seeds

Mealworms, egg, larva,
  pupa, adult stages
Moss, *Polytrichum*

Paramecium caudatum culture

Radish seedlings
  2-week-old
Rhizobium bacteria
Rodent

Snail

Water plants

Prepared Slides

cat ovary, transverse cross section
compact bone
  with Haversian system
Cnidarian (*Hydra*)

earthworm (*Lumbricus terrestris*)

flatworm (*Dugesia*)

Helianthus, root
Helianthus, stem
hydra, longitudinal section
hydra, whole mount

moss antheridia and archegonia
moss protonema

rat epidiymis,
  transverse cross section
rat testis,
  longitudinal cross section

roundworm
(*Ascaris lumbricoides*)

3 types of human tissues

Zea root

Zea stem

Preserved Specimens

Anole

Bird specimens or illustrations

Frog

Grantia sponge

Squid

Other Biological Supplies

Antibiotic disks: aureomycin, chloromycetin, penicillin, streptomycin, tetracycline, terramycin

Bacteriophage culture, T-4

DNA samples

Methyl cellulose

Nitrogen-free nutrients

Nutrient agar plates, sterile

Nutrient broth, sterile

Urine samples, simulated
(See investigation)

Water
samples (See investigation)
pond
sea

Chemical Supplies

Acid
acetic, 10%
hydrochloric, 20%
hydrochloric, 1%

Alcohol, ethyl, 95%

Benedict's solution

Biuret reagent

Bromthymol blue solution

Ethanol, 95%

Gum arabic solution, 1%

Iodine solution

Methylene blue stain

Sodium chloride (NaCl)
solution, 0.9%

SDS solution, 10%,
(sodium dodecylsulfate)

Sudan III stain

Water, distilled or deionized

Consumables

Apple (or potato)

Apple juice, unsweetened, 50%

Balloon, round

Beans
pink (pinto)
red
white

Bone, uncooked pork or beef

Bottle, 2-L soft drink

Bread

Butter

Cabbage, purple

Carrot

Cheese, cheddar

Cheesecloth

Chorine bleach
solution concentrated

Disinfectants: chlorine bleach, household cleaner, household disinfectant, phenol

Corn oil

Cotton balls

Cotton swabs, sterile

Eggs

Evergreen sprigs

Filter paper
(approximately 8 cm diameter)
disks, sterile

Fruit, citrus

Gelatin solution, 1%

Gloves, plastic

Glue or transparent tape

Honey solution, 4%

Horticultural vermiculite
or perlite

Ice

Index cards

Lettuce

Liver, fresh beef or pork

Matches

Notepad

Oatmeal

Paper bags
brown

Paper towels

Paper,
construction: green, yellow, brown, red, black, white
white, unlined

Petroleum jelly

pH test paper

Plastic bag
clear
food

Plastic spoons

Plastic wrap

Potatoes

Rodent food

Syrup

Tape
masking
transparent

Tomatoes (two different varieties)

Tongue depressors

Toothpicks

Twist ties

Weighing containers

Bibliography

Adamovic, Charles and Hedden, Carol J. 1997. Problem-solving Skills. *The Science Teacher* 64(4):20-23.

Ardizzone, Leonisa. 1997. A Course for Each Student. *The Science Teacher* 65(2):38-40.

Atwater, Mary M. 1995. The Multicultural Science Classroom. *The Science Teacher* 62(2):20-23.

Chiappetta, Eugene L. and Fillman David A. 1998. Clarifying the Place of Essential Topics and Unifying Principles in High School Biology. *School Science and Mathematics* 98(1):12-18.

Colburn, Alan and Clough, Michael P. 1997. Implementing the Learning Cycle: A Gradual Shift to a New Teaching Approach. *The Science Teacher* 64(5):30-34.

Collins, James W. et al. 2000. Texas Safety Standards: Kindergarten–Grade 12. Austin: The University of Texas at Austin, Charles A. Dana Center.

Council for Environmental Education. (2000). *Project Wild: K-12 Activity Guide*. Gaithersburg, MD: The Council for Environmental Education.

Crandall, Bill and Varrella, Gary. 1995. Issue-based Science: SS&C in Iowa – Connecting Science to the Real World. *The Science Teacher* 62(7):42-45.

Decoster, Patricia A. 1995. Questioning Answers: Analyzing Essays to Enhance Critical Thinking Skills. *The Science Teacher* 62(2):46-49.

Ebenezer, Jazlin V. and Lau, Eddy. 2003. Science on the Internet: A Resource for K–12 Teachers, 2/E. Upper Saddle River, NJ: Prentice-Hall.

Eyster, Linda S. 1997. A Comprehensive Rubric: Helping Teachers Grade Process-Oriented Tasks. *The Science Teacher* 64(9):18-21.

Francis, Joseph W. 2000. Use of Internet Resources in the Biology Lecture Classroom. *The American Biology Teacher* 62(2):90-93.

Goodman, L. and Berntson, G. 2000. The Art of Asking Questions: Using Directed Inquiry in the Classroom. *The American Biology Teacher* 62(7):473-477.

Heuschele, Ann. "It All Looks the Same to Me": An Exercise in Critical Observation. *The American Biology Teacher* 61(6):434-437.

Hinman, Richard L. 1998. Content and Science Inquiry. *The Science Teacher* 65(7):25-27.

Holyoak, Alan R. 1998. A Plan for Writing Throughout (not just across) the Biology Curriculum. *The American Biology Teacher* 60(5):186-190.

Johansen, Carol K. and Harris, David E. 2000. Teaching the Ethics of Biology. *The American Biology Teacher* 62(5):352-358.

Klapper, Michael H. 1995. Beyond the Scientific Method: Should Science be Taught as a More Creative Process. *The Science Teacher* 62(6):36-40.

Krest, Margie and Carle, Daria O. 1999. Teaching Scientific Writing: A Model for Integrating Research, Writing, and Critical Thinking. *The American Biology Teacher* 61(3):223-227.

Lawson, Anton E. 2000. Managing the Inquiry Classroom: Problems and Solutions. *The American Biology Teacher* 62(9):641-648.

Liggitt-Fox, Dianna. 1997. Fighting Student Misconceptions: Three Effective Strategies. *Science Scope* 20(5):28-30.

Lord, Thomas. 1998. Cooperative Learning that Really Works in Biology Teaching: Using Constructivist-based Activities to Challenge Student Teams. *The American Biology Teacher* 60(8):580-588.

McCormick, Terry L. 1995. Problem-Solving Projects: Integrating Technology into the Science Classroom. *The Science Teacher* 62(3):27-29.

Melear, Claudia. 1995. Multiculturalism in Science Education. *The American Biology Teacher* 57(1):21-27.

National Research Council. (1999). *How People Learn: Brain, Mind, Experience, and School*. Washington, D.C.: National Academy Press.

National Research Council. (2000). *Inquiry and the National Science Education Standards: A Guide for Teaching and Learning*. Washington, D.C.: National Academy Press.

Pheeney, Pierette. 1998. A Portfolio Primer: Helping Teachers Make the Most of this Assessment Tool. *The Science Teacher* 65(7):36-39.

Pierce, Wendy. 1998. Linking Learning to Labs. *Science Scope* 21(4):17-19.

Smithhenry, Dennis. 1997. Creating a Scientific Community: Set the Tone Early for Yearlong Cooperative Learning. *The Science Teacher* 64(8):44-47.

Wright, Emmett L. and Govindarjan, Girish. 1995. Discrepant Event Demonstrations: Motivating Students to Learn Science Concepts. *The Science Teacher* 62(1):24-28.

Young, Jay A. 1997. Chemical Safety – Part I: Safety in the Handling of Hazardous Chemicals. *The Science Teacher* 64(3):43-45.

Young, Jay A. 1997. Chemical Safety – Part II: Tips for Dealing with Laboratory hazards. *The Science Teacher* 64(4):40-43.

Laboratory Procedures

The purpose of this section is to provide some general information about preparing solutions and media, making substitutions for pH indicators, and culturing live materials. For more specific information regarding the preparation and use of solutions, media, and organisms in a particular Laboratory Investigation, consult the on-page annotations.

Solutions

General guidelines for preparing solutions and media include the following:

1. Prepare necessary solutions well in advance of the investigations in which they will be used. Each solution should be clearly labeled with its name, concentration, date of preparation, and any appropriate warnings such as toxic or flammable.

2. Always use clean glassware that has been washed with a low-sudsing laboratory soap. All glassware should be rinsed thoroughly in distilled water before use.

3. Mix each solution in a beaker or flask that holds 100 to 300 mL more than the amount of solution being prepared.

4. Use distilled water to make all preparations. Tap water may contain chemicals that alter the properties of solutions.

5. Pour concentrated acids and bases into water, stirring constantly. Never pour water into concentrated acids or bases.

6. Add solvents to solutes. Stir until solute is completely dissolved.

7. Store stains in dropper bottles.

Percentage Solutions: Volume/Volume To prepare a solution of a given percentage, dissolve the number of milliliters of solute equal to the percentage in enough solvent to make 100 mL of solution. For example, a 10% solution of hydrochloric acid (HCl) can be made by adding 10 mL of concentrated HCl to enough distilled water to bring the volume to 100 mL.

Percentage Solutions: Mass/Volume To prepare a solution of a given percentage, dissolve the number of grams of solute equal to the percentage in enough solvent to make 100 mL of the solution. For example, a 3% solution of sodium chloride (NaCl) can be made by adding 3 g NaCl to a graduated cylinder and then adding enough distilled water to bring the volume to 100 mL.

Reducing the Concentration of a Solution To reduce the concentration of an existing solution, pour the number of milliliters of the existing solution that is equal to the percentage of the new concentration into a graduated cylinder. Add enough distilled water to bring the volume in milliliters to an amount equal to the percentage of the original solution. For example, to reduce an 80% glucose solution to 20%, pour 20 mL of 80% glucose solution into a graduated cylinder. Add enough distilled water to bring the volume to 80 mL of 20% glucose.

Indicator Substitutions

In the biology laboratory, the pH indicators that are suggested for use can often be replaced by others that are equally effective. The following table lists some common indicators, the pH values at which they undergo a color change, and the expected color change.

Indicator	pH Value at Which Color Change Occurs	Color Change
thymol blue (acid)	1.5–2.5	red to yellow
bromphenol blue	3.0–4.5	yellow to blue
Congo red	3.0–5.0	blue to red
methyl orange	3.0–4.5	orange-red to yellow
litmus	4.5–8.5	red to blue
alizarin red	5.0–7.0	yellow to red
bromcresol purple	5.5–7.0	yellow to purple
bromthymol blue	6.0–7.5	yellow to blue
phenol red	6.5–8.0	yellow to red
neutral red	7.0–8.0	red to yellow
cresol red	7.0–9.0	yellow to red
thymol blue (alkaline)	8.0–10.0	yellow to blue
phenolpthalein	8.0–10.0	colorless to red
alizarin yellow	10.0–12.0	colorless to yellow

Live Organisms

The live organisms used in the *Biology Laboratory Manual* are readily available and can be cultured and maintained in a classroom or laboratory environment. Organisms are available from biological supply houses and often from pet stores or supermarkets. Some organisms can be collected locally from ponds, streams, fields, and forests. Only release native organisms back into the local environment.

In many schools, circumstances require that laboratory supplies, including live organisms, be ordered a year in advance. If this situation exists at your school, you may need to maintain cultures of organisms for long periods of time. The following directions on how to care for and maintain live organisms can be easily followed by you or a student laboratory assistant.

Careful attention to directions and the use of proper equipment and materials is important in caring for live organisms. Be especially careful when using glassware. Be sure that all glassware is clean and free of any soap residue.

Ideally, glassware used to culture organisms should be new and untouched by chemicals, including soap. Laboratory glassware often retains traces of the chemicals it has contacted even after it has been cleaned—and even the faintest traces of some chemicals can have a serious impact on live organisms. Because the organisms used in the Laboratory Investigations are quite hardy, they can be cultured under less than ideal conditions. However, you may want to set aside some glassware to use exclusively for culturing organisms and preparing media. This glassware should not come in contact with chemicals harsher than laboratory soap.

You should refer to pages T29–T31 and page 11 for guidelines for using live animals and safety rules regarding animals, respectively.

Algae Order specific species of algae such as *Fucus* from a biological supply company. Follow the instructions provided by the supplier to maintain the algae cultures. A salt mixture for preparing artificial seawater for *Fucus* culture can be purchased from an aquarium supply shop. Loosely place algae in jars of artificial seawater. Store the uncovered jars in a cool room beneath fluorescent lights.

Anoles Anoles and other small lizards may be raised in a terrarium constructed from a fine mesh cage or from a glass aquarium. If an aquarium is used, the top of the lizards' living quarters should be made of screen for good ventilation. The living quarters should contain some twigs on which the lizards can climb. Spray the plants in the terrarium daily to supply water for the lizards; they will lick up droplets of moisture from leaves but will seldom, if ever, drink water from a dish. The lizards subsist mainly on live insects. You may feed the lizards by offering them small crickets or occasionally mealworms held with forceps. Alternatively, you may place live insects such as crickets and fruit flies in the terrarium. You may wish to cover the top of the terrarium with a few layers of cheesecloth.

Aquatic plants Aquatic plants are common freshwater aquarium plants and are generally available from pet stores. Aquatic plants can also be collected throughout most of the year from ponds and slow-moving streams. To maintain aquatic plants in the classroom, fill an aquarium or large (4-L) glass jar with pond or spring water. If pond or spring water is not available, fill the container with tap water and set it aside for at least 24 hours before introducing the aquatic plants. Float aquatic plants loosely on the surface of the water. Overcrowding of the aquatic plants will cause them to deteriorate. Replenish water as necessary due to water loss from evaporation. Nutrients for aquatic plants can be provided by adding six to eight guppies or mature duckweed culture to the aquarium. Do not add snails to the aquatic plants: they will quickly eat and destroy the plants. Nutrients also can be provided by adding dilute (1%) commercial fertilizer (5–10–5) to the water. Provide a minimum of 15 hours of fluorescent light each day.

Bacteria Pure cultures of bacteria can be obtained from a biological supply company. Make sure that you are familiar with bacteriological techniques and have all necessary equipment and supplies—autoclaves, incubators, media, plates, slants, etc.—before using any bacteria in the biology laboratory. Never use pathogenic bacteria, but always treat all bacteria cultures as if they were pathogenic.

Bacteria are easily cultured in tubes of nutrient broth. To prepare the nutrient broth, bring 350 mL distilled water to a boil in a 500-mL beaker. Slowly add 3 g dehydrated nutrient broth, stirring constantly. Pour the broth into small test tubes and insert a cotton plug into each tube. Sterilize the tubes of broth for 15 minutes at 15 pounds pressure in an autoclave or pressure cooker. The sterilized tubes can be stored in a refrigerator until they are used. Transfer bacteria to the tubes of sterile nutrient broth using an inoculating loop and following sterile technique. Store inoculated tubes at room temperature for two to three days to allow the bacteria to grow. Tubes of bacteria can also be incubated at 37°C for 24 hours and then be used immediately. Subcultures and dilutions of the cultures can be made at two-week intervals. Cultures remain viable stored in a refrigerator for several weeks.

Bacteria may also be cultured on agar plates or slants. Biological supply companies often provide bacterial cultures on slants. Make subcultures of bacteria as soon as possible after receiving the original cultures. You can extend the life of slant cultures by covering the slants with a thin layer of sterile mineral oil and storing them in a refrigerator. These oil-covered slants will usually survive for several months.

Mealworms These larvae of *Tenebrio* beetles may be obtained from pet stores or from biological supply companies. They can be cultured in jars half-filled with slightly moist bran, oatmeal, or corn-flakes. The jars should be covered with cheesecloth or a fine wire mesh so that adult beetles cannot fly away. Adult beetles may be fed bits of raw carrots or potatoes.

Mosses and liverworts Mosses and liverworts may be obtained from biological supply companies or collected in woodland areas. A moist, covered terrarium in medium light provides the best growing conditions. If molds start to grow in the terrarium, remove the cover and reduce the amount of water until the molds disappear. Sprinkling a small amount of powdered sulfur in the terrarium may also discourage molds.

Plants Terrestrial plants such as *Coleus*, geraniums, and *Mimosa pudica* can be obtained from biological supply companies. Follow the supplier's directions regarding frequency of watering, exposure to light, and fertilizing. *Coleus* can be easily propagated from stem cuttings.

Protists Protists such as *Euglena*, *Amoeba*, *Stentor*, and *Paramecium* can be cultured in the classroom. Protists are easily cultured in stackable containers, such as finger bowls, Syracuse dishes, watch glasses, and petri dishes. The successful culturing of protists requires clean glassware. If possible, sterilize all glassware in an autoclave or pressure cooker. If sterilization is not possible, thoroughly wash all glassware in a solution of 10% nitric acid. Take care to avoid burns when working with nitric acid. Rinse the glassware several times with distilled water. Chemical and soap residues are harmful to protists and may prevent their successful culturing.

Pure stock cultures of protists can be purchased from a biological supply company. Mixed species of protists can be collected from ponds and slow-moving streams.

Cultures of protists can be successfully grown in pond water. Before using pond water, filter it through several layers of muslin or cheesecloth to remove debris. Protists can also be cultured in pasteurized spring water with a pH near 7. To pasteurize spring water, place 12 to 16 L spring water in a large enameled container. Heat the water to 65°C for 15 minutes. Pasteurized spring water can be stored up to two weeks in covered plastic containers. Longer storage requires repasteurization at two-week intervals to control the growth of hydrogen sulfide bacteria. Pond or pasteurized spring water should be used in the preparation of growth media. The following recipe for wheat medium is a good all-purpose growth medium for most protists.

- Wheat Medium: Collect wheat seeds that have not been sprayed with pesticides; obtain the seeds from farmers or order them from a biological supply company. Dried split peas or rice (not the quick-cooking variety) can be substituted for wheat seeds. Place 50 to 75 wheat seeds in a glass jar, seal the jar, and place it in an 82°C (180°F) oven for four hours. Or place 50 to 75 wheat seeds in a screw-top test tube filled with spring water. In an autoclave or pressure cooker, heat the test tubes for 15 minutes at 15 pounds pressure. In a culture dish, add three to five wheat seeds to pasteurized spring water. Add 3 to 4 mL stock protist culture to the dish. Loosely cover the culture dish and set it aside in a dimly lit area of the laboratory. Replenish evaporated water with distilled, pond, pasteurized spring, or tap water that has been allowed to stand uncovered at room temperature for at least 24 hours.

Amoeba Amebas are easily grown in a special salt solution called Chalkley's solution mixed with rice or a population of small ciliates such as *Chilomonas*.

- Chalkley's Solution: To prepare 1 L of stock solution, mix 1 g sodium chloride (NaCl), 0.04 g potassium chloride (KCl), and 0.06 g calcium chloride ($CaCl_2$) to 1 L distilled water. Stir until completely dissolved. The salts in the solution closely resemble those found in pond water. To use Chalkley's solution, add 100 mL of the prepared stock solution to 900 mL distilled water. This diluted solution is called the working solution.

- Chalkley's Solution-Rice Medium: Place about 250 mL Chalkley's working solution into several finger bowls or similar containers. To each container, add four or five grains of polished rice (not the quick-cooking variety). Place 50 to 100 *Amoeba* in each dish. Stack the dishes and cover the top dish with a loosely fitting lid. Place the cultures in a dark location at room temperature for two to four weeks. Once the cultures are established, occasionally add a few rice grains or several drops of *Chilomonas* culture to replenish the food supply.

Amoeba will need to be subcultured about once every 4 to five weeks. To subculture *Amoeba*, drain off about half the liquid. Divide the remaining liquid containing the *Amoeba* into two new culture dishes containing Chalkley's solution-rice medium. Set the cultures aside in a dark location for two to four weeks until the cultures become clearly established.

Chlamydomonas *Chlamydomonas* does well in Chalkley's solution-rice medium and in wheat-grain medium. Like *Euglena* and other photosynthetic protists, *Chlamydomonas* requires light.

Diatoms Although commercial media for diatoms are available, diatoms usually do not survive for long in the classroom.

Euglena *Euglena* cultures thrive in water that contains relatively large amounts of organic matter. *Euglena* can be grown successfully in three different media.

- Manure-Wheat Medium: Bring to a boil 250 mL spring water containing three wheat grains and six rabbit or sheep pellets (or equivalent mass of fresh or dried horse or cow manure). Boil for 15 minutes. Pour the mixture into a deep container such as a mayonnaise jar or large beaker. Set the container aside at room temperature for two days. Add *Euglena* from a pure culture. Cover the culture and place it near a window with diffuse light. In about two weeks, a large population of *Euglena* will be present, indicated by a greenish tinge to the water.

- Wheat-Rice-Milk Medium: For five minutes, boil a mixture of 20 wheat grains, 15 rice grains (not the quick-cooking variety), 5 mL nonfat milk, and 500 mL pasteurized spring water. Set the mixture aside overnight before adding *Euglena* from a pure culture. Store the culture in dim light near a window for about two weeks or until the *Euglena* culture becomes established.

- Rice Medium: Boil seven or eight grains of rice (not the quick-cooking variety) in 475 mL distilled water or old aquarium water for about one minute. Pour the mixture into a shallow dish. Allow the dish to stand at room temperature until a bacterial scum forms on the surface, about one week. Add *Euglena* from a pure culture and cover. Place the infusion in dim light near a window for six to eight weeks to allow the *Euglena* culture to develop and grow. Replenish water as necessary, using distilled or old aquarium water.

Euglena cultures can be maintained up to a year before subculturing becomes necessary.

Paramecium Paramecia can be successfully cultured in an infusion of dried lettuce leaves. To pre-pare the infusion, remove several large outer leaves from a head of lettuce. Place the leaves in an oven at low temperature for several hours to dry. Remove the lettuce leaves when they have become crisp and brown. Discard any blackened or charred leaves. Grind the dried leaves with a mortar and pestle. The ground leaves can be stored almost indefinitely in a tightly sealed glass container. In an Erlenmeyer flask, add 1.5 g powdered lettuce leaves to 1 L boiling distilled water. Boil for five minutes. Filter the infusion into smaller Erlenmeyer flasks. Seal the flasks with cotton plugs. Sterilize the flasks for 15 minutes at 15 pounds pressure in an autoclave or pressure cooker. Allow the infusion to stand overnight. Using sterile pipettes and flasks, add two parts of the lettuce infusions to one part distilled water. Add several drops of pure concentrated *Paramecium* culture to each flask. Stopper the flasks with cotton plugs. Set the cultures in dim light at room temperature for one to two weeks.

Paramecia need to be subcultured every month. Place several drops of the existing culture into flasks of dilute lettuce infusion.

Physarum polycephalum Slime molds, such as *Physarum polycephalum*, can be cultured on filter paper and oatmeal. Wrap a small glass bowl with a piece of filter paper or a paper towel so the the mouth of the bowl is covered by a smooth flat paper surface. Place the covered bowl in a large container such as a battery jar so that the mouth of the bowl and the flat paper surface face upward. Partially fill the battery jar with water so that the water level is about three-quarters of the way up the sides of the bowl. Place the slime mold on the filter paper. Sprinkle about 0.2 g oatmeal or pulverized rolled oats into the paper. Feed the slime mold with oatmeal every one to two days. The slime mold can be stored in a dormant state by drying the filter paper at room temperature and placing it in sealed containers in a refrigerator. The slime mold will survive for a year or two under these conditions.

Stentor The easiest way to grow *Stentor* is in a medium made of Chalkley's solution, wheat, and *Chilomonas*.

- Chalkley's Solution-Wheat-*Chilomonas* Medium: Boil five to six wheat grains in distilled water for about one minute. Add the boiled wheat grains and 5 mL dense *Chilomonas* culture to 100 mL working Chalkley's solution. (See directions for the preparation of Chalkley's solution under *Amoeba*). Allow the medium to stand at room temperature for two days. Add 10 to 20 *Stentor* to the medium. Cover the culture and place it in a cool, even-temperature room for two to three weeks. Replenish evaporated water with distilled water or pasteurized spring water as necessary.

The *Stentor* culture should last about six months without subculturing. Add one additional boiled wheat grain per month to the culture to maintain the food supply.

Radish seedlings Plant radish seeds in a light and porous mixture of soil and vermiculite. Plant seeds about 1 cm below the soil surface and about 2 to 3 cm apart. Keep soil evenly moist before and after seedlings emerge. Before seedlings emerge, the container in which they are planted can be covered with plastic wrap. The plastic wrap forms a mini-greenhouse, conserving heat and moisture. Remove the plastic once the seedlings emerge.

Rodents Small rodents such as hamsters, gerbils, mice, and rats may be housed in cages that are available commercially or in glass aquaria with a screen top. If you choose to raise mice, make sure that the classroom is well-ventilated, as mice have an offensive odor. Separate males and females to avoid unwanted litters. Clean the rodents' habitat daily (except for the first two days after the birth of a litter). The rodents should be provided with an exercise wheel and chewing sticks; some may require a salt lick. Make sure that a supply of fresh water is avaible at all times. Use a glass or plastic water fountain rather than a water bowl; open bowls become fouled easily. Rodents can be fed commercial food pellets supplemented with pieces of fresh vegetables such as carrots.

Snails Freshwater snails will flourish in an established aquarium with aquatic plants provided for food. Remove dead snails immmediately to prevent fouling of the water. Snails can help keep the glass in a freshwater aquarium relatively free of algae. Place two medium-sized snails in the aquarium for each gallon of water.

The following notes deal with organisms that are not used in the Laboratory Investigations. You may wish to culture these organisms for enrichment activities, independent student projects, or teacher demonstrations.

Bread mold Spores of the black bread mold, *Rhizopus stolonifer*, can be ordered from a biological supply company. Spores of bread mold also are commonly found on dry onions from a supermarket. Sprinkle purchased spores over the surface of a piece of wet bread in a dish or rub a moist cotton swab over the surface of an onion to collect spores and then rub the swab across the bread surface to transfer the spores. Seal the dish tightly and set it aside at room temperature. Mold should appear in about three days. After all investigations requiring mold are complete, allow the covered dish of mold to dry out. This procedure provides spores for the following year.

Brine shrimp The brine shrimp *Artemia* is a good source of food for hydras, fish, and other aquatic animals. It is also rather interesting to observe in its own right, as it exhibits a strong positive response to light.

Brine shrimp eggs are available from pet stores, tropical fish stores, and biological supply companies. Hatch brine shrimp eggs in a shallow glass dish containing a dilute (4%) solution of sodium chloride. Sprinkle 0.5 mL brine shrimp eggs on the surface of the water. Larvae will hatch in 18 to 72 hours, depending on the temperature of the water. At a constant temperature of 21°C, brine shrimp eggs usually hatch within 48 hours. Aerating the water with an airstone increases the hatching success rate.

Brine shrimp will grow to maturity in about 20 days if they are cultured in a well-aerated aquarium at temperatures below 25°C. They can be fed a yeast suspension supplemented with scrapings of algae from the sides of aquaria.

To capture brine shrimp for observation or for feeding to other organisms, shine a light at one side of the container. Siphon off the brine shrimp with a piece of plastic tubing or a kitchen bulb baster. Before being fed to hydras or other fresh-water organisms, brine shrimp must first be washed with distilled water to remove any traces of salt. To wash the brine shrimp, pour them through a filter or fine mesh net. Rinse them thoroughly with a gentle stream of tap or distilled water. Brine shrimp can survive only a few hours in fresh water, so remove and wash only as many as are needed.

Clams Clams and other bivalves can be maintained for a few days in an aquarium. Marine clams can also be stored for short periods of time in large beakers filled with a 4% solution of sodium chloride.

Crickets Crickets are quite easy to raise, and they provide a good source of food for other animals in the classroom. You may collect crickets in fields and other grassy areas or obtain them from a biological supply company. Crickets can be kept in a glass aquarium that has a secure screen top. Put about a centimeter of cat pan filler or clean sand on the bottom of the aquarium. Provide the crickets with small rocks and branches for hiding and climbing. Place a small container filled with wet cotton on the bottom of the aquarium to help maintain the humidity in the crickets' habitat and provide a source of water. Keep the cotton wet at all times. The crickets may be fed on dry dog food and bits of fresh fruits and vegetables. Avoid overcrowding. Crickets tend to be cannibalistic, especially at high population densities.

Daphnia *Daphnia* are available from a biological supply company. To culture *Daphnia*, nearly fill a 4-L jar with pasteurized spring water or tap water that has been allowed to stand at room temperature at least 24 hours. To the water add green unicellular algae or 100 mL of an established *Euglena* culture. Add several *Daphnia* to the jar and place the jar near a light source. Replenish the water and *Euglena* culture as necessary. Subculture the *Daphnia* about every three weeks.

Drosophila Fruit flies can be collected from fruit and vegetable markets or puchased from biological supply companies. Fruit flies with specific traits for use in genetics investigations must be ordered from a biological supply company far enough in advance to allow for the desired increase in the population size of the flies. Store flies in clear plastic or glass vials or jars with stoppers that allow for air exchanges. Stoppers must be escape-proof. Include in each vial a small piece of paper towel on which the flies can perch. Store the vials in a warm (18°–20°C) area away from bright light.

Fruit flies can be cultured on a few slices of overripe banana that have been sprinkled with a few grains of yeast. They can also be cultured on one of a large number of commercial or "home-made" media. The recipe for one particularly effective home-made medium is as follows.

- Banana-Agar Medium: Bring 625 mL water to a boil. Add 20 g agar powder and boil until thoroughly dissolved, stirring constantly. Add 25 mL white corn syrup and 250 mL mashed, very ripe bananas. Add 20 g dried brewer's yeast. Bring this mixture to a boil. If desired, add 20 g of a commercial mold inhibitor at this point. Stir mixture until all ingredients are thoroughly mixed. Pour into sterile culture vials as needed.

Fill a culture bottle with about 1 to 2 cm of medium. Insert a piece of crumpled paper toweling into the medium before it hardens. This provides a surface for egg-laying and pupation. Bottles may be stoppered with pieces of foam rubber or cotton wrapped in cheesecloth.

The life cycle of *Drosophila* takes about two weeks and varies with temperature. At 20°C, the life cycle usually takes 15 days. A magnifying glass is useful in sexing adult fruit flies. Males, which are slightly smaller than females, have a wide pigmented band that covers the posterior third of their rounded abdomen. Females have 5 to 8 thin bands on their slightly pointed abdomen.

Because female *Drosophila* store sperm within their body for some time after mating, virgin females must be obtained for genetic crosses. One way of ensuring that the females in a culture are virgin is to remove all the adult flies in a culture as pupae begin to form. The emerging female flies will be virgin for the first 10 hours.

Fruit flies must be anesthetized so that they can be examined. Traditionally, ether has been used; however, there are a number of commercial anesthetics available that are much less volatile. You can obtain anesthetizers from biological supply companies or construct them yourself.

To construct an anesthetizer, you will need a bottle whose mouth is the same size as that of the culture bottles, a cork stopper that fits the bottle, a nail about 3 cm long, cotton or gauze, and thread. Push the nail into the cork stopper so that the head of the nail is flush with the top of the stopper and the point of the nail protrudes from the bottom side of the stopper. Cover the nail with cotton; secure the cotton with thread. When ready to use the anesthetizer, put a few drops of anesthetic on the cotton.

To transfer flies from the culture bottle to the anesthetizer, tap the side of the culture bottle so that the flies fall to the bottom of the bottle. Quickly place the mouth of the anesthetizer over the mouth of the culture bottle. Invert the culture bottle and tap it so the flies (but not the medium or larvae) fall into the anesthetizer. Then quickly separate and stopper the bottles.

When the flies stop moving, spill them onto a sheet of white paper. Have on hand a petri dish cover that has a piece of filter paper taped to the inside. If the flies begin reviving too soon, put a drop or two of anesthetic on the filter paper and then cover the flies for a few seconds until they are reanesthetized.

Manipulate the flies using a small paintbrush. Transfer dead or unwanted flies to the "morgue"—a container of mineral oil. When transferring flies into a culture bottle, make sure that they fall on the paper toweling. If they fall on the medium, they will get stuck and die.

Duckweed Duckweed can be purchased from a biological supply company or collected from ponds and slow-moving streams in spring and early summer. A manure medium for duckweed can be prepared by adding 10 mL fresh or dried cow manure to 2 L tap water that has been allowed to stand at least 24 hours. Boil this mixture for 15 minutes and then allow it to cool. Pour the manure medium into several large jars. Add about 50 duckweed clusters to each jar. Duckweed can also be maintained on the surface of an established aquarium that contains snails and fish.

Earthworms Earthworms are readily collected when they come to the surface at night or after a heavy rain. They can also be obtained from a biological supply company. Food and habitats for worms are available commercially. You can also house worms in wooden containers such as cigar boxes. Fill the container with 5 to 15 centimeters of moist soil or peat moss. Keep the container covered and store it at a temperature of about 15°C. Make sure the soil remains moist. Twice a week, bury some lettuce and bits of bread soaked in milk in the soil.

Ferns Ferns may be grown in clay pots or terraria. The soil should be kept moist but not wet. Most ferns prefer medium light and relatively cool temperatures. Certain ferns, such as the bracken fern, should not be placed in direct or strong sunlight. Fern gametophytes take at least six weeks to grow from spores. The spores from crushed sori may be cultured in flowerpots, on the surface of an inverted flowerpot, or in sterile agar medium.

Frogs Live adult frogs can be maintained for short periods of time in plastic containers approximately 35 × 25 × 11 cm. Add enough tap water to half cover the frogs. At one end, insert an upside-down glass dish on which the frogs can rest out of the water. Provide hiding places by including broken pieces of clay pots. Cover the container to prevent escape. Clean the water every two to three days. Feed the frogs live insects or worms daily.

Eggs of *Xenopus* and *Rana pipiens* are recommended for hatching in the classroom. Use only tap water that has been allowed to stand at least 24 hours at room temperature to hatch the eggs and raise the tadpoles. Separate the eggs into clumps of about 10. Place the eggs in shallow containers of water. Maintain the eggs at room temperature and near a window where they can receive direct sunlight at least part of the day. Ten immature tadpoles can be maintained in a liter of water. Begin feeding tadpoles when strands of fecal matter appear in the water. Twice a week, feed tadpoles dry yeast or dry pea-soup powder. Clean the water as necessary. Larger tadpoles should be kept one each in a liter of water.

Goldfish The hardiest and least expensive type of goldfish are the wild-type fishes that are generally sold in pet stores as food for exotic fishes. Goldfish may also be obtained from biological supply companies.

Goldfish can be maintained in an aquarium or large glass container. Use tap water that has stood at room temperature at least 24 hours. If possible, use an aquarium with a corner or under-gravel filter to clean the water. Feed the goldfish daily, using commercial food, crushed dog or cat food, or dry high-protein baby cereal. Approximately one-half teaspoon of food is adequate for five fish. Keep the water clean to avoid contamination by bacteria and fungi.

Grasshoppers Collect live grasshoppers from nearby fields. Maintain live grasshoppers in glass jars or aquariums with mesh or screen coverings. Provide twigs on which the grasshoppers can crawl and perch, water, and food such as leaves of lettuce and spinach.

Hydra Hydras are easily grown in a culture dish containing a 5-cm sprig of an aquatic plant and pasteurized spring water (pH 7). (See the section on *Amoeba* for directions on the preparation of pasteurized spring water.) Place 20 to 30 hydras in the culture dish. Place the dish near a fluorescent light where it will receive 16 hours of light per day. Hydras are active carnivorous feeders that will eat only live food. Providing an adequate food supply is the most difficult aspect of maintaining hydras in the classroom. Feed hydras the washed larvae of brine shrimp, *Daphnia,* or chopped *Tubifex* worms every other day. Hydras require clean water. About 30 minutes after each feeding, remove uneaten brine shrimp and other debris from the bottom of the dish with a medicine dropper. Remove half the water from the dish and replace it with pasteurized spring water. Replace the aquatic plant as it deteriorates. When the population reaches 50 hydras, begin a new culture with half of the individuals from the existing culture.

Lichens Lichens may be obtained from biological supply companies. Alternatively, you may collect lichens from the surfaces of rocks, buildings, and dead trees. Spraying the attached lichens with water softens them and loosens their hold. Use a sharp knife to gently remove the lichens and place them in a cardboard box. The lichens can be stored in loosely covered cardboard boxes in a cool dry location. Spraying the lichens with water before they are used in the investigation softens them somewhat and reduces their brittleness.

Pill bugs Terrestrial isopods such as pill bugs, wood lice, and sow bugs can be raised in a terrarium that contains damp, rich humus with small rocks under which the isopods can hide. These isopods will eat small pieces of apples, raw potatoes, and lettuce.

Planarians Planarians such as *Dugesia* can be collected from the underside of logs and stones in bodies of cold, clear fresh water. They can also be obtained from biological supply companies. Planarians should be kept in black or opaque containers such as enameled pans at a temperature of about 18°C. The water should be changed frequently. Feed the planarians bits of raw liver, *Tubifex* worms, or egg yolk. Remove excess food with a medicine dropper or pipette after several hours to avoid fouling the water.

Vinegar eels Order *Anguilla aceti* or *Turbatrix aceti* from a biological supply company. These roundworms are harmless and nonparasitic, and are commonly found in bulk cider vinegar. Vinegar eels can also be obtained from local cider mills or vinegar manufacturers. Ask for pure bulk vinegar that contains "mother of vinegar." To culture vinegar eels, place about 200 mL unadulterated cider vinegar (from a grocery store) and 2 tablespoons of commercial vinegar eel medium into finger bowls or similar containers. A 2-cm cube of peeled raw apple can be substituted for commercial vinegar eel medium. Add vinegar eels. Cover containers loosely and place them in a dimly lit location. No further care is necessary. Subculture every three months if required.

Yeast To prepare an actively growing culture of yeast, dissolve 0.1 g dry yeast and 5 g sucrose in 75 mL distilled water. Mix thoroughly. The yeast culture should be used within two to four days. This culture should provide enough yeast for three classes of 30 students each.

Suppliers of Laboratory Materials and Equipment

Analytical Scientific, Ltd.
11049 Bandera Road
San Antonio, TX 78250

Ann Arbor Biologicals
6780 Jackson Road
Ann Arbor, MI 48103

Apple Computer, Inc.
1 Infinite Loop
Cupertino, CA 95014
www.apple.com

Arbor Scientific
P.O. Box 2750
Ann Arbor, MI 48106
www.arborsci.com

Bausch & Lomb
Scientific Optical Products
    Division
1400 North Goodman Street
Rochester, NY 14692-0450

Bio-Rad
1000 Alfred Nobel Drive
Hercules, CA 94547

California Corporation of
    Biochemical Research
3625 Medford Street
Los Angeles, CA 90063

Carolina Biological Supply
    Company
2700 York Road
Burlington, NC 27215

Central Scientific Company
    (CENCO)
3300 Cenco Parkway
Franklin Park, IL 60131
www.cenconet.com

Chem Scientific, Inc.
1250 Washington Street
Norwood, MA 02062

Connecticut Valley Biological
    Supply Company, Inc.
82 Valley Road
Southampton, MA 01073

Delta Biologicals
P.O. Box 26666
Tucson, AZ 85726-6666

Edmund Scientific Company
101 East Gloucester Pike
Barrington, NJ 08007-1380
www.edsci.com

Edvotek
P.O. Box 1232
West Bethesda, MD 20827

Fisher Education Company
485 Frontage Road
Burr Ridge, IL 60521

Flinn Scientific, Inc.
P.O. Box 219
Batavia, IL 60510
www.flinnsci.com

Forestry Suppliers, Inc.
P.O. Box 8397
205 West Rankin Street
Jackson, MS 39204
www.forestry-suppliers.com

Frey Scientific Company
905 Hickory Lane
Mansfield, OH 44905
www.freyscientific.com

General Supply Corporation
P.O. Box 9347
Jackson, MS 39286-9347
www.generalsupplycorp.com

Grau-Hall Scientific
    Corporation
6401 Elvas Avenue
Sacramento, CA 95819
www.grauhall.com

H & H Research, Inc.
P.O. Box 5156, Station One
Wilmington, NC 28403

Hach Company
P.O. Box 389
Loveland, CO 80539-0389
www.hach.com

Harvard Apparatus Company
84 October Hill Road
Holliston, MA 01746

Hubbard Scientific Company
P.O. Box 2121
401 W. Hickory Street
Fort Collins, CO 80522
www.hubbardscott.com

Kons Scientific Company, Inc.
P.O. Box 3
Germantown, WI 53022-0003

La Pine Scientific Company
13636 Western Avenue
P.O. Box 780
Blue Island, IL 60018

Lab-Aids, Inc.
17 Colt Court
Ronkonkoma, NY 11779
www.lab-aids.com

Learning Things, Inc.
P.O. Box 436
Arlington, MA 02476-0052

William A. Lemberger Company
2500 Waukau Avenue
P.O. Box 2482
Oshkosh, WI 54903

McKilligan Supply Corporation
435 Main Street
Johnson City, NY 13790-1998

Ben Meadows Company
P.O. Box 20200
Canton, GA 30114

Nasco
901 Janesville Avenue
Fort Atkinson, WI 53538

Nasco West, Inc.
4825 Stoddard Road
Modesto, CA 95356-9318

Niles Biological
9298 Elder Creek Road
Sacramento, CA 95829

Parco Scientific Company
P.O. Box 189
316 Youngstown-Kingsville Road
Vienna, OH 44473
www.parcoscientific.com

Phipps and Bird, Inc.
1519 Summit Avenue
Richmond, VA 23230
www.phippsbird.com

Sargent-Welch Scientific Company
P.O. Box 5229
Buffalo Grove, IL 60089-5229
www.sargentwelch.com

Schoolmasters Science
P.O. Box 1941
745 State Circle
Ann Arbor, MI 48106
www.schoolmasters.com

Science Kit and Boreal Labs
P.O. Box 5003
777 East Park Drive
Tonawanda, NY 14150
www.sciencekit.com

Scientific Glass Apparatus
Company
735 Broad Street
Bloomfield, NJ 07003

Southern Precision Instrument
Company
3419 East Commerce Street
San Antonio, TX 78820

Spectrum Educational Supplies
Limited
125 Mary Street
Aurora, Ontario, Canada
www.spectrumed.com

Swift Instruments, Inc.
P.O. Box 562
1190 North 4th Street
San Jose, CA 95112

Triarch, Inc.
P.O. Box 98
Ripon, WI 59471

Ward's Natural Science
Establishment, Inc.
P.O. Box 92912
Rochester, NY 14692-9012
www.wardsci.com

Wildlife Supply Company
95 Botsford Place
Buffalo, NY 14216
www.wildco.com

Wilkens-Anderson Company
4525 West Division Street
Chicago, IL 60651
www.waco-lab-supply.com

Guidelines for the Use and Care of Animals

Animals are an essential part of a biology curriculum. Few things are as interesting and motivating to students as animals. The judicious use of live or preserved animals can help students realize that the study of biology is relevant, fascinating, rewarding, and not merely another dull textbook exercise.

Although there are many advantages to providing biology students with opportunities to study real animals, it is important to be aware of and sensitive to ethical and practical concerns. The purpose of this section is to discuss some realistic guidelines for using animals in a secondary classroom. The final decision regarding the use of animals in your classroom should take into consideration these recommendations, the safety rules on pages 9–11 of *Laboratory Manual A*, local and school guidelines, your personal views, and your assessment of your students' needs, interests, maturity, and ability to behave responsibly.

1. Whenever possible, live animals should be observed in their natural habitats or in zoos, parks, and aquaria.

2. Check the state and federal codes regarding animal welfare that apply in your area. You may also wish to refer to guidelines published by the National Science Teachers' Association, the National Association of Biology Teachers, and the International Science Fair. Make students aware of all safety rules and regulations regarding animals.

3. Before bringing a live animal into the classroom, determine whether a proper habitat can be maintained in the classroom situation. Such a habitat includes temperature, space, and type of food. Students should have a clear understanding of the appropriate care needed by the live animals brought in the classroom. Do not allow students to tap on animal enclosures or otherwise disturb the animals.

4. No wild vertebrate animals should be brought into the classroom. Purchase animals from a reputable dealer only.

5. Live animals should be nonpoisonous and healthy. Any mammals used in the classroom should be vaccinated against rabies unless the animals were purchased recently from a reliable scientific supply company. Quarantine any animal to make sure it is disease-free before bringing it into the classroom.

6. Make sure that the living quarters of classroom animals are clean, located away from stressful situations, appropriately spacious, and secure enough to confine the animal. You may wish to lock cages to prevent the accidental release of animals; the small padlocks used on luggage are good for this purpose.

7. Remove wastes from animal living quarters daily. Thoroughly clean animal living quarters periodically to ensure that they are odor- and germ-free. Provide a daily supply of fresh water and any other need specific to the particular animal.

8. Provide for the care of the animals during weekends and school vacations. Inform the custodial staff of the presence of animals and warn them of any special requirements. For example, turning off the aquarium pump to save electricity or spraying the classroom for insects can be fatal to animal collections.

9. Students should be instructed as to how to handle each species brought into the classroom. For example, students can receive painful wounds from the improper handling of some fishes, mollusks, and sea urchins.

10. Animals should be handled only if necessary. If an animal is frightened or excited, pregnant, feeding, or with its young, special handling is required.

11. Students should thoroughly wash their hands with soap and warm water after handling animals or their cages.

12. Animals should be returned to their natural habitat after an observation period of not longer than 14 days. However, laboratory-bred animals or species that are not indigenous to an area should not be released into the environment.

13. If an animal must be euthanized, do not allow students to watch. Do the sacrificing humanely. Contact the local humane society for advice.

14. Before performing any experiment involving live animals, check local and state regulations. In some states, certification is required before a teacher is permitted to experiment with animals.

15. No animal studies involving anesthetic drugs, pathogenic organisms, toxicological products, carcinogens, or radiation should be performed.

16. Any experiment requiring live animals should have a clearly defined objective relating to the teaching/learning of some scientific principle.

17. No experimental procedures that will cause pain, discomfort, or harm to vertebrates should be done in the classroom or at home.

18. Surgical procedures should not be performed on live vertebrate animals.

19. If fertilized bird eggs are opened, the embryo should be destroyed humanely two days before it would have hatched, at the latest.

20. Whenever possible, substitute plants or invertebrate animals for vertebrates.

21. When working with preserved animals, make sure that students maintain a serious and respectful attitude toward the specimens.

Handling Ethical Issues

There is much controversy regarding the use of animals in science research. This controversy extends to preserved animals in dissections as well as live animals in experiments. Although the battle over what uses of animals are appropriate in a biology classroom can be frustrating and emotionally charged, it can also provide an opportunity for students to closely examine a current issue. You may wish to have students read current literature on the subject and contact groups and individuals with varying points of view.

Stress that it is important to make a rational, informed decision before taking a stand on any issue. Point out that it is vital to know and understand the arguments on both sides of an issue. Help students analyze the sources they find in terms of slant, bias, and the reliability and objectivity of the author(s). Teach them to learn to distinguish between fact and opinion. Encourage them to question what they read and hear. Challenge them to discover the hidden assumptions and implications of different points of view.

If dissections are a part of your curriculum and a student chooses to avoid dissections because of ethical concerns, you should respect that student's opinion. Point out, however, that no simulation or videotape can replace hands-on, first-hand experience.

NABT Guidelines for the Use of Live Animals

> The National Association of Biology Teachers (NABT) has developed the following set of guidelines to be used when working with live animals.

Living things are the subject of biology, and their direct study is an appropriate and necessary part of biology teaching. Textbook instruction alone cannot provide students with a basic understanding of life and life processes. We further recognize the importance of research to understanding life processes and providing information on health, disease, medical care, and agriculture.

The abuse of any living organism for experimentation or any other purpose is intolerable in any segment of society. Because biology deals specifically with living things, professional biological educators must be especially congnizant of their responsibility to prevent inhumane treatment to living organisms in the name of science and research. This responsibility should extend beyond the confines of the teacher's classroom to the rest of the school and community.

The National Association of Biology Teachers, in speaking to the dilemma of providing a sound biological education, while addressing the problem of humane experimentation, presents the following guidelines on the use of live animals.

A. Biological experimentation should lead to and be consistent with respect for life and all living things. Humane treatment and care of animals should be an integral part of any lesson that includes living animals.

B. All aspects of exercises and/or experiments dealing with living things must be within the comprehension and capabilities of the students involved. It is recongnized that these parameters are necessarily vague, but it is expected that competent teachers of biology can recognize these limitations.

C. Lower orders of life such as bacteria, fungi, prozoans, and invertebrates can reveal much basic biological information and are preferable as subjects for invasive studies wherever and whenever possible.

D. Vertebrate animals may be used as experimental organisms in the following situations:

1. Observations of normal living patterns of wild animals in the free living state or in zoological parks, gardens, or aquaria.

2. Observations of normal living patterns of pets, fish, or domestic animals.

3. Observations of biological phenomena, i.e., including ovulation in frogs through hormone injections that do not cause discomfort or adverse effects to the animals.

E. Animals should be properly cared for as described in the following guidelines:

1. Appropriate quarters for the animals being used should be provided in a place free from undue stresses. If housed in the classroom itself, animals should not be constantly subjected to disturbances that might be caused by students in the classroom or other upsetting activities.

2. All animals used in teaching or research programs must receive proper care. Quarters should provide for sanitation, protection from the elements, and have sufficient space for normal behavioral and postural requirements of the species. Quarters shall be easily cleaned, ventilated, and lighted. Proper temperature regulation shall be provided.

3. Proper food and clean drinking water for those animals requiring water shall be available at all times in suitable containers.

4. Animals' care shall be supervised by a science teacher experienced in proper animal care.

5. If euthanasia is necessary, animals shall be sacrificed in an approved, humane manner by an adult experienced in the use of such procedures. Laboratory animals should not be released in the environment if they were not originally a part of the native fauna. The introduction of nonnative species which may become feral must be avoided.

6. The procurement and use of wild or domestic animals must comply with existing local, state, or federal rules regarding the same.

F. Animal studies should be carried out under the provisions of the following guidelines:

1. All animal studies should be carried out under the direct supervision of a competent science teacher. It is the responsibility of that teacher to ensure that the student has the necessary comprehension for the study being done.

2. Students should not be allowed to take animals home to carry out experimental studies. These studies should be done in a suitable area in the school.

3. Students doing projects with vertebrate animals should adhere to the following:

   a. No experimental procedures should be attempted that would subject vertebrate animals to pain or distinct discomfort, or interfere with their health in any way. Pithing of live frogs should be carried out by a teacher experienced in such procedures and should not be part of the general class activity.

   b. Students should not perform surgery on living vertebrate animals except under the direct supervision of a qualified biomedical scientist.

4. Experimental procedures should not involve the use of microorganisms pathogenic to humans or other animals, ionizing radiation, carcinogens, drugs, or chemicals at toxic levels, drugs known to produce adverse or teratogenic effects, pain causing drugs, alcohol in any form, electric shock, exercise until exhaustion, or other distressing stimuli.

5. Behavioral studies should use only positive reinforcement in training studies.

6. Egg embryos subjected to experimental manipulation must be destroyed humanely at least two days prior to hatching. Normal egg embryos allowed to hatch must be treated humanely within these guidelines.

7. The administration of anesthetics should be carried out by a qualified science teacher competent in such procedures. (The legal ramifications of student use of anesthetics are complex and such use should be avoided.)

G. The use of living animals for science fair projects and displays shall be in accordance with these guidelines. In addition, no living vertebrate animals shall be used in displays for science fair exhibitions.

H. It is recognized that an exceptionally talented student may wish to conduct original research in the biological or medical sciences. In those cases where the research value of a specific project is obvious by its potential contribution to science, but its execution would be otherwise prohibited by the guidelines governing the selection of an appropriate experimental animal or procedure, exceptions can be obtained if:

1. the project is approved by and carried out under the direct supervision of a qualified biomedical scientist or a designated adult supervisor in the field of investigation; and

2. the project is carried out in an appropriate research facility; and

3. the project is carried out with the utmost regard for the humane care and treatment of the animals involved in the project; and

4. a research plan is developed and approved by the qualified biomedical scientist prior to the start of any research.

Laboratory Manual A

Biology

Prentice Hall

Upper Saddle River, New Jersey
Needham, Massachusetts

ISBN 0-13-115284-X

5 6 7 8 9 10   07 06

Contents

The symbol 🔍 indicates Design-an-Experiment investigations.

Unit 1   The Nature of Life

Unit 2   Ecology

Unit 3   Cells

Unit 4   Genetics

Unit 5   Evolution

Safety in the Biology Laboratory

Working in the biology laboratory can be interesting, exciting, and rewarding. But it can also be quite dangerous if you are not serious and alert and if proper safety precautions are not taken at all times. You are responsible for maintaining an enjoyable, instructional, and safe environment in the biology laboratory. Unsafe practices endanger not only you but the people around you as well.

Read the following information about safety in the biology laboratory carefully. Review applicable safety information before you begin each Laboratory Investigation. If you have any questions about safety or laboratory procedures, be sure to ask your teacher.

Safety Symbol Guide

All the investigations in this laboratory manual have been designed with safety in mind. If you follow the instructions, you should have a safe and interesting year in the laboratory. Before beginning any investigation, make sure you read the safety rules on pages 8–11 of *Laboratory Manual A*.

The safety symbols shown on page 8 are used throughout *Laboratory Manual A*. They appear first next to the Safety section of an investigation and then next to certain steps in an investigation where specific safety precautions are required. The symbols alert you to the need for special safety precautions. The description of each symbol indicates the precaution(s) you should take whenever you see the symbol in an investigation.

Safety Symbols

These symbols alert you to possible dangers.

Safety Goggles Always wear safety goggles to protect your eyes in any activity involving chemicals, flames, or heating, or the possibility of broken glassware.

Laboratory Apron Wear a laboratory apron to protect your skin and clothing.

Breakage You are working with breakable materials, such as glassware. Handle breakable materials with care. Do not touch broken glassware.

Heat-resistant Gloves Use hand protection when handling hot materials. Hot equipment or hot water can cause burns. Do not touch hot objects with your bare hands.

Plastic Gloves Wear disposable plastic gloves to protect yourself from chemicals or organisms that could be harmful. Keep your hands away from your face. Dispose of the gloves according to your teacher's instructions at the end of the activity.

Heating Use a clamp or tongs to pick up hot glassware. Do not touch hot objects with your bare hands.

Sharp Object Pointed-tip scissors, scalpels, knives, needles, pins, or tacks can cut or puncture your skin. Always direct a sharp edge or point away from yourself and others. Use sharp instruments only as directed.

Electric Shock Avoid the possibility of electric shock. Never use electrical equipment around water, or when equipment is wet or your hands are wet. Be sure cords are untangled and cannot trip anyone. Disconnect the equipment when it is not in use.

Corrosive Chemical Avoid getting acids or other corrosive chemicals on your skin or clothing, or in your eyes. Do not inhale the vapors. Wash your hands when you are finished with the activity.

Poison Do not let any poisonous chemical come in contact with your skin, and do not inhale its vapors. Wash your hands when you are finished with the activity.

Physical Safety When an experiment involves physical activity, take precautions to avoid injuring yourself or others. Follow instructions from your teacher. Alert your teacher if there is any reason you should not participate in the activity.

Animal Safety Treat live animals with care to avoid harming the animals or yourself. Working with animal parts or preserved animals also may require caution. Wash your hands when you are finished.

Plant Safety Handle plants only as directed by your teacher. If you are allergic to certain plants, tell your teacher before doing an activity in which plants are used. Avoid touching poisonous plants or plants with thorns. Wash your hands when you are finished with the activity.

Flames You may be working with flames from a Bunsen burner, candle, or matches. Tie back loose hair and clothing. Follow instructions from your teacher about lighting and extinguishing flames.

No Flames Flammable materials may be present. Make sure no flames, sparks, or exposed heat sources are present.

Fumes When poisonous or unpleasant vapors may be involved, work in a ventilated area. Avoid inhaling vapors directly. Only test an odor when directed to do so by your teacher, and use a wafting motion to direct the vapor toward your nose.

Disposal Chemicals and other used materials must be disposed of safely. Follow the instructions from your teacher.

Hand Washing Wash your hands thoroughly. Use antibacterial soap and warm water. Lather both sides of your hands and between your fingers. Rinse well.

General Safety Awareness You may see this symbol when none of the other symbols appears. In this case, follow the specific instructions provided. You may also see this symbol when you are asked to develop your own procedure. Have your teacher approve your plan before you go further.

Science Safety Rules

One of the first things a scientist learns is that working in the laboratory can be an exciting experience. But the laboratory can also be quite dangerous if proper safety rules are not followed at all times. To prepare yourself for a safe year in the laboratory, read over the following safety rules. Then read them a second time. Make sure you understand each rule. If you do not, ask your teacher to explain any rules you are unsure of.

Dress Code

1. Many materials in the laboratory can cause eye injury. To protect yourself from possible injury, wear safety goggles whenever you are working with chemicals, burners, or any substance that might get into your eyes. Never wear contact lenses in the laboratory.

2. Wear a laboratory apron or coat whenever you are working with chemicals or heated substances.

3. Tie back long hair to keep your hair away from any chemicals, burners and candles, or other laboratory equipment.

4. Remove or tie back any article of clothing or jewelry that can hang down and touch chemicals and flames. Do not wear sandals or open-toed shoes in the laboratory. Never walk around the laboratory barefoot or in stocking feet.

General Safety Rules

5. Be serious and alert when working in the laboratory. Never "horse around" in the laboratory.

6. Be prepared to work when you arrive in the laboratory. Be sure that you understand the procedure to be employed in any laboratory investigation and the possible hazards associated with it.

7. Read all directions for an investigation several times. Follow the directions exactly as they are written. If you are in doubt about any part of the investigation, ask your teacher for assistance.

8. Never perform activities that are not authorized by your teacher. Obtain permission before "experimenting" on your own.

9. Never handle any equipment unless you have specific permission.

10. Take extreme care not to spill any material in the laboratory. If spills occur, ask your teacher immediately about the proper cleanup procedure. Never simply pour chemicals or other substances into the sink or trash container.

11. Never eat or taste anything or apply cosmetics in the laboratory unless directed to do so. This includes food, drinks, candy, and gum, as well as chemicals. Wash your hands before and after performing every investigation.

12. Know the location and proper use of safety equipment such as the fire extinguisher, emergency blanket, first-aid kit, emergency shower, and eyewash station.

13. Notify your teacher of any medical problems you may have, such as allergies or asthma.

14. Keep your laboratory area clean and free of unnecessary books, papers, and equipment.

First Aid

15. Report all accidents, no matter how minor, to your teacher immediately.

16. Learn what to do in case of specific accidents such as getting acid in your eyes or on your skin. (Rinse acids off your body with lots of water.)

17. Become aware of the location of the first-aid kit. Your teacher should administer any required first aid due to injury. Or your teacher may send you to the school nurse or call a physician.

18. Know where and how to report an accident or fire. Find out the location of the fire extinguisher, phone, and fire alarm. Keep a list of important phone numbers such as the fire department and school

nurse near the phone. Report any fires to your teacher at once.

Heating and Fire Safety

19. Never use a heat source such as a candle or burner without wearing safety goggles.

20. Never heat a chemical you are not instructed to heat. A chemical that is harmless when cool can be dangerous when heated.

21. Maintain a clean work area and keep all materials away from flames.

22. Never reach across a flame.

23. Make sure you know how to light a Bunsen burner. (Your teacher will demonstrate the proper procedure for lighting a burner.) If the flame leaps out of a burner toward you, turn the gas off immediately. Do not touch the burner. It may be hot. And never leave a lighted burner unattended.

24. Point a test tube or bottle that is being heated away from you and others. Chemicals can splash or boil out of a heated test tube.

25. Never heat a liquid in a closed container. The expanding gases produced may blow the container apart, injuring you or others.

26. Never pick up a container that has been heated without first holding the back of your hand near it. If you can feel the heat on the back of your hand, the container may be too hot to handle. Use a clamp, tongs, or heat-resistant gloves when handling hot containers.

Using Chemicals Safely

27. Never mix chemicals for the "fun of it." You might produce a dangerous, possibly explosive, substance.

28. Never touch, taste, or smell a chemical that you do not know for a fact is harmless. Many chemicals are poisonous. If you are instructed to note the fumes in an investigation, gently wave your hand over the opening of a container and direct the fumes toward your nose. Do not inhale the fumes directly from the container.

29. Use only those chemicals needed in the investigation. Keep all lids closed when a chemical is not being used. Notify your teacher whenever chemicals are spilled.

30. Dispose of all chemicals as instructed by your teacher. To avoid contamination, never return chemicals to their original containers.

31. Be extra careful when working with acids or bases. Pour such chemicals over the sink, not over your work bench.

32. When diluting an acid, pour the acid into water. Never pour water into the acid.

33. Rinse any acids off your skin or clothing with water. Immediately notify your teacher of any acid spill.

Using Glassware Safely

34. Never force glass tubing into a rubber stopper. A turning motion and lubricant will be helpful when inserting glass tubing into rubber stoppers or rubber tubing. Your teacher will demonstrate the proper way to insert glass tubing.

35. Never heat glassware that is not thoroughly dry. Use a wire screen to protect glassware from any flame.

36. Keep in mind that hot glassware will not appear hot. Never pick up glassware without first checking to see if it is hot.

37. If you are instructed to cut glass tubing, fire polish the ends immediately to remove sharp edges.

38. Never use broken or chipped glassware. If glassware breaks, notify your teacher and dispose of the glassware in the proper trash container.

39. Never eat or drink from laboratory glassware. Clean glassware thoroughly before putting it away.

Using Sharp Instruments

40. Handle scalpels or razor blades with extreme care. Never cut material toward you; cut away from you.

41. Be careful when handling sharp, pointed objects such as scissors, pins, and dissecting probes.

42. Notify your teacher immediately if you cut yourself or receive a cut.

Handling Living Organisms

43. No investigations that will cause pain, discomfort, or harm to mammals, birds, reptiles, fish, and amphibians should be done in the classroom or at home.

44. Treat all living things with care and respect. Do not touch any organism in the classroom or laboratory unless given permission to do so. Many plants are poisonous or have thorns, and even tame animals may bite or scratch if alarmed.

45. Animals should be handled only if necessary. If an animal is excited or frightened, pregnant, feeding, or with its young, special handling is required.

46. Your teacher will instruct you as to how to handle each species that may be brought into the classroom.

47. Treat all microorganisms as if they were harmful. Use antiseptic procedure, as directed by your teacher, when working with microbes. Dispose of microbes as your teacher directs.

48. Clean your hands thoroughly after handling animals or the cage containing animals.

49. Wear gloves when handling small mammals. Report animal bites or stings to your teacher at once.

End-of-Investigation Rules

50. When an investigation is completed, clean up your work area and return all equipment to its proper place.

51. Wash your hands with soap and warm water after every investigation.

52. Turn off all burners before leaving the laboratory. Check that the gas line leading to the burner is off as well.

Safety Contract

Once you have read all the safety information on pages 7–11 in *Laboratory Manual A* and are sure you understand all the rules, fill out the safety contract that follows. Signing this contract tells your teacher that you are aware of the rules of the laboratory. Return your signed contract to your teacher. You will not be allowed to work in the laboratory until you have returned your signed contract.

SAFETY CONTRACT

I, _____, have read the

Safety in the Biology Laboratory section on pages 7–11 in *Biology*

Laboratory Manual A. I understand its contents completely, and agree to

follow all the safety rules and guidelines that have been established in

each of the following areas:

(please check)

☐ Dress Code   ☐ Using Glassware Safely

☐ General Safety Rules   ☐ Using Sharp Instruments

☐ First Aid   ☐ Handling Living Organisms

☐ Heating and Fire Safety   ☐ End-of-Investigation Rules

☐ Using Chemicals Safely

Signature _____ Date _____

How to Use the Laboratory Manual

This is probably the most exciting time in history to be studying biology. The science of biology is progressing rapidly. Biology is directly related to many of today's most important news stories. Cloning of animals; AIDS; animal rights; genetic fingerprinting; acid rain; and efforts to save endangered species all involve biology.

In order to gain a working knowledge of biology, you need to understand some of the processes that scientists use to find answers to problems. The Laboratory Investigations and activities in *Laboratory Manual A* enable you to learn about and practice methods used by scientists in their quest to increase human knowledge.

In each Laboratory Investigation, your objective is to solve a problem using scientific methods. Each Laboratory Investigation follows a standard outline that will help you tackle the problem in a systematic and organized manner. One Laboratory Investigation in each unit (except Unit 1) is a Design an Experiment activity that follows a slightly different outline.

Introduction The Introduction provides information you will need to complete the investigation, and ties the Laboratory Investigation to concepts discussed in the textbook. The Introduction corresponds to the first step in any scientific work—gathering information about the topic so that you can develop a hypothesis.

Problem This section presents a problem in the form of a question. Your job is to solve the problem based on your observations.

Pre-Lab Discussion After reading the Laboratory Investigation, answering the questions in this section will help you to clarify the purpose of the investigation. By asking you the reasons for specific steps in the Procedure, this section prepares you to carry out the Laboratory Investigation. Questions in this section may also highlight safety concerns to which you should pay careful attention.

Materials A list of all required materials appears at the beginning of the investigation. The quantity of material for each investigation is indicated for individual students, pairs of students, or groups of students.

Safety The Safety section warns you of potential hazards and tells you about precautions you should take to decrease the risk of accidents. The safety symbols that are relevant to the Laboratory Investigation appear next to the title of the Safety section. They also appear next to certain steps of the Procedure.

Procedure This section provides detailed step-by-step instructions. Diagrams are included where necessary. The Procedure enables you to test the hypothesis.

Make sure you read the entire Procedure carefully before you begin the investigation. Look for safety symbols and notes. If safety symbols appear next to a step in the Procedure, you should follow the corresponding safety precaution(s) for that step and all following steps. **CAUTION** statements within the steps of the Procedure warn of possible hazards. **Notes** in the Procedure provide special directions.

In keeping with scientific methods, you will record your data by filling in data tables, graphing data, labeling diagrams, drawing observed structures, and answering questions.

Analysis and Conclusions Two steps of the scientific method—analyzing data and forming a conclusion—are represented in this section. Here, you are to analyze and interpret your experimental results. This section may also challenge you to apply your conclusions to real-life situations or related experiments.

Going Further This section suggests additional activities for you to pursue on your own. Some of these are extensions of the Laboratory Investigation that you might perform with your teacher's permission. Others involve library research.

Presenting Data

To seek answers to problems or questions they have about the world, scientists typically perform many experiments in the laboratory. In doing so, they observe physical characteristics and processes, select areas for study, and review the scientific literature to gain background information about the topic they are investigating. They then form hypotheses, test these hypotheses through controlled experiments, record and analyze data, and develop a conclusion about the correctness of the hypotheses. Finally, they report their findings in detail, giving enough information about their experimental procedure so that other scientists are able to replicate the experiments and verify the results.

The Laboratory Investigations in *Laboratory Manual A* provide an opportunity for you to investigate scientific problems in the same manner as that of a typical scientist. As you perform these investigations, you will employ many of the techniques and steps of the scientific method a working scientist does. Some of the most important skills you will acquire are associated with the step of the scientific method known as recording and analyzing data. Three of these skills are creating and filling in data tables, making drawings, and finding averages. Another set of skills useful in presenting data is examined in the Laboratory Skills activity titled Using Graphing Skills.

It is important to record data precisely—even if the results of an investigation appear to be wrong. And it is extremely important to keep in mind that developing laboratory skills and data analysis skills is actually more valuable than simply arriving at the correct answers. If you analyze your data correctly—even if the data are not perfect— you will be learning to think as a scientist thinks. And that is the purpose of this laboratory manual and your experience in the biology laboratory.

Data Tables

When scientists conduct various experiments and do research, they collect vast amounts of information: for example, measurements, descriptions, and other observations. To communicate and interpret this information, they must record it in an organized fashion. Scientists use data tables for this purpose.

You will be responsible for completing data tables for many of the Laboratory Investigations. Each column in a data table has a heading. The column headings explain where particular data are to be placed. The completed data tables will help you interpret the information you collected and answer the questions found at the end of each Laboratory Investigation.

Name_____ Class_____ Date _____

EXERCISE 1

Given the following information, complete Data Table 1. Then interpret the data and answer the five questions that follow.

Information: The following hair colors were found among three classes of students:

Class 1:	brown— 20	Class 2:	brown— 18	Class 3:	brown— 15
	black— 1		black— 0		black— 4
	blond— 4		blond— 6		blond— 15

Data Table

Hair Color	Class 1	Class 2	Class 3	Total
Brown	20	18	15	53
Black	1	0	4	5
Blond	4	6	15	25

1. What type of information is being gathered?

Hair color among three classes of students.

2. Which hair color occurs most often?

Brown.

3. From the information in the Data Table, can you give the number of boys with black hair?

No.

4. What information can you give about the number of students with black hair?

Total of 5.

5. Which class has the most blond students?

Class 3.

6. How many students made up the entire student population?

83.

EXERCISE 2

Given the following information, organize the data into a table. Use the blank area provided in Figure 1 to draw in the necessary columns and rows. Then interpret the data and answer the questions that follow.

Information: On an expedition around the world, several scientists collected the venom of various snakes. One of the tests that the scientists conducted determined the toxicity of the venom of each snake. Other data obtained by the scientists included the mortality percentage, or relative death rate, from the bites of various snakes.

The snakes observed were the (1) southern United States copperhead, (2) western diamondback rattlesnake, (3) eastern coral snake, (4) king cobra, (5) Indian krait, (6) European viper, (7) bushmaster, (8) fer-de-lance, (9) black-necked cobra, (10) puff adder.

The mortality percentage of people bitten by the snakes varied from 100% to less than 1%. The scientists noted the mortality percentage for each of the snakes was (1) less than 1%, (2) 5–15%, (3) 5–20%, (4) greater than 40%, (5) 77%, (6) 1–5%, (7) usually 100%, (8) 10–20%, (9) 11–40%, and (10) 11–40%.

Snakes Observed	Mortality Percentage
Copperhead	less than 1%
Rattlesnake	5–15%
Coral snake	5–20%
King Cobra	greater than 40%
Indian krait	77%
European viper	1–5%
Bushmaster	usually 100%
Fer-de-lance	10–20%
Black-necked cobra	11–40%
Puff adder	11–40%

Figure 1

1. Which snake's venom has the highest mortality rate?
   Bushmaster.

2. Which snake's venom has the lowest mortality rate?
   Southern United States copperhead.

3. From the information recorded, can you determine the snake whose venom works the most rapidly? The least rapidly?
   No. No.

4. Which two snakes' venom have the same mortality rate?
   Black-necked cobra and the puff adder.

5. How many types of snakes were observed?
   10.

DRAWINGS

Laboratory drawings can be made using several methods. Some drawings are made in circles that represent the viewing field of a microscope or another type of magnifier. When completing these drawings, be sure to include the magnification at which you viewed the object. Other laboratory drawings represent organisms or parts of organisms. These drawings show the relative size, shape, and location of anatomical structures. When completing representative drawings, make the structures as clear and as accurate as possible.

Most laboratory drawings are labeled. Use the following guidelines to help make your laboratory drawings clear and legible.

- Use a ruler to draw label lines.
- Label lines should point to the center of the structure being labeled.
- Do not write on the label lines.
- Print all labels horizontally.
- Label the right-hand side of the drawing, if possible.
- Do not cross label lines.

EXERCISE 3

The following drawing was made without using the guidelines above. Circle those parts of the drawing that do not follow the guidelines. Then, on the lines provided, explain how the drawing should be done.

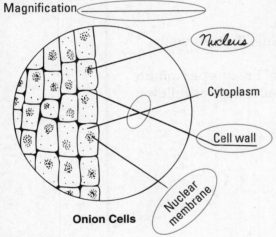

Magnification should be inserted. Nucleus label should be printed. Cell wall label should appear at the end of the label line. Nuclear membrane label should be printed horizontally. Label lines should not cross.

Onion Cells

Figure 2

AVERAGES

Occasionally you will be required to find the average of data gathered from an investigation. To find an average, add the items in the group together and then divide the total by the number of items. For example, if there were five students of different ages—12, 13, 14, 17, and 19—how would you find the average age of the group? Add the five ages together and divide the total by 5, which is the number of items (students) in the group. What is the average age of this group of students? Your answer should be 15 years old.

EXERCISE 4

In a garden the heights of six sunflowers are 135.0 cm, 162.5 cm, 180.0 cm, 235.0 cm, 185.0 cm, and 167.5 cm. What is the average height of the sunflowers?

177.5 cm.

EXERCISE 5

Find the average for the following group of data. Then use the results to answer the questions that follow.

In an experiment on plant growth and overcrowding, plants of the following heights are in three equal-sized containers.

Flowerpot 1:   20.0 cm and 18.2 cm
Flowerpot 2:   12.0 cm, 10.8 cm, 11.2 cm, and 12.4 cm
Flowerpot 3:   7.5 cm, 8.0 cm, 6.0 cm, 6.2 cm, 5.8 cm, and 7.3 cm

1. What is the average height of the plants in each flowerpot?

   Flowerpot 1: 19.1 cm;

   Flowerpot 2: 11.6 cm; Flowerpot 3: 6.8 cm.

2. In which flowerpot did the plants grow the tallest? Explain.

   The plants in Flowerpot 1 grew the tallest because they had more room to grow. Also the competition for food

   and water was less in Flowerpot 1 than in the other flowerpots.

EXERCISE 6

Find the averages for the following groups of data. Express your answers to the nearest tenth.

In a sample group of students, the number of breaths per minute was measured at rest and after exercise. The results were as follows:

At rest
Males: 10.1, 13.0, 12.5, 10.2, 13.1, 11.8
Females: 10.4, 13.0, 12.1, 11.9, 10.5, 12.8

After exercise
Males: 18.9, 23.7, 22.6, 21.3, 19.2, 20.6
Females: 25.0, 26.7, 29.0, 35.3, 33.1, 31.7

1. What is the average number of breaths per minute for males at rest? 11.8.
   Females at rest? 11.8.

2. What is the average number of breaths per minute for males after exercise? 21.1.
   Females after exercise? 30.1.

3. How many students make up the sample group? 12.0

4. What is the average number of breaths per minute for the entire group at rest? 11.8.
   After exercise? 25.6.

5. Do males or females take more breaths per minute at rest? Neither, the results are the same.
   After exercise? Females.

Recognizing Laboratory Safety

You may want to refer students to safety information appearing in Appendix B of the textbook.
Time required: 50 minutes

Introduction

An important part of your study of biology will be working in a laboratory. In the laboratory, you and your classmates will learn biology by actively conducting and observing experiments. Working directly with living things will provide opportunities for you to better understand the principles of biology discussed in your textbook or talked about in class.

Most of the laboratory work you will do is quite safe. However, some laboratory equipment, chemicals, and specimens can be dangerous if handled improperly. Laboratory accidents do not just happen. They are caused by carelessness, improper handling of equipment and specimens, or inappropriate behavior.

In this investigation, you will learn how to prevent accidents and thus work safely in a laboratory. You will review some safety guidelines and become acquainted with the location and proper use of safety equipment in your classroom laboratory.

Problem

What are the proper practices for working safely in a biology laboratory?

Pre-Lab Discussion

Read the entire investigation. Then, work with a partner to answer the following questions.

1. Why might eating or drinking in the laboratory be dangerous?
   Traces of poisonous substances may be on the lab tables. Crumbs or the sticky remains of food may, in turn,

   contaminate the lab.

2. How can reading through the entire investigation before beginning the Procedure help prevent accidents?
   Reading through the entire investigation insures a knowledge of the steps of the investigation, which will help to

   proceed in a calm, knowledgeable way. It also highlights safety precautions to pay attention to.

3. Look around the room. What safety equipment do you recognize?
   Answers will vary. Students should recognize the fire extinguishers and first-aid kits.

4. What safety procedures should you follow when cleaning up at the end of an investigation?
   Pay careful attention when washing glassware, and follow the teacher's directions for disposing of chemicals.

5. Can minor safety procedures be skipped in order to finish the investigation before the bell rings?
   Never skip safety procedures, no matter how minor.

Materials *(per group)*

Biology textbook
Laboratory safety equipment (for demonstration)

Procedure

1. Carefully read the list of laboratory safety rules listed in Appendix B of your textbook.

2. Special symbols are used throughout this laboratory manual to call attention to investigations that require extra caution. Use Appendix B in your textbook as a reference to describe what each symbol printed below means.

1. Student is working with glassware that can easily be broken. _____
_____

2. Student is working with fire source. _____
_____

3. Student should put on heat-resistant gloves to avoid burning his or her hands. _____
_____

4. Student is working with chemicals that could be hazardous. _____
_____

5. Student is performing an experiment in which the eyes and face should be protected by safety goggles.
_____

6. Student is working with a sharp instrument. _____
_____

7. Student is using electricity in the laboratory. _____
_____

8. Student is working with live animals. _____
_____

3. Your teacher will point out the location of the safety equipment in your classroom laboratory. Pay special attention to instructions for using such equipment as fire extinguishers, eyewash fountains, emergency blankets, emergency showers, and items in first-aid kits. Use the space provided below to list the location of all safety equipment in your laboratory.

Student responses will depend on the specific safety features of your

classroom laboratory.

Be sure to show the location of all safety equipment in your laboratory. Also give instructions on its proper use. Guidelines pertaining to the use of special equipment, fire drill procedures, or penalties for misbehavior in lab might also be discussed at this time.

Analysis and Conclusions

Observing Look at each of the following drawings and explain why the laboratory activities pictured are unsafe.

1. Safety goggles should always be worn whenever a person is working with chemicals, alcohol or Bunsen burners, or any substance that might get into the eyes.

2. When heating a test tube, always point its open end away from yourself or others. Wear heat-resistant gloves when holding a heated object.

3. Never heat a liquid in a closed container. The expanding gases produced may blow the container apart.

4. Never eat or drink from laboratory glassware. The last material in the glassware may have been poisonous and traces of it may still remain in the glassware.

_____

_____

_____

_____

Going Further

Many houseplants and some plants found in biology laboratories are poisonous. Use appropriate library resources to do research on several common poisonous plants. Share your research with your classmates. You may prepare a booklet describing common poisonous plants. Use drawings or photographs to illustrate your booklet.

Identifying Laboratory Equipment

Time required: 40 minutes

Introduction

Scientists use a variety of tools to explore the world around them. Tools are very important in the advancement of science. The type of tools scientists use depends on the problems they are trying to solve. A scientist may use something as simple as a metric ruler to measure the length of a leaf. At another time, the same scientist may use a complex computer to analyze large amounts of data concerning hundreds of leaves.

In this investigation, you will identify pieces of laboratory equipment likely to be found in a biology laboratory. You will also learn the function of each piece of laboratory equipment.

Problem

What are the names and functions of some of the pieces of laboratory equipment found in a typical biology laboratory?

Pre-Lab Discussion

Read the entire investigation. Then, work with a partner to answer the following questions.

1. What kinds of measurements might you need to make in the laboratory?

Length, mass, volume, temperature.

2. What kinds of equipment would you need for these tasks?

Metric ruler, triple-beam balance, graduated cylinder, thermometer.

3. Why are there several types of glassware marked for measuring?

Different sizes of glassware, such as the graduated beaker or the graduated cylinder, allow for more accurate

measurements of specific volumes.

4. How might glassware be used differently?

Some are used for measuring, some are used for tests or experiments. Ten test tubes are more appropriate for

running several different tests on a solution than ten graduated cylinders.

5. When might you need to use a thermometer in the lab?

To make sure the experimental and the control groups are at the same temperature. To record the temperature

at which a reaction occurs.

Safety

Handle all glassware carefully. Be careful when handling sharp instruments. Always handle the microscope with extreme care. You are responsible for its proper care and use. Use caution when handling glass slides, as they can break easily and cut you. Note all safety alert symbols next to the steps in the Procedure and review the meanings of each symbol by referring to Safety Symbols on page 8.

Equipment should be set up for display before students begin the investigation.

Procedure

1. Look at the drawings of the laboratory equipment in Figure 1. In the space provided, write the name of each piece of laboratory equipment.

2. Carefully inspect the different types of laboratory equipment that have been set out by your teacher. In the space provided write the function of each piece of laboratory equipment.

A. hand lens; magnifies small objects

B. dissecting tray; holds specimen for dissection

C. dissecting pins; hold specimen on dissecting tray

D. forceps; grasps small objects

E. dissecting scissors; cut specimens to be studied

F. dissecting probe; pointed object used to examine specimens

G. scalpel; cuts specimens to be dissected

H. safety goggles; protect eyes from fire and chemicals

I. triple-beam balance; measures mass

J. graduated cylinder; measures liquids

K. test tube; holds liquids

L. beaker; holds and measures liquids

M. test-tube rack; holds test tubes

N. Bunsen burner; heats objects

O. dropper pipette; measures out drops of liquid

P. pipette; transfers measured amounts of liquid

Q. compound microscope; magnifies very small objects

R. microscope slide; holds object for examination with the compound microscope

S. coverslip; covers material on a glass slide

T. petri dish; shallow dish used for bacterial cultures

U. thermometer; measures temperature

V. funnel; transfers liquid from one container to another; filters materials with filter paper

W. metric ruler; measures length

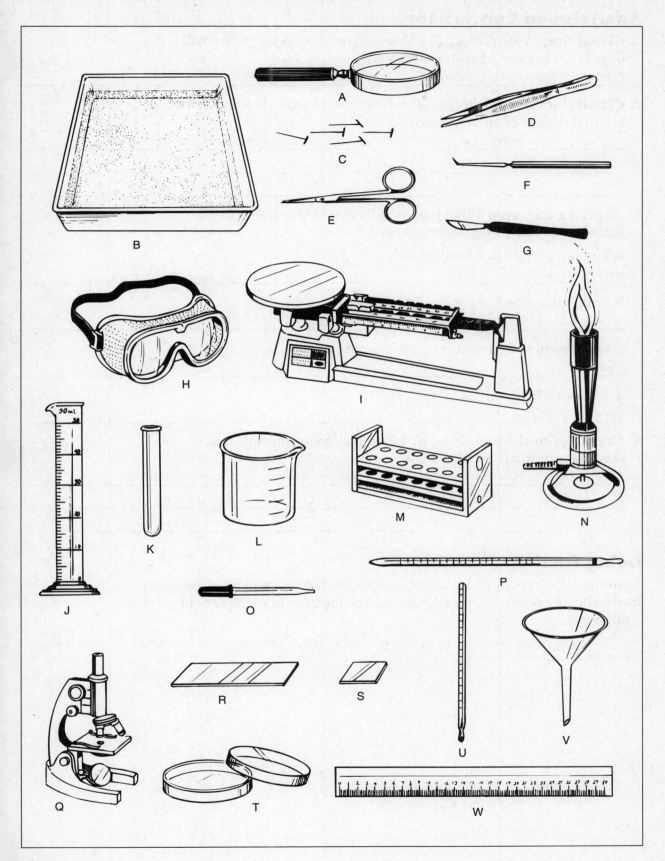

Figure 1

Analysis and Conclusions

1. **Classifying** Which laboratory tools can be used to magnify small objects so they can be seen more easily?

   Compound microscope and hand lens.

2. **Classifying** Which laboratory tools are useful when looking at the internal organs of an earthworm?

   Dissecting tray, dissecting pins, dissecting scissors, forceps, probe, scalpel, and hand lens.

3. **Applying Concepts** What tool or tools would you use to make each of the following measurements?

   a. amount of milk in a small glass

   Graduated cylinder.

   b. length of a sheet of paper

   Metric ruler.

   c. temperature of the water in a swimming pool

   Thermometer.

   d. mass of a baseball

   Triple-beam balance.

4. **Drawing Conclusions** How do laboratory tools improve the observations made by a scientist?

   Certain laboratory tools can be used to extend the range and accuracy of the scientist's senses.

Going Further

Examine other types of laboratory equipment that you will be using in the biology laboratory. Try to determine the function of each piece of equipment.

You may wish to include items such as a hot plate, inoculating loop, Erlenmeyer or Florence flask, test-tube holder, beaker tongs, depression slide, or dissecting microscope.

Making Metric Measurements

You may want to refer students to reading about the metric system in Section 1-4 and in Appendix C of the textbook.
Time required: 50 minutes

Introduction

In many biology investigations, precise measurements must be made before observations can be interpreted. For everyday measuring, we still use English units such as the inch, quart, and pound. For scientific work, and for everyday measuring in most countries, the International System of Units (SI) is used. Eventually our country will use SI units for everyday measuring too.

Like our money system, SI is a metric system. All units are based on the number 10. In the SI system it is easy to change one unit to another because all units are related to one another by a power of 10.

In this investigation, you will review SI units for measuring length, liquid volume, and mass. You will also learn how to use some common laboratory equipment used for measuring.

Problem

How are metric units of measurement used in the laboratory?

Pre-Lab Discussion

Read the entire investigation. Then, work with a partner to answer the following questions.

1. Why do scientists and other people in most countries use the metric system for measurements?

   It is easier to convert to other units within the system. The SI system is the universal language of

   measurement for scientists.

2. Why is it easy to change from one unit to another in the SI system?

   All units are related to one another by the power of ten.

3. What connections can you identify between the metric units for length and volume?

   Metric units of volume are derived by cubing metric units of length. A common metric unit of length is the

   meter. Volume is measured by multiplying length by width by height, all of which are measured in meters.

   Therefore, the metric unit of volume is the cubic meter (m³).

4. Why is it difficult to convert miles to yards or feet?

   In the English system there is no uniform relationship between units. For example, a yard is equal to 3 feet

   or 36 inches.

5. Name several aspects of everyday life that will change when our country converts to SI units.

   Examples include: Signs for miles per hour on the highway; food products that are weighed in ounces or pounds.

Materials (per group)

meter stick
metric ruler
small test tube
rubber stopper

coin
triple-beam balance
50-mL beaker
100-mL graduated cylinder

Safety 🔲 🔳

Handle all glassware carefully. Note all safety alert symbols next to the steps in the Procedure and review the meanings of each symbol by referring to Safety Symbols on page 8.

Procedure

Part A. Measuring Length

1. Use the meter stick to measure the length, width, and height of your laboratory table or desk in meters. Record your measurements to the nearest hundredth of a meter in Data Table 1.

2. Convert the measurements from meters to centimeters and then to millimeters. Record these measurements in Data Table 1.

3. Use a metric ruler to measure the length of a small test tube and the diameter of its mouth in centimeters. Record your measurements to the nearest millimeter in Data Table 2.

4. Convert the measurements from centimeters to millimeters. Record these measurements in Data Table 2.

Data Table 1

Lab Table Measurements			
Dimension	m	cm	mm
Length	Answers will depend on student observations.		
Width			
Height			

Data Table 2

Test Tube Measurements		
Dimension	cm	mm
Length	Answers will depend on student observations.	
Diameter of mouth		

Name_____ Class_____ Date _____

Part B. Measuring the Volume of a Liquid

 1. Fill the test tube to the top with water. Pour the water into the graduated cylinder.

2. The surface of the liquid will be slightly curved. This curved surface is called a meniscus. To measure the volume accurately, your eye must be at the same level as the bottom of the meniscus. See Figure 1. Record the volume of the water from the test tube to the nearest milliliter in Data Table 3.

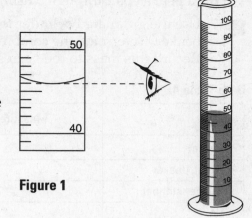

Figure 1

Data Table 3

Measurement of Volume	
Object	**Volume (mL)**
Water in test tube	Answers will depend on student observations.

Part C. Measuring Mass

 1. Place the 50-mL beaker on the pan of the balance. Be sure that the riders on the triple-beam balance are moved all the way to the left and that the pointer rests on zero. See Figure 2.

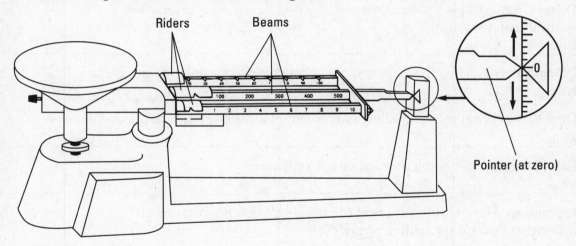

Figure 2

2. Move the rider on the middle beam to the right one notch at a time until the pointer drops below zero. Move the rider left one notch.

3. Move the rider on the back beam one notch at a time until the pointer again drops below zero. Move the rider left one notch.

4. Slide the rider along the front beam until the pointer stops at zero. The mass of the object is equal to the sum of the readings on the three beams.

5. Record the mass of the beaker to the nearest tenth of a gram in Data Table 4 on p. 30. Remove the beaker.

6. Repeat steps 2 through 5 using the rubber stopper and then the coin.

7. Use the graduated cylinder to place exactly 40 mL of water in the beaker. Determine the combined mass of the beaker and water. Record this mass to the nearest tenth of a gram in Data Table 4.

Data Table 4

Measurement of Mass	
Object	Mass (g)
50-mL beaker	
Rubber stopper	Answers will depend on student observations.
Coin	
50-mL beaker plus 40 mL of water	

Analysis and Conclusions

1. **Calculating** How do you convert meters to centimeters? Centimeters to millimeters?

   To convert meters to centimeters, multiply by 100. To convert centimeters to millimeters, multiply by 10.

2. **Observing** What is the largest volume of liquid your graduated cylinder can measure?

   100 mL.

3. **Observing** What is the smallest volume of a liquid your graduated cylinder can measure?

   1 mL.

4. **Calculating** What is the largest mass of an object your balance can measure?

   610 g.

5. **Observing** What is the smallest mass of an object your balance can measure?

   0.1 g.

6. **Calculating** What is the mass of 40 mL of water?

   40 g.

7. **Predicting** How would you find the mass of a certain amount of water that you poured into a paper cup?

   First find the mass of the paper cup. Then pour the water into the paper cup and find their combined mass.

   Subtract the mass of the paper cup from the combined mass.

8. **Calculating** In this investigation you found the mass of 40 mL of water. Based on your observations, what is the mass of 1 mL of water?

   1 mL of water has a mass of 1 g.

Going Further

If other types of laboratory balances are available, such as an electronic balance or a double-pan balance, use them to find the masses of several different objects. Compare the accuracy of the different balances.

Applying the Scientific Method

You may want to tell students to read about the scientific method in Sections 1-1 and 1-2. Time required: 30 minutes and a 15-minute observation period after one week

Introduction

The scientific method is a procedure used to gather information and test ideas. Scientists use the scientific method to answer questions about life and living organisms. Experimentation is an important part of the scientific method. In order to ensure that the results of an experiment are due to the variable being tested, a scientist must have both an experimental setup and a control setup. The experimental setup and the control setup differ only in the variable being tested.

In this investigation, you will form a hypothesis, test it, and draw a conclusion based on your observations.

Problem

Is light necessary for the sprouting of a potato?

Pre-Lab Discussion

Read the entire investigation. Then, work with a partner to answer the following questions.

1. Under what conditions do potatoes usually grow?
   Underground in darkness.

2. Why is it important to seal the plastic bags?
   To prevent other factors from affecting the experiment.

3. How does cutting one potato in half help limit the variables of the experiment?
   By using the same potato, we can be positive that both halves have the same growth potential at the
   beginning of the experiment.

4. Why is it necessary to keep both potato halves on moist paper towels?
   Water is necessary for plant growth.

5. What evidence will tell you whether or not light is necessary for sprouting a potato?
   Which potato half has more sprouts, the potato in the dark or the potato in the light.

Materials (per group)

1 medium-sized potato
2 plastic bags with twist ties
knife
2 paper towels

Have students wash the potato with a brush because some potatoes have a wax coating that can inhibit growth. Students can reduce the risk of microbial contamination by using tongs to dip the potato halves in bleach for 30 seconds and then rinsing them thoroughly with running water before placing them in plastic bags. Students should wear laboratory aprons, safety goggles, and plastic gloves when working around bleach.

Safety 🗑 ✂ 🔥

Put on a laboratory apron. Be careful when handling sharp instruments. Note all safety alert symbols next to the steps in the Procedure and review the meanings of each symbol by referring to Safety Symbols on page 8.

Procedure

1. With the members of your group, discuss whether or not the potato needs light to sprout. Based on your discussion, record your hypothesis in the space provided below.
   Hypothesis:

   Hypotheses should be specific and testable.

✂ 2. Wash the potato with a brush. Carefully cut the potato in half lengthwise. Count the number of eyes on the potato half to be put in the dark and on the half to be put in the light. Record this information in the Data Table.

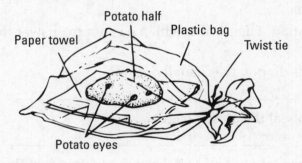

Paper towel Potato half Plastic bag Twist tie

Potato eyes

Figure 1

3. Fold each paper towel repeatedly until you have a rectangle about the same size as your potato halves. Moisten the towels with water. Place a folded paper towel in each plastic bag.

4. Place a potato half in each plastic bag with the cut surface on the paper towel. Tie each bag with a twist tie. See Figure 1.

5. Place one of the plastic bags in a cool place that receives light. Place the other plastic bag in a dark place. Be sure that the potato halves remain on top of the paper towels and that both potato halves are kept cool and at the same temperature.

6. After one week, open each plastic bag and count the number of sprouts. Record this information in the Data Table.

7. To calculate the percentage of eyes sprouting, divide the number of sprouts by the number of eyes and multiply the result by 100. Record your answers in the Data Table.

8. Have one person from your group go to the chalkboard to record your group's data in the table that has been drawn by your teacher.

🔥 9. Wash your hands with soap and warm water before leaving the lab.

Data Table

	Number of Eyes	Number of Sprouts	Percentage of Eyes Sprouting
Potato half in dark			
Potato half in light			

Analysis and Conclusions

1. **Observing** Did more sprouts grow in the light or in the dark?
   Potato halves in the dark should grow a greater percentage of sprouts.

2. **Controlling Variables** What was the control setup in this investigation?
   The potato halves in the dark because potatoes normally grow underground in the absence of light.

3. **Controlling Variables** What was the experimental setup in this investigation?
   The potato halves exposed to the light.

4. **Drawing Conclusions** What conclusion can you draw from this investigation?
   Light inhibits sprouting in potatoes.

5. **Evaluating and Revising** How does your hypothesis compare with your results after completing the investigation?
   Answers will depend on the student's original hypothesis.

6. **Controlling Variables** Why was it important to keep both the control setup and the experimental setup at the same temperature throughout the experiment?
   By keeping the temperature constant, you can be sure that the results of the experimental setup were due
   only to the absence or presence of light and not to differences in temperature.

Going Further
Devise an experiment to see if another variable, such as temperature or water, affects the number of sprouts a potato produces.

Laboratory Skills 5

Using a Compound Light Microscope

Refer students to reading in Section 1-4 and Appendix D about the compound microscope before performing this lab. Time required: 50 minutes

Introduction

Many objects are too small to be seen by the eye alone. They can be seen, however, with the use of an instrument that magnifies, or visually enlarges, the object. One such instrument, which is of great importance to biologists and other scientists, is the compound light microscope. A compound light microscope consists of a light source or mirror that illuminates the object to be observed, an objective lens that magnifies the image of the object, and an eyepiece (ocular lens) that further magnifies the image of the object and projects it into the viewer's eye.

Objects, or specimens, to be observed under a microscope are generally prepared in one of two ways. Prepared or permanent slides are made to last a long time. They are usually purchased from biological supply houses. Temporary or wet-mount slides are made to last only a short time—usually one laboratory period.

The microscope is an expensive precision instrument that requires special care and handling. In this investigation, you will learn the parts of a compound light microscope, the functions of those parts, and the proper use and care of the microscope. You will also learn the technique of preparing wet-mount slides.

Problem

What is the proper use of a compound light microscope?

Pre-Lab Discussion

Read the entire investigation. Then, work with a partner to answer the following questions.

1. Why might it be a good idea to keep your microscope at least 10 cm from the edge of the table?
   To keep from knocking the microscope off the table.

2. Why should a microscope slide and coverslip be held by their edges?
   To prevent fingertips and smudges from getting on them and interfering with the view of the object under the microscope.

3. Why do scientists use microscopes?
   To study things not easily visible to the naked eye.

4. Why should you use lens paper only once?
   Lens paper that has been used may collect dust that could scratch the next lens on which it is used.

5. Why is it important to eliminate air bubbles from the slide?
   Air bubbles might cause distortion or confuse the image.

Materials *(per group)*

compound light microscope
prepared slide
lens paper
soft cloth (or cheesecloth)
newspaper

microscope slide
coverslip
dissecting probe
dropper pipette
scissors

Before class, make sure all microscopes are in correct storage postion with a cover on, with the lowest-power objective in place, and with the lowest-power objective as near to the stage as possible.

Safety 🔲 ✂️ 🔥 🦺

Put on a laboratory apron. Always handle the microscope with extreme care. You are responsible for its proper care and use. Use caution when handling microscope slides, as they can break easily and cut you. Never use direct sunlight as a light source for a compound light microscope. The sunlight reflecting through the microscope could damage your eye. Be careful when handling sharp instruments. Observe proper laboratory procedures when using electrical equipment. Note all safety alert symbols next to the steps in the Procedure and review the meanings of each symbol by referring to Safety Symbols on page 8.

Procedure

Part A. Care of the Compound Light Microscope

1. Figure 1 shows the proper way to carry a microscope. Always carry the microscope with both hands. Grasp the arm of the microscope with one hand and place your other hand under the base. Always hold the microscope in an upright position so that the eyepiece cannot fall out. Place a microscope on your worktable or desk at least 10 cm from the edge. Position the microscope with the arm facing you.

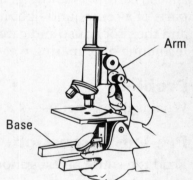

Figure 1

2. Notice the numbers etched on the objectives and on the eyepiece. Each number is followed by an "X" that means "times." For example, the low-power objective may have the number "10X" on its side, as shown in Figure 2. That objective magnifies an object 10 times its normal size. Record the magnifications of your microscope in the Data Table. The total magnification of a microscope is calculated by multiplying the magnification of the objective by the magnification of the eyepiece. For example:

magnification of objective	×	magnification of eyepiece	=	total magnification
10X	×	10X	=	100X

Use the formula to complete the Data Table.

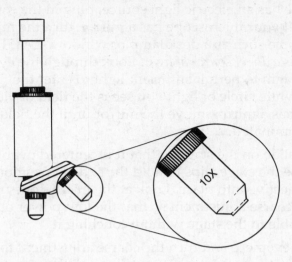

Figure 2

Data Table

Objective	Magnification of Objective	Magnification of Eyepiece	Total Magnification
Low power	10X	10X	100X
High power	43X	10X	430X
Other	Answers will depend on microscopes used.		

4. Before you use the microscope, clean the lenses of the objectives and eyepiece with lens paper. **Note:** *To avoid scratching the lenses, never clean or wipe them with anything other than lens paper. Use a new piece of lens paper on each lens you clean. Never touch a lens with your finger. The oils on your skin may attract dust or lint that could scratch the lens.*

Part B. Use of a Compound Light Microscope

1. Look at the microscope from the side. Locate the coarse adjustment knob that moves the objectives up and down. Practice moving the coarse adjustment knob to see how it moves the objectives with each turn.

2. Turn the coarse adjustment so that the low-power objective is positioned about 3 cm from the stage. Locate the revolving nosepiece. Turn the nosepiece until you hear the high-power objective click into position. See Figure 3. When an objective clicks into position, it is in the proper alignment for light to pass from the light source through the objective into the viewer's eye. Now turn the nosepiece until the low-power objective clicks back into position. **Note:** *Always look at the microscope from the side when moving an objective so that the microscope does not hit or damage the slide.*

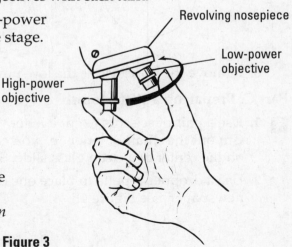

Revolving nosepiece

Low-power objective

High-power objective

Figure 3

3. If your microscope has an electric light source, plug in the cord and turn on the light. If your microscope has a mirror, turn the mirror toward a light source such as a desk lamp or window. **CAUTION:** *Never use the sun as a direct source of light.* Look through the eyepiece. Adjust the diaphragm to permit sufficient light to enter the microscope. The white circle of light you see is the field of view. If your microscope has a mirror, move the mirror until the field of view is evenly illuminated.

4. Place a prepared slide on the stage so that it is centered over the stage opening. Use the stage clips to hold the slide in position. Turn the low-power objective into place. Look at the microscope from the side and turn the coarse adjustment so that the low-power objective is as close as possible to the stage without touching it.

5. Look through the eyepiece and turn the coarse adjustment to move the low-power objective away from the stage until the object comes into focus. To avoid eyestrain, keep both eyes open while looking through a microscope. **CAUTION:** *To avoid moving the objective into the slide, never lower the objective toward the stage while looking through the eyepiece.*

6. Turn the fine adjustment to bring the object into sharp focus. You may wish to adjust the diaphragm so that you can see the object more clearly. In the appropriate space below, draw what you see through the microscope. Record the magnification.

7. Look at the microscope from the side and rotate the nosepiece until the high-power objective clicks into position. Look through the eyepiece. Turn the fine adjustment to bring the object on the slide into focus. **CAUTION:** *Never use the coarse adjustment when focusing the high-power objective lens. This could break your slide or damage the lens.* In the appropriate space below, draw what you see through the microscope. Record the magnification.

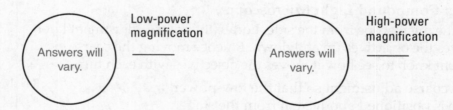

Low-power magnification _____

Answers will vary.

High-power magnification _____

Answers will vary.

8. Remove the slide. Move the low-power objective into position.

Part C. Preparing a Wet Mount

1. Use a pair of scissors to cut a letter "e" from a piece of newspaper. Cut out the smallest letter "e" you can find. Position the "e" upright on the center of a clean glass slide. See Figure 4A.

2. Use a dropper pipette to place one drop of water on the cut piece of newspaper. See Figure 4B.

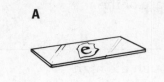

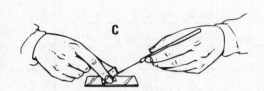
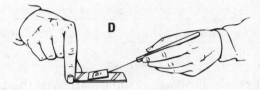

Figure 4

3. Hold a clean coverslip in your fingers as shown in Figure 4C. Make sure the bottom edge of the coverslip is in the drop of water. Use a dissecting probe to slowly lower the coverslip onto the wet newspaper. Slowly lowering the coverslip prevents air bubbles from being trapped between the slide and the coverslip. The type of slide you have just made is called a wet mount. Practice making a wet mount until you can do so without trapping air bubbles on the slide.

4. Center the wet mount on the stage with the letter "e" in its normal upright position. **Note:** *Make sure the bottom of the slide is dry before you place it on the stage.* Turn the low-power objective into position and bring the "e" into focus. In the appropriate place below, draw the letter "e" as seen through the microscope. Record the magnification.

5. While looking through the eyepiece, move the slide to the left. Notice the way the letter seems to move. Now move the slide to the right. Again notice the way the letter seems to move. Move the slide up and down and observe the direction the letter moves.

6. Turn the high-power objective into position and bring the letter "e" into focus. In the appropriate place below, draw the letter "e" as seen through the microscope. Record the magnification.

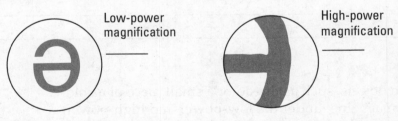

Low-power magnification _____

High-power magnification _____

A student's inability to bring an object into focus may have one or more causes: dirty lenses on ocular or objectives, dirty slide, slide not centered over stage opening, incorrect amount of light, mirror improperly positioned, objective not properly aligned, objective raised too high, or objective not raised high enough.

7. Take apart the wet mount. Clean the slide and coverslip with soap and water. Carefully dry the slide and coverslip with paper towels and return them to their boxes.

8. Rotate the low-power objective into position and use the coarse adjustment to place it as close to the stage as possible without touching. Carefully pick up the microscope and return it to its storage area.

Analysis and Conclusions

1. **Inferring** Why do you place one hand under the base of the microscope as you carry it?

   To support the weight of the microscope and to prevent dropping it.

2. **Observing** How is the image of an object seen through the high-power objective different from the image seen through the low-power objective?

   The high-power objective will have a narrower field of view, but the image seen through it will be larger

   and contain more detail than an image seen through the low-power objective.

3. **Observing** How does the position of the letter "e" as seen through the microscope differ from the way an "e" normally appears?

   The letter "e" is upside down and backward.

4. **Inferring** Explain why a specimen to be viewed under the microscope must be thin.

   Light must be able to pass through the specimen in order for you to see microscopic detail. The light is

   reflected from the mirror below the stage, through the specimen, the objective lens, the body of the

   microscope, and the eyepiece to your eye.

5. **Inferring** Why should you never use coarse adjustment when focusing the high-power objective lens?

   This could break or scratch the lens. The high-power objective lens is the longest lens, and using

   coarse adjustment could smash it into the slide.

6. **Drawing Conclusions** Suppose you were observing an organism through the microscope and noticed that it moved toward the bottom of the slide and then it moved to the right. What does this tell you about the actual movement of the organism?

   Specimens viewed through the microscope appear to move in a direction exactly opposite to that of their

   actual movement on the slide. In this case, the organism actually moved toward the top of the slide and

   then to the left.

Going Further

View some common objects, such as thread or a small piece of a color photograph from a magazine, under the low-power and high-power objectives of the microscope. Make a drawing for each object. Describe the appearance of the objects when viewed under a microscope.

Using the Bunsen Burner

Time required: 20 minutes

Introduction

Sometimes a biologist needs to heat materials. In the laboratory, one of the most efficient ways to do this is to use a Bunsen burner. Bunsen burners are made in a variety of designs. In every one, however, a mixture of air and gas is burned. In most Bunsen burners, the amounts of air and gas can be controlled. In some laboratories, electric hot plates or portable gas burners are used instead of Bunsen burners.

In this investigation, you will learn the parts of the Bunsen burner and their functions. You will also learn how to use the Bunsen burner safely in the laboratory.

Problem

How can the Bunsen burner be safely used to heat materials in the laboratory?

Pre-Lab Discussion

Read the entire investigation. Then, work with a partner to answer the following questions.

1. Why is it important to wear safety goggles when using a Bunsen burner?

To protect the eyes from an injury that might occur as a substance or object reacts to the heat

being applied to it.

2. Why is it important to tie back loose hair and clothing when using a Bunsen burner?

To prevent hair and clothing from catching fire as they brush past a flame.

3. In addition to the items mentioned in questions 1 and 2, what other safety precautions should be followed before lighting a Bunsen burner?

Students should know the locations of fire extinguishers, fire blankets, emergency showers, and

emergency shutoff valves, and how to use them. Students should also know the locations of fire alarms

and emergency exits.

4. How is using a Bunsen burner different from using a candle?

In a Bunsen burner, air and gas mix before they ignite. A candle uses the air that is outside of it to feed its

flame. The flame of a Bunsen burner is hotter than a candle's flame.

5. Why is it important to make sure that the volume of water and the starting temperature are the same in each trial?

The amount of heat given off by the flame must be the only variable in the experiment.

Materials *(per group)*

Bunsen burner
ring stand
2 250-mL beakers
wire gauze
metric ruler

beaker tongs
iron ring
100-mL graduated cylinder
flint striker or matches
clock with second hand

Safety ⬛🔥🔥📋💨

Put on a laboratory apron. Put on safety goggles. Handle all glassware carefully. Tie back loose hair and clothing when using the Bunsen burner. Use extreme care when working with heated equipment or materials to avoid burns. Note all safety alert symbols next to the steps in the Procedure and review the meanings of each symbol by referring to Safety Symbols on page 8.

Procedure

1. Examine your burner when it is *not* connected to the gas outlet. If your burner is the type that can easily be taken apart, unscrew the barrel from the base and locate the parts shown in Figure 1. As you examine the parts, think about their functions.

   • The barrel is the area where the air and gas mix.

   • The collar can be turned to adjust the intake of air. If you turn the collar so that the holes are larger, more air will be drawn into the barrel.

   • The air intake openings are the holes in the collar through which air is drawn in.

   • The base supports the burner so that it does not tip over.

   • The gas intake tube brings the supply of gas from the outlet to the burner.

   • The spud is the small opening through which the gas flows. The small opening causes the gas to enter with great speed.

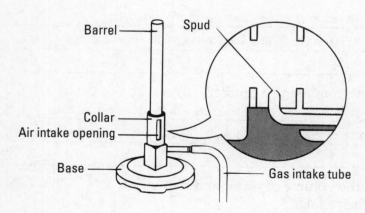

Figure 1

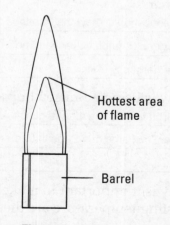

Figure 2

Name_____ Class_____ Date _____

 2. Reassemble the Bunsen burner if necessary and connect the gas intake tube to the gas outlet. **CAUTION:** *Put on safety goggles.* Make sure that the burner is placed away from flammable materials.

3. Adjust the collar so that the air intake openings are half open. If you use a match to light the burner, light the match and hold it about 2 cm above and just to the right of the barrel. Hold the match in this position while you open the gas outlet valve slowly until it is fully open. **CAUTION:** *To avoid burns on your hands, always use extreme care when handling lighted matches.* The burner can also be turned off by using the valve. Do not lean over the burner when lighting it.

4. If you use a flint striker to light the burner, hold the striker in the same position you would hold a lighted match. To light the burner with a striker, you must produce a spark at the same time you open the gas valve.

5. Practice lighting the burner several times. Every member of your group should be given the opportunity to light the burner.

6. The most efficient and hottest flame is blue in color and has distinct regions as shown in Figure 2. Adjust the collar so that the flame is blue and a pale blue inner cone is visible.

7. Adjust the flow of gas until the flame is about 6 cm high. Some burners have a valve in the base to regulate the flow of gas, but the flow of gas can always be adjusted at the gas outlet valve. After adjusting the flow of gas, shut off the burner. Leave your safety goggles on for the remainder of the investigation.

8. Arrange the apparatus as pictured in Figure 3.

 9. Adjust the iron ring so that the bottom of the beaker is about 2 cm above the mouth of the burner barrel. Measure 100 mL of water in the graduated cylinder and pour it into one of the beakers.

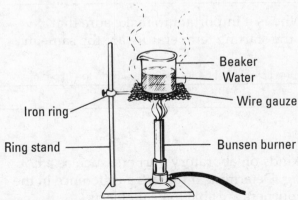

Figure 3

10. Light the burner and heat the beaker of water. The bottom of the beaker should just be touching the top of the inner cone of the flame. In the Data Table on p. 44, record the time it takes for the water to start boiling rapidly. Using the beaker tongs, carefully remove the beaker and pour out the water.

11. Repeat steps 9 and 10 with the other beaker supported at a height of about 8 cm above the mouth of the barrel. **CAUTION:** *When raising the iron ring, use heat-resistant gloves.* In the Data Table, record the time it takes for the water to start boiling rapidly at this height. **Note:** *Be sure that the starting temperature of the water is the same in each trial.*

In steps 10 and 11, caution students to ignore the appearance of *small* bubbles and wait until rapid boiling begins.

Data Table

Height Above Burner (cm)	Time to Boil (min)
2	Answers will depend on student observations.
8	Answers will depend on student observations.

Analysis and Conclusions

1. Inferring What would happen if the air intake openings were made very small?

The gas would not burn as well. The flame would become yellow. The flame would not be as hot.

2. Drawing Conclusions If the burner does not light after the gas outlet valve is opened, what might be wrong?

The spud or gas intake tube might be clogged.

3. Observing At what height, 2 cm or 8 cm, did the water come to a rapid boil faster?

The water should come to a rapid boil faster at a height of 2 cm.

4. Drawing Conclusions Why is it necessary to know how to adjust the flow rates of the air and gas when using a Bunsen burner?

In a Bunsen burner, air and gas mix before they ignite. They are both required to produce a flame. Adjusting the air and gas regulates the size and strength of the flame.

5. Controlling Variables Why is it important to make sure that the volume of water and the starting temperature are the same in each trial?

The amount of heat given off by the flame must be the only variable in the experiment.

Going Further

Test the ability of different kinds of laboratory burners, such as a hot plate, to heat water to boiling. Determine if there is a difference in the speed with which different burners are able to heat objects.

Preparing Laboratory Solutions

You may want to refer students to reading in Section 2-2 about solutions.
Time required: 40 minutes

Introduction

A solution is a type of mixture in which one substance dissolves in another. In a solution, the substance that is dissolved is called the solute. The substance that does the dissolving is called the solvent. The most common solvent is water. Most solutions cannot easily be separated by simple physical means such as filtering.

Solutions in which water is the solvent, or aqueous solutions, are important to all types of living organisms. Marine microorganisms spend their entire lives in the ocean, an aqueous solution of water, salt, and other substances. Most of the nutrients needed by plants are in aqueous solution in moist soil. Plasma, the liquid part of the blood, is an aqueous solution containing dissolved nutrients and gases.

In this investigation, you will learn some of the techniques used to prepare laboratory solutions. You will also learn some of the proper uses of a triple-beam balance and a filtering apparatus.

Problem

What are some of the different ways in which laboratory solutions can be prepared?

Pre-Lab Discussion

Read the entire investigation. Then, work with a partner to answer the following questions.

1. What does the percentage concentration of a solution mean?

   The percent of a solute in a solution.

2. What is the difference between the mass/volume concentration of a solution and its volume/volume concentration?

   A mass/volume concentration is the mass of a solute in a given volume of solution. A volume/volume

   concentration is the volume of a (liquid) solute in a given volume of solution.

3. Why is it difficult to dilute a solution accurately?

   A small error in the volume of the solution being diluted can drastically change the dilution.

4. What is the relationship between a 30% sodium chloride solution and a 3% sodium chloride solution in terms of the number of solute molecules in each solution?

   The 30% solution contains ten times more solute molecules than the 3% solution.

5. Why is a chemical placed on a piece of weighing paper instead of directly on the pan of a balance when its mass is being measured?

   If a chemical were placed directly on the pan of a triple-beam balance, it could react with the metal pan or

   become contaminated by another substance that had been previously placed on the pan.

Materials *(per group)*

sodium chloride

10 mL of red food coloring

100-mL graduated cylinder

filter paper

funnel

2 100-mL beakers

weighing paper

triple-beam balance

scoop

10-mL graduated cylinder

ring stand

iron ring

Filter paper or a piece of writing paper can be used as weighing paper.

Safety

Put on a laboratory apron. Put on safety goggles. Handle all glassware carefully. Always use special caution when working with laboratory chemicals, as they may irritate the skin or cause staining of the skin or clothing. Never touch or taste any chemical unless instructed to do so. Wash your hands with soap and warm water before leaving the lab. Note all safety alert symbols next to the steps in the Procedure and review the meanings of each symbol by referring to Safety Symbols on page 8.

Procedure

Part A. Preparing the Mass/Volume Solution

1. To prepare a solution of a given percentage, dissolve the number of grams of solid solute equal to the percentage in enough water to make 100 mL of the solution. To prepare a 5% sodium chloride solution, place a piece of weighing paper on the pan of the triple-beam balance and find its mass.

2. Add exactly 5 g to the value of the mass of the weighing paper and move the riders of the balance to this number.

3. Using the scoop, add a small amount of sodium chloride at a time to the paper on the balance until the pointer rests on zero.

4. Add the 5 grams of sodium chloride to the 100-mL graduated cylinder.

5. Add enough water to bring the volume of the solution to 100 mL. What happens to the sodium chloride crystals?

   The sodium chloride crystals dissolve and disappear as the water is mixed with them.

6. Dispose of this solution according to your teacher's instructions.

Part B. Preparing a Volume/Volume Solution

1. To prepare a solution of a given percentage, dissolve the number of milliliters of liquid solute equal to the percentage in enough solvent to make 100 mL of the solution. To prepare a 10% colored water solution, measure 10 mL of red food coloring in the 10-mL graduated cylinder and pour it into the large graduated cylinder. **CAUTION:** *Use caution with red food coloring to avoid staining your hands or clothing.*

2. Add enough water to the large graduated cylinder to bring the volume to 100 mL. What happens to the red food coloring as water is mixed with it?

The red food coloring is diluted by the water and its color changes to a lighter red.

3. Keep this solution for use in Part C of this investigation.

Part C. Reducing the Concentration of a Solution

1. To reduce the concentration of a solution, pour the number of milliliters of the existing solution that is equal to the percentage of the new concentration into a graduated cylinder. Add enough solvent to bring the volume in milliliters to an amount equal to the percentage of the original solution. To reduce a 10% colored water solution to a 1% solution, pour the 10% colored water solution you prepared in Part B into a 100-mL beaker.

2. Measure 1 mL of the 10% solution in the 10-mL graduated cylinder.

3. Add enough water to the graduated cylinder to bring the volume to 10 mL. What differences do you observe between the 10% and 1% solutions of colored water?

The 10% solution of colored water appears darker in color than the 1% solution.

4. Dispose of the 1% solution according to your teacher's instructions. Keep the 10% solution for use in Part D of this investigation.

Part D. Filtering

1. Prepare a filter paper as shown in Figure 1. Fold a circle of filter paper across the middle. Fold the resulting half circle to form a quarter circle. Open the folded paper into a cone, leaving the triple layer on one side and a single layer on the other.

2. Support a funnel as shown in Figure 2. Place the cone of the filter paper in the funnel and wet the paper so that it adheres smoothly to the walls of the funnel. Set a clean beaker beneath the funnel in such a way that the stem of the funnel touches the side of the beaker.

3. Pour the 10% colored water solution prepared in Part B slowly into the funnel. Do not let the mixture overflow the filter paper. As the mixture filters through the filter paper, record your observations in the Data Table on p. 48.

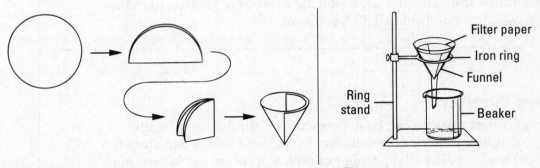

Figure 1

Figure 2

Filter paper

Iron ring

Funnel

Ring stand

Beaker

4. After all of the solution has passed through the filter paper into the beaker, observe the appearance of the filter paper. Record your observations in the Data Table.

5. Carefully remove the filter paper from the funnel and dispose of it and the colored water solution according to your teacher's instructions. Wash your hands with soap and warm water before leaving the lab.

Data Table

Appearance of Liquid Before Filtering	Appearance of Liquid After Filtering	Appearance of Filter Paper After Filtering
Red	Red	No materials collected.

Analysis and Conclusions

1. **Comparing and Contrasting** Relate the colors of the 10% and 1% colored water solutions to the number of solute molecules each solution contains.

   The darker 10% solution contains a greater number of solute molecules per unit of volume than the

   lighter 1% solution.

2. **Observing** Was the filter paper successful in separating the two parts of the red food coloring solution? Use your observations to support your answer.

   No. The solution remained red after filtering, indicating that both the red food color molecules and water

   molecules went through the filter paper.

3. **Communicating Results** Describe the procedure needed to prepare a 30% sugar solution.

   Use a triple-beam balance to measure 30 g of sugar. Add the 30 g of sugar to a graduated cylinder.

   Add water to the 100-mL mark of the graduated cylinder.

4. **Communicating Results** Describe the procedure needed to produce a 20% liquid bleach solution.

   Add 20 mL liquid bleach to a graduated cylinder. Add water to the 100-mL mark of the graduated cylinder.

5. **Communicating Results** Describe the procedure needed to reduce an 80% starch solution to a 20% solution.

   Pour 20 mL of 80% starch solution into a graduated cylinder. Add enough water to bring the volume to

   80mL of 20% starch solution.

Going Further

Solution concentrations can be expressed in a number of different ways, including molarity (the number of moles of solute per liter of solution) and molality (the number of moles of solute per kilogram of solvent). Using a chemistry reference text, describe the procedures used to prepare 1 molar and 1 molal concentrations.

Using Graphing Skills

Time required: 30 minutes

Introduction

Recorded data can be plotted on a graph. A graph is a pictorial representation of information recorded in a data table. It is used to show a relationship between two or more different factors. Two common types of graphs are line graphs and bar graphs.

In this investigation, you will interpret and construct a bar graph and a line graph.

Problem

How do you correctly interpret and construct a line graph and a bar graph?

Pre-Lab Discussion

Read the entire investigation. Then, work with a partner to answer the following questions.

1. Would a line graph or a bar graph be better for showing the number of birds of each color in a population?

   Bar graph.

2. How could you plot more than one responding variable on a line graph?

   Using multiple lines on a line graph with a corresponding key as to the responding variable that each

   line represents.

3. Where do you place the manipulated variable on a line graph?

   The x-axis.

4. Which type of graph would you use to show comparisons? Explain the reason for your answer.

   Bar graph. On bar graphs the x-axis can have labels instead of a numerical scale.

5. Why is it important to have all parts of a graph clearly labeled and drawn?

   Graphs that are clearly labeled are much less likely to be misread or misinterpreted.

Procedure

Part A. Interpreting Graphs

1. The type of graph that best shows the relationship between two variables is the line graph. A line graph has one or more lines connecting a series of points. See Figure 1. Along the horizontal axis, or x-axis, you will find the manipulated variable in the experiment. Along the vertical axis or y-axis, you will find the responding variable.

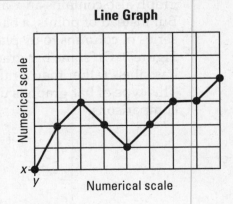

Line Graph

y-axis label: Numerical scale
x-axis label: Numerical scale

Figure 1

2. Use the line graph in Figure 2 to answer questions a through f below.
   a. Which plant grew the tallest? _Plant 2._____
   b. How many plants grew to be at least 6 cm tall? _All the plants._____
   c. Which plant grew the fastest in the first five days? _Plant 3._____
   d. Which line represents plant 2? _The dotted line._____
   e. After 10 days, how much had plant 3 grown? _6 cm._____
   f. How long did it take for plant 1 to grow 6 cm? _15 days._____

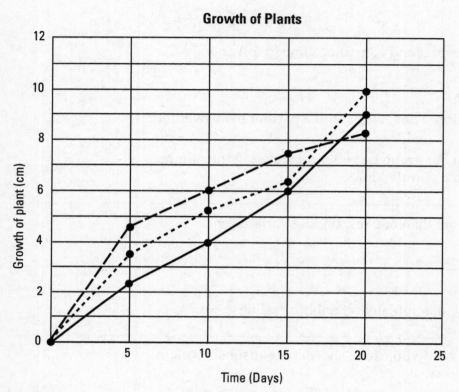

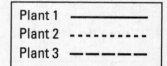

Figure 2

3. A bar graph is another way of showing relationships between variables. A bar graph also contains an *x*-axis and a *y*-axis. But instead of points, a bar graph uses a series of columns to display data. See Figure 3. On some bar graphs, the *x*-axis has labels rather than a numerical scale. This type of bar graph is used only to show comparisons.

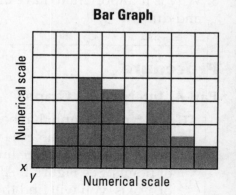

Figure 3

4. Use the bar graph in Figure 4 to answer questions a through e below.

    a. At birth, what is the average number of red blood cells per mm³ of blood?

    5.7 million.

    b. What appears to happen to the number of red blood cells between birth and 2 months?

    It decreases.

    c. What happens to the number of red blood cells between the ages of 6 and 8 years?

    It stays the same.

    d. Between what ages is a human likely to have 4.6 million red blood cells?

    Between 6 months to 12 months.

    e. After 14 years of age, do males or females have a higher red blood cell count?

    Males.

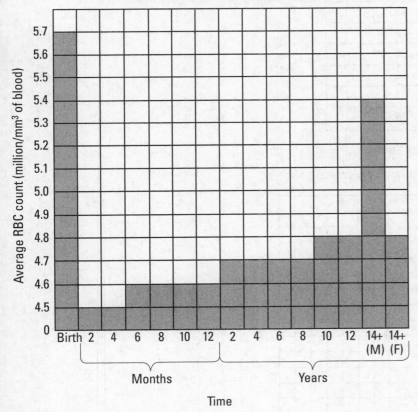

Figure 4

Part B. Constructing Graphs

1. When plotting data on a graph, you must decide which variable to place along the *x*-axis and which variable to place along the *y*-axis. Label the axes of your graph accordingly. Then you must decide on the scale of each axis; that is, how much each unit along the axis represents. Scales should be chosen to make the graph as large as possible within the limits of the paper and still include the largest item of data. If the scale unit is too large, your graph will be cramped into a small area and will be hard to read and interpret. If the scale unit is too small, the graph will run off the paper. Scale units should also be selected for ease of locating points on the graph. Multiples of 1, 2, 5, or 10 are easiest to work with.

2. Use the information recorded in Data Table 1 to construct a line graph on the grid provided below. You should label each axis, mark an appropriate scale on each axis, plot the data, connect the points, and give your graph a title.

Data Table 1

Temperature (°C)	Breathing Rate (per minute)
10	15
15	25
18	30
20	38
23	60
25	57
27	25

Breathing Rate of the Freshwater Sunfish

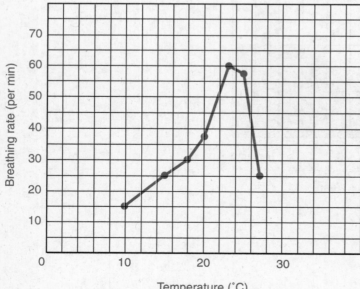

Breathing Rate of the Freshwater Sunfish

3. Use the information recorded in Data Table 2 to construct a bar graph on the grid provided below. You should label each axis, mark an appropriate scale on each axis, plot the data, darken the columns of the graph, and give your graph a title.

Data Table 2

Month	Jan.	Feb.	Mar.	April	May	June	July	Aug.	Sept.	Oct.	Nov.	Dec.
Rainfall (mL)	15	21	28	24	16	8	2	1	2	3	5	10

Average Rainfall in Willamette Valley

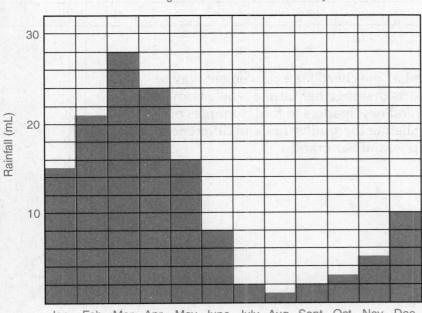

Average Rainfall in Willamette Valley

Analysis and Conclusions

1. Comparing and Contrasting How is a graph similar to a data table?

A graph is a pictorial representation of the information found in a data table.

2. Comparing and Contrasting How is a line graph different from a bar graph?

A line graph contains a series of points connected together. A bar graph uses a series of columns to display data.

3. Using Graphs Does a steep curve on a line graph indicate a rapid or slow rate of change?

A rapid rate of change.

4. **Using Graphs** You are conducting an experiment to measure the gain in mass of a young mouse over a ten-week period. In constructing a graph to represent your data, which variable should you place along the x-axis and which variable should you place along the y-axis? Explain your answer.

Because the manipulated variable should be placed along the x-axis, the time should be plotted there.

The more responding variable, the gain in mass of the mouse, should be placed along the y-axis.

5. **Using Graphs** What is an advantage of using multiple lines in a line graph? (See Figure 2.)

The use of multiple lines on a line graph allows for the comparison of several different experiments with

similar data.

Going Further

A circle graph (sometimes called a "pie chart") is a convenient way to show the relative sizes of the parts that together form a whole body of data. Look through magazines and newspapers to find examples of circle graphs. Construct a chart listing the similarities and differences between circle graphs, line graphs, and bar graphs.

Chapter 1   The Science of Biology

Observing the Uncertainty of Measurements

You may want to refer students to Section 1–4 and Appendix C in the textbook for a discussion of measurements and the metric system.
Time required: 40 minutes

Introduction

Scientists use a wide variety of tools to make precise measurements. Some of the tools include a balance that measures mass in grams, a ruler or meter stick that measures length in centimeters, and a graduated cylinder that measures volume in milliliters. The accuracy of a measurement depends on three things: the accuracy of the measuring instrument, the ability of the observer to read the scale properly, and the degree of precision of the measuring instrument. In this investigation you will practice the skill of making accurate measurements using a variety of measuring instruments.

Explain the difference between the precision design of the instrument and the skill required to make accurate observations using the instrument. Compare two different sizes of graduated cylinders or a bathroom scale and a laboratory balance to demonstrate the differences in the precision of two similar instruments.

Problem

Are there differences between measurements made by two different observers?

Pre-Lab Discussion

Read the entire investigation. Then, work with a partner to answer the following questions.

1. Why is it necessary to have a particular tool for each task?

   The tools are designed to measure a particular physical feature. No single tool can be used for measuring

   mass, length, and volume.

2. What might be a better tool for measuring the size of your classroom?

   A longer measuring tool such as a metric tape.

3. What is an advantage of using metric tools over a yardstick or ruler?

   Metric measurements are based on units of 10, so it is possible to express numbers in decimal fractions and

   scientific notation. The English system of inches and feet requires fractions such as $\frac{1}{2}$, which make

   computations more difficult.

4. Is it necessary for the same person in a group to make each measurement?

   No, the variability in measurements among the class members is likely to occur no matter which member of

   the group makes the measurements.

5. Would you expect every group's measurement of the temperature of the ice water to be the same?

   Yes. As long as the ice and liquid water are well mixed, the temperature should remain at 0˚C until all the ice

   has melted.

Materials *(per station)*

Station 1: meter stick

Station 2: meter stick

Station 3: 30-cm ruler

regular object *Provide a cubic or rectangular object.*

Station 4: 100-mL graduated cylinder

150-mL beaker of colored liquid *Use food coloring or water-soluble ink to prepare colored liquid.*

Station 5: triple-beam balance

small pebble

Station 6: 100-mL graduated cylinder

150-mL beaker of water

irregular object *a small stone*

Station 7: Celsius thermometer *A non-mercury thermometer is recommended.*

250-mL beaker of ice and water

paper towel

Safety 🧪🧤🖐

Put on a laboratory apron. Put on safety goggles. Handle glassware and thermometers carefully. Note all safety alert symbols next to the numbered steps in the Procedure and review the meaning of each symbol by referring to Safety Symbols on page 8.

Procedure

1. Station 1: Use the meter stick to measure the length and width of your science classroom. If the room has an irregular shape, measure the longest width and the longest length. Express your measurements to the nearest tenth of a meter and record them in the Data Table.

2. Station 2: Use the meter stick to measure the length and width of your desk or lab table. If the table has an irregular shape, measure the longest width and the longest length. Express your measurements to the nearest tenth of a centimeter and record them in the Data Table.

3. Station 3: Use the metric ruler to find the volume of the regular object. Volume is found by multiplying the length times the width times the height of the object. Express the volume in cubic centimeters (cm³) and record it in the Data Table.

4. Station 4: Use the graduated cylinder to find the volume of the colored liquid in the beaker. **CAUTION:** *Be careful to avoid breakage when working with glassware.* Remember to always read a graduated cylinder at the bottom curve of the meniscus. Pour the liquid back into the beaker. Express your measurement in milliliters and record it in the Data Table.

Before the class begins, prepare a class data table on the board or at a computer terminal so that each group can record its data for each station. Remind students to also make their own record for each station.

Assign each pair of students a starting station. For large classes, double the number of stations so that students can work in pairs.(In this case, provide duplicate objects at each station.) When a group completes one station, it should move on to the next free station. Students can do the stations in any order as long as they fill in their data tables accordingly. When they complete all the stations, they should record their data in the class data table you provide. Allow about 5 minutes per station for a total of 35–40 minutes. Allow additional time to make a record of the class data table and subsequent discussion of the class data.

5. Station 5: Make certain that the riders on the triple-beam balance are moved all the way to the left and that the pointer rests on zero. Place the pebble on the pan on the triple-beam balance. Move the riders until the pointer is at zero. Express your measurement to the nearest tenth of a gram and record it in the Data Table. Remove the pebble and return all riders to the far left of the balance.

6. Station 6: Fill the graduated cylinder half full with water from the beaker. Find the volume of the irregular object. Express the volume of the object in cubic centimeters (cm^3) and record it in the Data Table. Carefully remove the object from the graduated cylinder. Pour the water back into the beaker.

7. Station 7: Use the Celsius thermometer to find the temperature of the ice water. Express the temperature to the nearest 0.5°C and record it in the Data Table. Remove the thermometer and carefully dry it with a paper towel.

8. Compare your measurements from each station with those of classmates by having one member from your group record your data on the class data table your teacher provides. Make a copy of the class data table so that you can answer the questions that follow.

Data Table

Station	Object	Measurement (units)
1	classroom	
2	desk	Answers will depend on materials provided.
3		
4		
5	pebble	
6		
7	ice water	0°

Analysis and Conclusions

1. **Analyzing Data** Examine the results from all the group measurements. Did the groups get exactly the same measurement results for the task at the same station?

Probably not. It would be unusual for each observer to achieve the same level of accuracy.

2. **Inferring** Why is the graduated cylinder used instead of a ruler to measure the volume of the irregular object at Station 6?

The irregular object has no well-defined sides that can be easily measured so that the volume can then be calculated.

3. **Drawing Conclusions** What are two important guidelines to follow in making a good set of measurements?

First, select a tool that provides the correct scale for a precise measurement. Second, repeat the

measurement several times or have several observers make the same measurement.

4. **Comparing and Contrasting** Examine all the data collected and determine which set of measurements showed the greatest variability. What are some possible reasons the measurements are not consistent for a particular set of measurements?

Possible answers might include: 1. The scale on the instrument was not fine enough to be very precise; 2. It

was difficult to read the meniscus in the graduated cylinder; 3. The liquid in the beaker is lost with repeated

transfers.

5. **Predicting** At station 3, you calculated the volume of a regular object using a metric ruler. If you determined the volume of that object using the graduated cylinder technique at station 6, would you expect the results to be the same?

Both methods give the volume (length × width × height) of the same object and, therefore, it should be the

same, or nearly the same, for both.

Going Further

Test your prediction in question 5 by measuring the volume of the regular object at Station 3 by using the graduated cylinder technique at Station 6. Calculate the difference between the two measurements. How would you determine which is the more accurate?

Chapter 2   The Chemistry of Life

Identifying Organic Compounds

You may want to refer students to Section 2–3 of the textbook for a discussion of organic compounds before performing this investigation.
Time required: 60 minutes

Introduction

The most common organic compounds found in living organisms are lipids, carbohydrates, proteins, and nucleic acids. Common foods, which often consist of plant materials or substances derived from animals, are also combinations of these organic compounds. Substances called indicators can be used to test for the presence of organic compounds. An indicator is a substance that changes color in the presence of a particular compound. In this investigation, you will use several indicators to test for the presence of lipids, carbohydrates, and proteins in various foods.

Problem

What are the major types of organic compounds in some common foods?

Pre-Lab Discussion

Read the entire investigation. Then, work with a partner to answer the following questions.

1. What is an indicator? How are indicators used in this experiment?

   An indicator is a substance that changes color in the presence of a particular compound.

   In this investigation, indicators will be used to detect the presence of various organic

   compounds in foods.

2. What is the purpose of using distilled water as one of your test substances?

   Distilled water acts as a control and is used as a standard in color comparisons.

3. What is the controlled variable in Part C?

   The biuret reagent is a controlled variable.

4. What is the purpose of washing the test tubes thoroughly?

   Washing the test tubes eliminates contamination of the substance by a previously used indicator or

   food substance.

5. You have added Sudan III stain to each of the test tubes. What change indicates the presence of lipids?

   The Sudan III stain will dissolve in lipids and stain them red.

Materials *(per group)*

10 test tubes

Read all the information on chemical safety from any Materials Safety Data Sheet that accompanies a chemical.

test-tube rack

test-tube holder

masking tape

glass-marking pencil

10-mL graduated cylinder

Bunsen burner or hot plate

iodine solution   Dissolve 5 g potassium iodide and 1.5 g iodine crystals in 500 mL distilled water.

20 mL honey solution   Dissolve 20 mL honey in 500 mL distilled water.

20 mL egg white and water mixture   Mix egg whites from 3 eggs with 500 mL distilled water.

20 mL corn oil

20 mL lettuce and water mixture   Mix 20 mL macerated lettuce with 500 mL distilled water.

20 mL gelatin and water solution   Dissolve 3.5 g gelatin in 346.5 mL distilled water. Refrigerate until needed.

20 mL melted butter

20 mL potato and water mixture   Mix 20 mL macerated potato with 500 mL distilled water.

20 mL apple juice and water mixture   Mix 250 mL unsweetened apple juice with 250 mL distilled water.

20 mL distilled water

20 mL unknown substance   You might use clear meat broth (without flour or cornstarch), crackers and distilled water, oats and distilled water, olive oil, melted lard, orange juice, cream cheese and distilled water, or peanut butter and distilled water. Soak solid foods overnight to soften them. Then, mash softened food and mix with distilled water.

10 dropper pipettes

paper towels

600-mL beaker

brown paper bag

Sudan III stain

biuret reagent   Indicators are available from chemical supply houses and should be put in dropper bottles.

Benedict's solution   Biuret solution must be fresh.

Safety 🩺🏠🧤🧷⚗️🔥🧪☠️🧯

Put on a laboratory apron and safety goggles. Be careful to avoid breakage when working with glassware. Always use special caution when using any laboratory chemicals, as they may irritate the skin or cause staining of the skin or clothing. Never touch or taste any chemical unless instructed to do so. Use extreme care when working with heated equipment or materials to avoid burns. Wear plastic gloves when handling eggs or egg whites or tools that have been in contact with them. Wash hands thoroughly after carrying out this lab. Note all safety alert symbols and review their meanings on page 8.

Procedure
For suggestions for a shorter laboratory period, see the Note at the end of Going Further.

Part A. Testing for Lipids

🩺🧤 1. Place 9 test tubes in a test-tube rack. Use masking tape to make labels for each test tube. Write the name of a different food sample (listed in Materials) on each masking-tape label. Label the ninth test tube "distilled water."

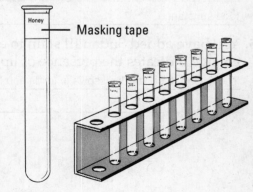

Masking tape

Figure 1

2. Use a graduated cylinder to transfer 5 mL of distilled water into the test tube labeled "distilled water." Use a glass-marking pencil to mark the test tube at the level of the water. Mark the other test tubes in the test-tube rack at the same level.

3. Use a separate dropper pipette to fill each of the other test tubes with 5 mL of the substance indicated on the masking-tape label. Add 5 drops of Sudan III stain to each test tube. Sudan III stain will dissolve in lipids and stain them red.

4. Gently shake the contents of each test tube. **CAUTION:** *Use extreme care when handling Sudan III to avoid staining hands or clothing.* In the Data Table, record any color changes and place a check mark next to those substances testing positively for lipids.

5. Wash the test tubes thoroughly but leave the labels on.

6. For another test for lipids, divide a piece of a brown paper bag into 10 equal sections. In each section, write the name of one test substance, as shown in Figure 2.

Honey	Egg white	Corn oil	Lettuce	Gelatin
Butter	Potato	Apple juice	Distilled water	

Figure 2
Empty square can be used later to test unknown substance.

7. In each section, place a small drop of the identified food onto the brown paper. With a paper towel, wipe off any excess pieces of food that may stick to the paper. Set the paper aside until the spots appear dry—about 10 to 15 minutes.

8. Hold the piece of brown paper up to a bright light or window. You will notice that some foods leave a translucent spot on the brown paper. The translucent spot indicates the presence of lipids.

Part B. Testing for Carbohydrates

1. Sugars and starches are two common types of carbohydrates. To test for starch, use the same dropper pipettes to refill each cleaned test tube with 5 mL of the substance indicated on the masking-tape label. Add 5 drops of iodine solution to each test tube. Iodine will change color from yellow-brown to blue-black in the presence of starch.

2. Gently shake the contents of each test tube. **CAUTION:** *Use extreme caution when using iodine as it is poisonous and can also stain hands and clothing.* In the Data Table, record any color changes and place a check mark next to those substances testing positive for starch.
   Explain to students that the iodine solution will not dissolve in lipids, but it will react at the interface between the two layers when the test tubes are shaken, if starch is present.

3. Wash the test tubes thoroughly.

4. For a sugar test, set up a hot-water bath as shown in Figure 3. Half fill the beaker with tap water. Heat the water to a gentle boil. **CAUTION:** *Use extreme care when working with hot water. Do not let the water splash onto your hands.*

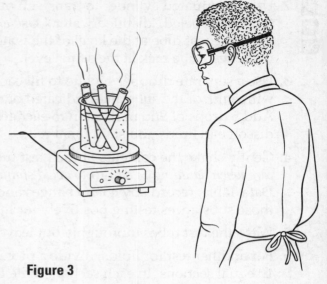

Figure 3

5. While the water bath is heating, fill each cleaned test tube with 5 mL of the substance indicated on the masking-tape label. Add 10 drops of Benedict's solution to each test tube. When heated, Benedict's solution will change color from blue to green, yellow, orange, or red in the presence of a simple sugar, or monosaccharide.

6. Gently shake the contents of each test tube. **CAUTION:** *Use extreme caution when using Benedict's solution to avoid staining hands or clothing.*

7. Place the test tubes in the hot-water bath. Heat the test tubes for 3 to 5 minutes. With the test-tube holder, remove the test tubes from the hot-water bath and place them back in the test-tube rack. **CAUTION:** *Never touch hot test tubes with your bare hands. Always use a test-tube holder to handle hot test tubes.* In the Data Table, record any color changes and place a check mark next to any substances that test positive for a simple sugar.

Benedict's solution will not react with sucrose. Avoid materials that contain sucrose.

8. After they have cooled, wash the test tubes thoroughly.

Part C. Testing for Proteins

1. Put 5 mL of the appropriate substance in each labeled test tube. Add 5 drops of biuret reagent to each test tube. **CAUTION:** *Biuret reagent contains sodium hydroxide, a strong base. If you splash any reagent on yourself, wash it off immediately with water. Call your teacher for assistance.*

2. Gently shake the contents of each test tube. Biuret reagent changes color from yellow to blue-violet in the presence of protein. In the Data Table, record any changes in color and place a check mark next to any substances that test positively for protein.

Disinfect all tools and surfaces that have been in contact with raw eggs. Wipe down all lab surfaces with 70% isopropyl alcohol or a disinfecting solution. Sterilize all equipment used in this investigation.

3. Wash test tubes thoroughly.

Part D. Testing an Unknown Substance for Organic Compounds

1. Obtain a sample of an unknown substance from your teacher and pour it into the remaining test tube. Repeat the tests described in Parts A, B, and C of the Procedure to determine the main organic compounds in your sample. Record your results in the Data Table.

2. Wash the test tube thoroughly.

3. Wash your hands with soap and warm water before leaving the lab.

Name_____ Class_____ Date _____

Data Table

Substance	Lipid Test		Carbohydrate Test				Protein Test	
	Sudan color	Lipids present (✓)	Iodine color	Starches present (✓)	Benedict's color	Sugars present (✓)	Biuret color	Proteins present (✓)
Honey					Orange	✓		
Egg white							Blue-violet	✓
Corn oil	Red	✓						
Lettuce								
Gelatin							Blue-violet	✓
Butter	Red	✓						
Potato			Black	✓				
Apple juice					Orange	✓		
Distilled water								
Unknown			Answers will vary depending on unknown.					

Analysis and Conclusions

1. **Classifying** Which test substances contain lipids?

   Corn oil and butter (possibly the unknown).

2. **Classifying** Which test substances contain starch?

   Potato (possibly the unknown).

3. **Classifying** Which test substances contain simple sugar?

   Honey and apple juice (possibly the unknown).

4. **Classifying** Which test substances contain protein?

   Egg white and gelatin (possibly the unknown).

5. **Observing** Which test substances did not test positive for any of the organic compounds?

   Lettuce (possibly the unknown).

6. **Drawing Conclusions** People with diabetes are instructed to avoid foods that are rich in carbohydrates. How could your observations in this investigation help you decide whether a food should be served to a person with diabetes?

   The food could be tested using iodine and/or Benedict's solution. If a color change occurs, the food might

   not be appropriate for diabetics.

7. **Inferring** Your brown lunch bag has a large, translucent spot on the bottom. What explanation could you give for this occurrence?

   Some food item in the lunch bag contains lipids. (Students might say the bag accidentally rested on a

   substance containing lipids.)

8. **Drawing Conclusions** What conclusion could you make if a positive test for any of the organic compounds occurred in the test tube containing only distilled water?

The test tube, distilled water, or indicators may have been contaminated. The tests should be conducted

again to achieve accurate results.

9. **Drawing Conclusions** A very thin slice is removed from a peanut and treated with Sudan III stain. Then a drop of Biuret reagent is added to the peanut slice. When you examine the peanut slice under a microscope, patches of red and blue-violet are visible. What conclusions can you draw from your examination?

Peanuts contain lipids and proteins.

Going Further

Test each food from a school lunch for the presence of lipids, starch, single sugars, and proteins. Construct a data table to summarize your findings.

A Shorter Laboratory Period:
If you wish to shorten this investigation, you may want to have your students omit Part D of the Procedure (testing of an unknown substance). It is also possible to have students test fewer than the eight listed food substances. If you wish to have students complete the entire investigation but do not feel that the time within one class period is adequate, schedule Parts A, B, and C for one class period and Part D for part of another class period.

Chapter 3   The Biosphere

Investigating Chemical Cycles in the Biosphere

You may want to refer students to Section 3–3 in the textbook for a discussion of the carbon and oxygen cycles. Time required: 30 minutes with 5 to 10 minutes of daily observation over a 7-day period

Introduction

Living things need certain nutrients in order to continue living. For example, animals need oxygen, water, vitamins, and other compounds. Plants require carbon dioxide, water, and other compounds. Nutrients, such as water, oxygen, carbon, nitrogen, and phosphorous, move through the biosphere and may be used over and over again. The process by which each nutrient is recycled is called a biogeochemical cycle. For example, during photosynthesis, carbon dioxide and water are taken in by plants. Molecules of water are split, releasing oxygen into the atmosphere. Many organisms use the oxygen in the atmosphere during cellular respiration. In this investigation, you will examine the role of carbon dioxide in four closed systems.

Problem

How does carbon dioxide cycle in the biosphere?

Pre-Lab Discussion

Read the entire investigation. Then, work with a partner to answer the following questions.

1. What are the manipulated variables in this experiment?

   The manipulated variables include the presence of plant sprigs and a snail in each test tube.

2. What are the controlled variables in this experiment?

   Controlled variables include the source and amount of pond water placed in each test tube, the

   amount and concentration of the bromthymol blue solution placed in each test tube, the intensity and

   amount of light received by each test tube, and the amount of time each test tube is observed under

   similar conditions.

3. What purpose does the bromthymol blue solution serve in this experiment?

   The bromthymol blue solution is used to indicate the presence or absence of carbon dioxide in each

   test tube. It will detect any carbon dioxide that builds up.

4. How will you know whether carbon dioxide is present in each test tube?

   The bromthymol blue solution will become yellow in the presence of carbon dioxide. If the solution

   remains blue, there is little or no carbon dioxide present in the test tube.

5. Predict the results of the experiment. What color do you expect the solution in each test tube to be after seven days?

   Students may expect test tube 2 to be yellow because the carbon dioxide given off by the snail will not be

   consumed and will build up whereas the carbon dioxide in tubes 1 and 3 will be consumed by the water

   plants. Students should predict no change in tube 4 because it is the control.

Materials *(per group)*

2 snails[1]
4 water plant cuttings[2]
pond water
masking tape
fluorescent plant lamp[3]
bromthymol blue solution in dropper bottle[4]
4 culture tubes with tops[5]
test-tube rack

Safety

Put on a laboratory apron. Put on safety goggles. Handle all glassware carefully. Always use special caution and wear disposable plastic gloves when working with laboratory chemicals, as they may irritate the skin or cause staining of the skin or clothing. Never touch or taste any chemical unless instructed to do so. Follow your teacher's directions and all appropriate safety procedures when handling live animals. To avoid possible contact with poisonous or prickly plants, use forceps or wear gloves when collecting plant specimens. Wash your hands thoroughly after carrying out this investigation. Plant parts and their juices can irritate your eyes and skin. Use forceps or wear gloves when handling plants. Note all safety alert symbols next to the steps in the Procedure and review the meanings of each symbol by referring to Safety Symbols on page 8.

Procedure

1. Work in groups of two or four students. **CAUTION:** *Wear your safety goggles and laboratory apron. Be careful to avoid breakage when working with glassware.* Obtain four culture tubes with tops. Use the masking tape to prepare four labels as shown in Figure 1. Place one label on each culture tube.

Tube 1	Tube 2	Tube 3	Tube 4
2 water plant cuttings and 1 snail	1 snail	2 water plant cuttings	No organisms
Name	Name	Name	Name
Date	Date	Date	Date

Figure 1

2. **CAUTION:** *Follow your teacher's directions and all safety precautions when handling plants and animals.* Into test tube 1, place two water plant cuttings and one live snail. Into tube 2, place one live snail. Into tube 3, place two water plant cuttings.

3. Fill all four tubes to the top with pond water. Add four drops of bromthymol blue solution to each tube. Seal each tube tightly. **CAUTION:** *Handle the bromthymol blue solution with care because it stains the skin and clothing. Wear plastic gloves.*

[1] Collect pond snails and water plants in the spring and early summer from local ponds, streams, or canals, or order them from a biological supply house or local pet store. If the snails are kept in an aquarium with fish, they should be cleaned before use in this investigation. Snails may be kept for short periods of time in a jar or indefinitely in an aquarium with aquatic plants. Collect 2 L of pond water per class, or age the same amount of tap water for at least 24 hours.

[2] Be sure sprigs of water plants are fresh and bright green. Use 10-cm pieces that include the growing tips.

[3] CAUTION: An incandescent light source can become hot and is a burning hazard. Do not use any lamp that can become hot.

[4] Dissolve 0.1 g bromthymol blue powder in 1 L distilled water. If solution appears green, add 4% sodium hydroxide solution to bromthymol blue drop by drop until color is blue. Bromthymol blue may also be purchased premixed from a biological supply house. Read all the information on chemical safety from any Materials Safety Data Sheet that accompanies a chemical.

[5] Screw-top culture tubes (20 x 200 mm) with caps can be ordered from a biological supply house. You may also use large test tubes or small jars. The reaction takes less time in a small container.

4. Set the tubes in a test-tube rack and place them all the same distance from a fluorescent plant lamp.

5. After 24 hours, observe the tubes. Notice if the organisms are still alive. Note any color change in the water. Bromthymol blue is an indicator. In the presence of carbon dioxide, it changes color from blue to yellow. Record your observations in the Data Table.

6. Observe the tubes every day for seven days. Record your observations in the Data Table.

7. Empty all the tubes and dispose of the organisms according to your teacher's directions. Wash your hands with soap and warm water before leaving the lab.

Data Table

Observations				
Day	Tube 1	Tube 2	Tube 3	Tube 4
1				
2				
3				
4				
5				
6				
7	all alive	yellow, snail dead	blue, plants yellowing	blue

Analysis and Conclusions

1. **Controlling Variables** What is the purpose of test tube 4?

   Tube 4 acts as an experimental control.

2. **Observing** What changes did you observe in the bromthymol blue solution in each test tube? Answers should be supported by students' data.

   Tube 1

   The bromthymol blue solution may or may not change color.

   Tube 2

   The bromthymol blue solution will change to yellow, indicating the presence of carbon dioxide.

   Tube 3

   The bromthymol blue solution may or may not change color.

   Tube 4

   There should be no change in color.

3. **Analyzing Data** At the end of seven days, what happened to the organisms in test tubes 1, 2, and 3? Explain the results you obtained.

   Answers should be supported by the data collected and will depend on students' interpretation of the data.

   In general, the organisms in test tubes 1 and 3 should have remained alive, while the snail in test tube 2

   may have died from lack of oxygen.

4. **Comparing and Contrasting** Compare and contrast the events that occurred in test tubes 1 and 3.

Answers should be supported by the data collected and will depend on students' interpretation of the data.

In general, the plants in test tube 1 emitted oxygen during photosynthesis, which was consumed by the snail.

At the same time, the snail and plants released carbon dioxide, which was used by the plants, as they carried

out cellular respiration. In test tube 3, the plants carried out both photosynthesis and cellular respiration.

5. **Predicting** Predict what would happen if the test tubes had all been placed in the dark for seven days. What if the test tubes were placed in the dark for many months? Explain your prediction.

After seven days, the plants would probably look sick. Students may predict that after many months of

darkness the plants would die because they would be unable to carry out photosynthesis. This would

cause the snails to eventually die from lack of food and oxygen.

6. **Drawing Conclusions** Could plants exist on Earth without animals? Could animals exist on Earth without plants? Use your data to explain your answers.

Answers should be supported by the data collected. Many students may conclude that plants could survive

on Earth without animals because plants carry out both photosynthesis and cellular respiration—using and

giving off carbon dioxide. Students may say that, barring technological advancements that could mimic the

oxygen cycle, animals require plants for oxygen and food to live on Earth.

7. **Drawing Conclusions** How does this investigation demonstrate the role of carbon dioxide in chemical cycling?

Answers should be supported by the data collected and will depend on students' interpretations. Students

may state that plants give off oxygen and fix carbon, which is used by animals. Animals, in turn, give off

carbon dioxide, which are used by plants.

Going Further

Repeat this investigation with different organisms or different combinations of organisms in each tube. You may also want to alter the size of the culture tubes or other containers. Be sure that all containers remain tightly sealed throughout the observation period. Report your observations and conclusions to the class.

Observing The Effect of Bacteria on Bean Plant Growth

You may want to refer students to Section 4–2 in the textbook for a discussion of the interactions between organisms in ecosystems and communities.

Time required: 40 minutes for initial set-up; 6-8 weeks for growth with minimal daily care; 40 minutes to collect data and make calculations

Introduction

Ecologists often study the interactions of organisms in ecosystems or communities. An understanding of these interactions provides fascinating insights into the very specialized functions of particular organisms. Relationships between organisms living together can be different in nature. Parasitism benefits one organism while the other is harmed, as in a tapeworm infestation of a cat or dog. In commensalism, one organism benefits and the other receives little or no benefit or harm, as in a bird nesting in a tree. Mutualism differs from each of these in that both organisms benefit, as in the case of lichens (close associations of algae and fungi). Some bacteria live closely associated with other organisms. One particular type of bacterium, *Rhizobium*, invades the roots of legume-type plants, causing nodules or swellings to develop on the roots. In this investigation, you will design and carry out a controlled experiment to determine whether the presence of *Rhizobium* affects bean plant growth.

Problem

How does the presence of *Rhizobium* bacteria affect the growth of plants?

Pre-Lab Discussion

Read the entire investigation. Then, work with a partner to answer the following questions.

1. Define the hypothesis that will be tested by your experiment.

Possible hypotheses might include that the bacteria are harmful to the plants and will decrease the length and

mass of the plants, or that the bacteria help the plant and increase their length and mass, or that the bacteria have

no effect on plant growth.

2. How could you test your predictions using the suggested materials?

Set up two separate pots and plant seeds inoculated with *Rhizobium* in the first pot and seeds without

Rhizobium in a second pot. After 6–8 weeks, measure the length and mass of the plants.

3. Which variables will be manipulated and which variables will be controlled?

The manipulated variable is inoculation of seeds with *Rhizobium.* Controlled variables include soil, water,

temperature, sunlight, planting depth of seeds, etc.

4. Discuss the possible outcomes of your experiment and explain the meaning of each.

Plants with *Rhizobium* may grow better (taller and more mass) or less well (shorter and less mass) than those

without, or there may be little difference in plant growth with or without *Rhizobium*. The difference in growth, if

any, indicates the effect of *Rhizobium* on the plants.

5. Suppose the control plants (those not inoculated with *Rhizobium*) developed the nodules that normally form as a result of invasion by bacteria. How could this be explained? Should this data be considered in drawing conclusions?

If plants form nodules, it means that contamination by the bacteria has occurred, and hence the plant has

grown in the presence of the bacteria. Such data cannot be used to support or contradict your predictions.

Suggested Materials *(per group)*

5-inch plastic pots (sterile)   If pots are not new, sterilize with bleach solution, rinse and dry.

distilled or deionized water   Do not use spring water.

legume seeds   Bush type lima beans of high viability work well.

horticultural vermiculite (less dusty) or perlite   You may choose to provide students with dust masks when they fill plant pots with vermiculite.

Rhizobium bacteria   harmless to humans and pets

fluorescent plant lamps   Gro-lux lamps work well.

nitrogen-free nutrients   Prepare by adding per 1 liter distilled water: 0.8 g potassium monohydrogen phosphate, 0.2 g potassium dihydrogen phosphate, 0.2 g magnesium sulfate, 0.1 g calcium sulfate, 0.01 g ferric sulfate. Read all the information on chemical safety from any Materials Safety Data Sheet that accompanies a chemical.

ruler

balance (grams)

You may request additional materials if you need them.

Safety ☣ ♨ ⚠ ✋ ⚗

Always use special caution and wear disposable plastic gloves when working with laboratory chemicals, as they may irritate the skin or stain skin or clothing. Follow your teacher's directions and all appropriate safety procedures when handling microorganisms. Note all safety symbols next to the steps in Design Your Experiment and review meanings of each symbol by referring to Safety Symbols on page 8.

Vermiculite is inert and sterile and is available at most garden supply stores. *Rhizobium* is available at garden supply stores and also from seed companies. Be sure that students set up the pot without the *Rhizobium* first and are extremely careful not to contaminate it with *Rhizobium*.

Depending on your lab space, it is possible to have students grow their plants at home. For uniformity and ease, all supplies should be provided to students. It is vital that before students begin their self-designed experiments, the procedure is carefully examined and approved by the instructor.

Design Your Experiment

1. Prepare a written experimental design in the space below.

Hypothesis:

Student responses will vary but should be that plants with *Rhizobium* bacteria

will grow more or less or there will be no difference in growth.

Manipulated variables:

inoculation of seeds with or presence of *Rhizobium*

Responding variables:

growth as determined from height and mass of plants

Controlled variables:

soil, water, temperature, sunlight, planting depth of seeds, temperature, etc.

Procedure:

An acceptable experimental design would be to label and fill the "without" pot with vermiculite, and plant

three seeds in it. Set the "with" pot up in the same way but inoculate the seeds with *Rhizobium* just before

planting. Students should water the plants until water comes out of the drainage holes. The pots should be

covered with plastic wrap between waterings until germination has occurred. Once the plants have their first

true leaves, they should be given N-free nutrients. At the end of 6–8 weeks, students should remove the

entire root mass from each pot and gently shake and rinse off all soil. All roots and nodules should be saved.

The root mass should be dipped into water repeatedly until all soil is washed off. Plant height should be

measured to the nearest millimeter. The mass of each plant should be measured to the nearest tenth of a

gram.

2. Once your teacher has approved your design, you may carry out your experiment. **CAUTION:** *Wear plastic gloves when handling laboratory chemicals and microorganisms.* Wash your hands with soap and warm water before leaving the lab.

Class results can be posted for analysis. If nodules are observed in "without" (control) plants, the data should not be used. It means that contamination has occurred and students should not be penalized. Explain fully to students why such data should not be included in the class results.

3. Record your data in the Data Table or create your own data table. If you need more space, use additional sheets of paper.

Data Table

	With *Rhizobium*	Without *Rhizobium*	Difference	Percent Difference
Plant height (cm)				
Plant mass (g)				
Observations of roots of bean plants				

4. Calculate the difference and the percentage difference in height and mass and record them in the data table.

Analysis and Conclusions

1. **Analyzing Data** How did the *Rhizobium* bacteria affect the growth of the bean plants?

It is likely that the plants grown from seeds inoculated with *Rhizobium* will show a longer length stem

and higher mass than those without.

2. **Drawing Conclusions** Do the results support or contradict your prediction? How strongly do the results support this conclusion? Explain.

Responses will depend upon student predictions and data. The results should indicate that the length

and mass are greater in plants with *Rhizobium* than those without. The percent increase in mass should

be about 8–9% while the percent increase in height should be about 3–4%.

3. **Evaluating** How would you describe the type of interaction or relationship between the bacteria and the bean plant? Support your answer.

The relationship is a mutualistic one. Bacteria play an important role in the nitrogen cycle by "fixing" or

making available the important element nitrogen that would otherwise be unavailable to plants.

4. **Comparing and Contrasting** Were the percentage increases for height and mass about the same? Do you think height or mass of the plant is more important?

Student responses will depend on data collected. The mass of the plant is probably more important than

the height.

5. **Predicting** Imagine this experiment is criticized because height and mass are not thought to be the ultimate goal of growing bean plants. Are there any variables other than height or mass that would be better indicators of success? Are these easily measured?

The production of beans is the ultimate goal. Fruit or seed production might be better predictors of success,

but they are not as easily measured.

Going Further

What question(s) did the results of your experiment raise? Design an experiment that would address one such question or that would logically follow from this experiment.

Sampling a Plant Community

You may want to refer students to Sections 5–1 and 5–2 in the textbook before performing this investigation.
Time required: two 50-minute sessions

Introduction

A population is any group of the same species that lives in the same area. Do you know what the human population density is in the area in which you live? The density is high if the area is a crowded city filled with apartment dwellers. The density is low if the area is rural and houses are far apart.

Ecologists are sometimes asked to carry out an environmental-impact study to see how developing an area of land will affect the living things there. To do this, ecologists must know exactly what species of plants and animals there are and how many individuals are likely to be disturbed. Finding the population of many species of plants and animals is a huge task. Ecologists often take a random sampling of parts of an area and then estimate what the population is like in the larger area. In this investigation, you will use a technique called the quadrat method for estimating the plant populations that inhabit a nearby area. Recall that population density is expressed as the number of individual organisms per unit area. You also will determine the population density of a nearby plant species and calculate what plants are dominant in the area.

Problem

How can the size of large populations be estimated?

Pre-Lab Discussion

Read the entire investigation. Then, work with a partner to answer the following questions.

1. What will you observe in the 10 m × 10 m square and record in Data Table 1?

   Students will observe and record the different species of plants present.

2. How will you use the plant guidebooks in this investigation?

   The guidebooks will help to identify and name each species of plant and to help categorize each

   species. They will also help identify any dangerous plants.

3. What will you do to make sure you get a random sampling of plants in the large square area?

   Sample answer: To ensure a random sampling, students may say that they will close their eyes and toss an

   object into the large square area. Then, mark off a 1 m × 1 m quadrat around the spot where the object landed

   and count the plants within the quadrat. They will repeat this two more times.

4. How might counting plants in three different quadrats give you a more accurate estimate of the total populations than counting plants in only one quadrat?

   Sample answer: There may be differences in the number of species in different areas of the large square.

   Taking three different samples will give a better picture of the populations for the entire square area.

5. Using the data you will collect in Data Table 2, what two steps must you take to calculate the approximate total population of a species in the large square?

Find the average number of the species in the three quadrats by adding the number in each quadrat

and dividing the sum by 3. Then, multiply the average quadrat population of that species by 100 to find

the total population.

Materials *(per pair)*

protective work gloves

meter stick or metric tape measure

16 stakes

rubber mallet

large ball of string

scissors

plant guidebooks to woody and nonwoody plants

notepad for use in the field

right triangle (measuring tool)

Find a suitable site in advance and get approval for its use (which might involve obtaining a permit from the appropriate authority). A suitable site should have a variety of plants that can be identified by students using plant guidebooks. You may wish to choose a site that will show a variety of plants from quadrat to quadrat because of different abiotic factors such as sunlight or water.
It would be best if the plot size were based on the size and density of the sampled plants. There should be enough plants in the plot for variety but not so many that students will be confused and unable to separate and count individual plants.

Safety 🔲🔳📦🔲

Be careful when handling sharp instruments. Use the mallet and other tools carefully. You will be observing and handling plants outdoors. Alert your teacher in advance to any allergies you may have. To avoid possible contact with poisonous or prickly plants, wear work gloves. Use the plant guidebooks to identify dangerous plants. Do not disturb the nests of any animals you may encounter. Treat living organisms with respect. Return or dispose of all materials according to the instructions of your teacher. Note all safety symbols next to the numbered steps in the Procedure and review the meaning of each symbol by referring to Safety Symbols on page 8.

Identify any allergies to plants or stinging insects that you or your students may have and take precautions to avoid these organisms.

Procedure

🔲 **1.** Work with a partner. As shown in Figure 1, use a tape measure or meter stick to measure off a square 10 m on a side. Then use the mallet to drive a stake into each of the four corners of the square. **CAUTION:** *Be careful not to injure yourself when using the mallet and stakes.*

You may substitute large nails for stakes in this investigation.

🔲 **2.** Loop the string around the stakes to mark off the square. Cut the string and tie the ends together. **CAUTION:** *Be careful when handling sharp tools.*

Point out that quadrat sampling techniques can be used for studying animals only if they are sessile or sedentary.

🔲 **3.** Take a survey of the kinds of plants you observe within the square. Use the categories shown in Data Table 1. Use plant guidebooks or other references to help you find the names of the species you observe. Write your observations in Data Table 1. **CAUTION:** *Be aware of any poisonous or prickly plants. Be sure to wear work gloves.*

4. Select an area within the site for your first small, sample area, or quadrat. Do so randomly by closing your eyes and tossing an object into the square. Around the spot where the object lands, measure off a square 1 m on a side. This square is your first quadrat.

5. Use string and stakes to mark off the boundaries of the quadrat as shown in Figure 2. The right-triangle tool will help you make the corners square.

6. Observe the plants in your quadrat as shown in Figure 3. Record in Data Table 2 the number of plants in each species. Large plants can be counted individually. If you are counting grass or ground cover, measure off several smaller squares 10 cm × 10 cm. Count the number of individual plants in each of the several smaller squares, take an average figure per small square, and multiply by 100 to get an estimate for the full quadrat.

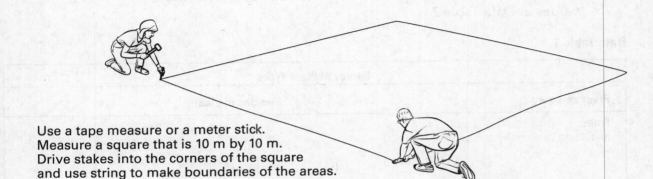

Use a tape measure or a meter stick.
Measure a square that is 10 m by 10 m.
Drive stakes into the corners of the square
and use string to make boundaries of the areas.

Figure 1

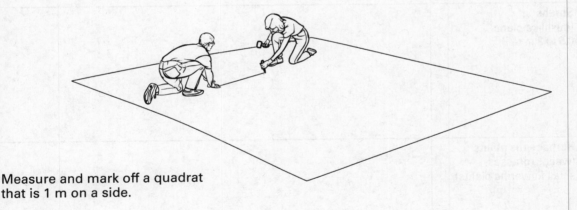

Measure and mark off a quadrat
that is 1 m on a side.

Figure 2

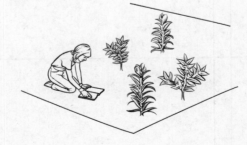

Use plant guidebooks to identify
the plants in the square.

Figure 3

The population density (number of individual plants per unit area) can be calculated by dividing the number of individuals by the size of the area sampled.

7. Repeat steps 4 through 6 twice more, to obtain population data for two more quadrats within the large square area.

8. When you have finished counting and identifying the plants, pull up the stakes, rewind the string, and return to class.

9. You now have a complete list of plant species and the number counted in each of three quadrats that are 1 m² in area. Average the numbers for each species by adding them and then dividing the total number by 3. This number is the species population density per square meter.

10. Estimate the approximate total population of each species by multiplying the average quadrat population by 100. Record these values in Data Table 2.

Data Table 1

Survey of Plant Types	
Plant category	**Species of plants**
Trees (including saplings)	Species will vary.
Shrubs (bushlike plants 0.5 to 3 m tall)	
Herbaceous plants (weeds, grasses, small flowering plants)	
Ground cover (mosses, lichens, and so on)	

Data Table 2

Populations in Quadrats					
Type of plant	Species name	Number in quadrat 1	Number in quadrat 2	Number in quadrat 3	Calculated total population in entire area, 10 m × 10 m

Analysis and Conclusions

1. **Analyzing Data** Interpret your data to determine the relative populations of plants in your 10 m × 10 m square. Are there mostly trees, shrubs, or herbaceous plants? What is the dominant species?

   Answers will depend on student data. Student responses should reflect an understanding of the categories

   of plant species and the meaning of the term dominant species.

2. **Comparing and Contrasting** Compare your results with other student teams in the class. Why were the population densities of the various species different from one part of the overall site to another? Comment on how abiotic factors such as sunlight, terrain, and availability of water may have had an effect.

   Answers will depend on student data. Students should offer hypotheses about which factors, such as

   variations in light, water, drainage, and soil type, might have caused specific differences in plant populations

   between different parts of the site.

3. **Inferring** Infer whether you would expect to see the plants in the same density 1 month, 6 months, or 1 year from now. Explain what the conditions may be like in all three cases.

   There may be changes in population density because of seasonal differences in conditions. A year later, the

   season will again be the same and the species will probably have similar densities to those they have now.

   However, other plant populations may have extended their ranges, or there may be a change in the abiotic

   factors to which certain species are especially sensitive.

4. **Formulating Hypotheses** Hypothesize about how your large square area might change if human activity or disease destroyed the dominant species.

   Answers will depend on student data. Students may suggest that if the dominant species were destroyed,

   another species that is not affected as adversely by the new environmental conditions would increase in number.

5. **Drawing Conclusions** Based on the results of this investigation, do you think that counting random samples is an accurate method for counting a large population? Explain your answer.

   Sample answer: Counting random samples is a fast, accurate way to count a large population.

   In this investigation, it would take a very long time to count each plant in the 10 m × 10 m square. If there are

   too many small plants, like grass, getting an accurate count of the large square area may be very difficult. It

   makes more sense to count samples in large areas.

Going Further

Based on the results of this investigation, develop a hypothesis about how the average population density of one kind of plant you sampled was affected by an abiotic factor such as water or light. Propose an experiment to test your hypothesis. If the necessary resources are available and you have your teacher's permission, perform the experiment.

Investigating Air and Water Pollution

You may want to refer students to Section 6–2 in the textbook for a discussion of pollution.
Time required:
    Part A–30 minutes
    Part B–30 minutes

Introduction

Although life on Earth depends on air and water, we are endangering these important resources by polluting them with harmful substances. The air we breathe contains the oxygen our cells need, but it also contains many other chemicals that can damage our bodies. Our atmosphere is polluted with smog, acid rain, carbon dioxide, and a variety of other chemicals that create problems for all organisms dependent on the atmosphere.

Despite the fact that the Earth's surface is 75 percent water, only a small fraction of that water is fresh water that can be used by living things. The pollution of our freshwater supply by chemicals, sewage, oil, and heated waste water interferes with many food chains. It also requires costly treatments to ensure the safety of our water supply. In this investigation, you will conduct tests to determine the types of pollutants present in samples of air and water taken from the area in which you live.

Problem

How can air and water pollution be detected?

Pre-Lab Discussion

Read the entire investigation. Then, work with a partner to answer the following questions.

1. How will you choose a location to test for air pollution?

   Answers will vary. Students may say that they will test areas that are near known pollutants, such as near

   the school parking lot or bus stop, or areas that they suspect may have pollutants, such as in a chemistry lab

   or an auto mechanics classroom.

2. Why are four particle traps used for each location?

   Having several samples at each location will provide the opportunity to average the data and increase

   the reliability of the data.

3. How will you compare the amount of air pollution at different locations?

   Air pollution will be compared in different locations by measuring the average number of particles collected

   in different locations over a set period of time.

4. Why should you stir each water sample before testing it for pollutants?

Stirring allows the tests to be conducted on a representative mixture of the particles in each sample.

For example, stirring will disperse any pollutants that might have settled to the bottom of a sample.

5. Examine water samples A, B, and C. Which of the samples do you think is clean and safe for human consumption? Explain your prediction.

Answers should be supported by students' observations. Students may conclude that sample B and/or C

is cleanest because they are clear and clean-looking.

Materials *(per group)*

4 microscope slides

petroleum jelly

tongue depressors   Wooden craft sticks can also be used.

4 petri dishes

glass-marking pencil

microscope

water samples A, B, and C

3 stirring rods

pH test paper

3 test tubes with stoppers

3 dropper pipettes

To 1 or 2 liters tap water (depending on class size), add the following:

Sample A–soil, gravel, leaf matter, small amounts of motor oil, and detergent

Sample B–single drops of sulfuric acid until a pH of between 2 and 4 is reached **CAUTION:** *wear safety goggles, a lab apron, and rubber gloves when working with sulfuric acid.*

Sample C–sodium sulfite until an odor of rotten eggs is produced **CAUTION:** *Do not use sulfites if you or any students are asthmatic.*

Safety 🔲🔲🔲🔲🔲🔲   Each group will need a small beaker of each sample.

Put on a laboratory apron. Put on safety goggles. Always use special caution and wear disposable plastic gloves when working with laboratory chemicals, as they may irritate the skin or cause staining of the skin or clothing. Never touch or taste any chemical unless instructed to do so. Always handle the microscope with extreme care. You are responsible for its proper care and use. Use caution when handling microscope slides as they can break easily and cut you. Note all safety alert symbols next to the steps in the Procedure and review the meaning of each symbol by referring to Safety Symbols on page 8.

Procedure

Part A. Air Pollution

1. Work in groups of two or four students. Obtain four glass slides, petroleum jelly, four tongue depressors, and four petri dishes. Make four particle traps by using a tongue depressor to smear the center of four glass slides with petroleum jelly. Place each particle trap in the bottom half of a petri dish. Cover each petri dish immediately. **CAUTION:** *Wear your safety goggles and laboratory apron. Handle all glassware carefully.*

2. Select one location on the school grounds for your particle traps. After obtaining your teacher's approval, place the four petri dishes containing the particle traps in the selected location. Make sure that the petri dishes are side by side.

3. Remove the lids of the petri dishes and expose the traps to the air for 20 minutes.

4. At the end of the exposure time, replace the lids. Use the glass-marking pencil to record the test location on the lid of each petri dish. Return to your classroom.

5. Carefully remove the particle trap from the first petri dish and place it on the stage of a microscope. Use the low-power objective to examine the slide. Count the number of trapped particles and record this number in Data Table 1. **CAUTION:** *Do not touch or taste the particles you collect. Wear plastic gloves. Always handle the microscope with extreme care, and do not use it around water or with wet hands. Never use direct sunlight as the light source for the microscope.*

6. Repeat step 5 for each of the remaining particle traps.

7. Calculate the average number of particles trapped at your selected location. Record this average in Data Table 1. To find the average number, add the number of particles counted on each trap and divide by 4.

8. Report your location and the average number of particles you trapped to the class. Using class data, complete Data Table 2.

9. Clean your laboratory equipment before proceeding with Part B of the investigation.

Part B. Water Pollution

1. Obtain water samples A, B, and C and the remaining materials listed under Materials. **CAUTION:** *Do not touch or taste the water samples. Wear plastic gloves.*

2. Describe the appearance of the water in sample A. Record your observations in Data Table 3.

3. Hold the sample away from your face and nose. Slowly wave your hand over the top of the container and inhale gently to determine if the water has an odor. **CAUTION:** *Do not inhale the fumes of the sample directly or repeatedly.* Record your observations in Data Table 3.

4. To determine the pH of the water sample, use a clean dropper pipette to place a drop of the water sample on the pH test paper. Immediately compare the color with the chart on the pH paper container. Record the pH in Data Table 3.

5. Pour water from the sample into a test tube until it is half full. To check for the presence of detergents, place a stopper in the test tube and shake for 10 seconds. Foam on the top of the sample indicates the presence of detergents. Record your observations in Data Table 3.

6. Repeat steps 2 through 5 with water samples B and C.

7. Wash your hands with soap and warm water before leaving the lab.

Data Table 1

Particle Trap	Number of Particles
1	
2	
3	
4	
Average	

Data Table 2

Particle Trap Location	Average Number of Trapped Particles

Data Table 3

Test For:	Sample A	Sample B	Sample C
Appearance	cloudy	clear	clear
Odor	foul	none	foul
pH	6	3	6.5
Detergents	present	absent	absent

Analysis and Conclusions

1. **Measuring** How did you measure air pollution in this investigation? What are some weaknesses in the way you measured air pollution?

Air pollution was measured in terms of the number of particles trapped from the air in different locations. This measurement is weak because air contains non-particulate pollutants (such as gases) and particles that cannot be detected with a compound light microscope.

2. **Inferring** Were there any particle traps in which you did not see any particles? Can you infer that air in such a location is free of pollutants?

Answers should be supported by the data collected. A particle trap that appears to be free of particles does not necessarily indicate that there is no pollution in the location tested because invisible gases and other chemicals that a particle trap cannot detect may be present in the area.

3. **Analyzing Data** In which location was the greatest average number of particles trapped? What factors do you think increased the average number of particles trapped in this location?

Answers should be supported by the data collected and will depend on students' interpretation of the data.

Sites that are near automobiles or exhaust vents should show greater particle densities than other sites.

4. **Predicting** In what types of weather you would expect air pollution to be the worst? Explain the basis of your prediction.

Answers will vary. On warm, humid days that have little air circulation air pollution will be worse in a polluted

area than on windy days.

5. **Drawing Conclusions** Do your data support your initial prediction about the water samples?

Answers should be supported by the data collected and will depend on students' initial predictions. Many

students may conclude that even clean-looking water might still contain dangerous pollutants that could not

be detected by the given tests.

6. **Evaluating** How might the air and water pollution tests used in this lab be improved?

Answers should be supported by the data collected and will depend on students' results. Students may

conclude that additional variables should be included in the air and water tests. For example, the air tests

might include noting qualitative information about each location tested.

Going Further

Conduct a study of the pollution in your community. Use the air and water pollution tests from this investigation to determine air and water quality, and make a visual survey to evaluate land pollution. Report your findings on a map of the area. Be sure to identify the major landmarks; roadways; and residential, commercial, and industrial areas of your community on the map. Your map key should explain any colors or symbols you used in reporting the data.

Observing Osmosis

You may want to refer students to Section 7–3 in the textbook for a discussion of osmosis before performing this lab.
Time required: 50 minutes

Introduction

Osmosis is the diffusion of water across a semipermeable membrane, from an area of high water concentration to an area of low water concentration. Osmosis also occurs in response to changing concentrations of water-soluble solutes. Osmosis can be observed in individual cells or in collections of cells, as in multicellular organisms or their structures. In this investigation you will use a shelled egg's external membrane to demonstrate how osmosis can occur in solutions where there are changes in the concentrations of solutes.

Problem

How does solute concentration affect the movement of water across a biological membrane?

Pre-Lab Discussion

Read the entire investigation. Then, work with a partner to answer the following questions.

1. Explain the meaning of the term *water-soluble*.

Water-soluble describes a substance that dissolves in water.

2. Why does the investigation ask you to blot the egg each time it is removed from a beaker?

The egg is blotted to remove any excess liquid that might add to the weight of the egg.

3. What are some differences between the liquids used in the investigation?

Water is less concentrated than syrup and flows more easily. Syrup is more concentrated and viscous.

4. What data will you record in Data Table 2?

The mass of the egg in syrup is recorded in Data Table 2.

5. Why do you need to record the times the egg was immersed?

This information will be used to make a graph of the mass of the eggs over time.

Materials *(per pair)*

2 decalcified eggs
paper towels
weighing container
2 250-mL beakers
distilled water

syrup
marker
2 plastic spoons
balance

Advance Preparation

Eggs   You can obtain chicken eggs and white vinegar from stores or from the school cafeteria. To decalcify eggs, place uncooked eggs in a large plastic container and cover them completely with white vinegar. Eggs do not need to be in a single layer. Allow eggs to decalcify for approximately 72 hours. To avoid the vinegar odor, place container in a well-ventilated area.

Syrup   You can obtain any type of syrup for use, such as pancake, waffle, or corn, from stores or from the school cafeteria.

Safety

Put on safety goggles. Put on a laboratory apron. Be careful to avoid breakage when working with glassware. Always use caution when working with laboratory chemicals, as they may irritate the skin or stain skin or clothing. Wear plastic gloves when handling eggs or egg whites or tools that have been in contact with them. Wash hands thoroughly after carrying out this lab. Note all safety symbols next to the steps in the Procedure and review the meaning of each symbol by referring to Safety Symbols on page 8.

Procedure

1. Wear your safety goggles, plastic gloves, and laboratory apron. Work in pairs. You will eventually share your data with other members of the class.

2. Obtain two decalcified eggs, provided by your teacher. Gently blot them on a paper towel and determine the mass of each, using correct procedure (use weighing paper or a container on the balance). Record the initial mass of each egg in the spaces provided in Data Tables 1 and 2.

3. Place one egg in a beaker. Fill this beaker with distilled water to just cover the egg. See Figure 1. In Data Table 1 record the time the egg is placed in the water. Note the appearance of the water at this time and record your observation in Data Table 3. **CAUTION:** *Be careful to avoid breaking glassware.*

Stress safety and disposal procedures.

Warn students that vinegar is dilute (3%) acetic acid and can cause injury and irritation to eyes and nasal passages.

The decalcified eggs are uncooked. Warn students to handle eggs very gently because they can easily break.

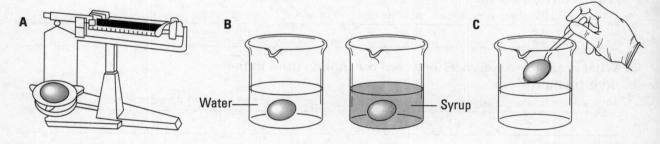

A Determine the initial mass of each egg.

B Place one egg in beaker, cover with water, and note the time. Place the other egg in second beaker, cover with syrup, and note the time.

C After egg has been immersed for 10 minutes, remove it from beaker with a spoon and set it on a paper towel.

Water — Syrup

Figure 1

4. Place the other egg in a beaker. Pour syrup into the beaker to just cover the egg. In Data Table 2 record the time the egg is placed in the syrup. Note the appearance of the syrup at this time and record your observation in Data Table 3.

5. Using the marker, label one plastic spoon *water* and the other spoon *syrup*. After 10 minutes have elapsed, use the correctly labeled plastic spoon to remove each egg from its beaker. Carefully blot the egg with a paper towel and determine the mass of the egg. See Figure 2. Record in Data Table 1 the mass of the egg that was immersed in water. Record in Data Table 2 the mass of the egg that was immersed in syrup. Gently return each egg to its appropriate beaker. Note the times again.

A

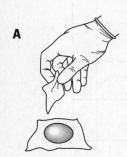

Carefully blot the egg dry.

B

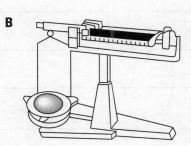

Determine the mass of the egg.

C

Carefully return the egg to its beaker and note the time. Then remove the second egg, blot dry, determine its mass, and return the second egg to the beaker of syrup. Continue the immersion and weighing process until the lab period ends.

Figure 2

6. Repeat step 5 every 10 minutes, as long as time permits. Record the masses of the eggs for each 10-minute interval in Data Table 1 or Data Table 2.

7. After you have completed the last mass determination of the eggs in water and syrup, record the appearance of the water and syrup in Data Table 3. **CAUTION:** *Wash your hands thoroughly after carrying out this lab.*

8. Determine the percent change in mass of each egg for each 10-minute interval by using the following formula:

$$\frac{(\text{mass after immersion} - \text{initial mass}) \times 100}{\text{initial mass}}$$

Record this percent mass change in Data Tables 1 and 2.

Data Table 1: Egg in Distilled Water

Time (minutes)	Mass (grams)	% Mass change
In _____ Out _____	Initial mass _____	
In _____ Out _____	After 10 min. _____	0.2
In _____ Out _____	After 20 min. _____	0.4
In _____ Out _____	After 30 min. _____	0.8
In _____ Out _____	After 40 min. _____	1.3
In _____ Out _____	After 50 min. _____	1.9

Data Table 2: Egg in Syrup

Time (minutes)	Mass (grams)	% Mass change
In _____ Out _____	Initial mass _____	
In _____ Out _____	After 10 min. _____	−0.2
In _____ Out _____	After 20 min. _____	−0.3
In _____ Out _____	After 30 min. _____	−0.7
In _____ Out _____	After 40 min. _____	−1.3
In _____ Out _____	After 50 min. _____	−2.0

Data Table 3: Appearances of Liquids

	Initial	Final
Water	clear	clear
Syrup	dark and thick	lighter and thinner

9. Graph the percent change in mass of each egg versus time using Figure 3. Use a different symbol or color for each egg.

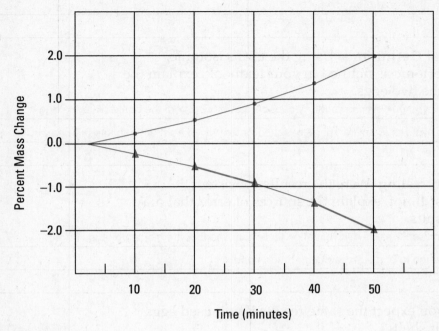

Key to symbols
- Distilled water
▲ Syrup

Figure 3

Analysis and Conclusions

1. **Observing** Did any egg gain mass over time? If so, which one(s)?

   The egg in distilled water gained mass over time.

2. **Observing** Did any egg lose mass over time? If so, which one(s)?

   The egg in syrup lost mass over time.

3. **Observing** Describe any changes in the appearance of the water or the syrup.

   The appearance of the water should not change. If the investigation runs for at least 50 minutes, the syrup may

   look paler and be more dilute.

4. **Inferring** Explain why there were changes in the mass of the eggs, either a loss or gain.

   Water moves from an area of high water concentration to low water concentration. The egg in distilled water

   will gain mass, and the egg in syrup will lose mass because of the movement of water.

5. **Formulating Hypotheses** Explain any changes you observed in the appearance of the water or the syrup.

There was no change in the water. Because water moved from the egg to the syrup, the syrup's color

became paler, and the syrup became more dilute.

6. **Forming Operational Definitions** Using the terms isotonic, hypotonic, and hypertonic as defined in your textbook, explain the changes in mass of the two eggs.

The egg in water was in a hypotonic environment, because water moved from the beaker into the egg.

The egg in syrup was in a hypertonic environment, because water moved from the egg into the beaker.

7. **Comparing and Contrasting** Were the results consistent throughout the class? If not, explain the sources of error that may have affected the results.

Results may vary due to improper mass determination technique, inadequate blotting of eggs prior to

measuring mass, and damage to egg surface due to rough handling.

8. **Predicting** Would you expect the same results if you used eggs that were still in their shells?

No. Although the shell may allow water to move into the egg, the egg has no room to expand. Some mass

differences may be detectable, but a longer time period would be necessary for the lab.

9. **Inferring** What might you infer if the syrup's color became darker as time progressed?

Water moved from the syrup into the egg because of a higher water concentration in the syrup and a lower

water concentration in the egg.

10. **Formulating Hypotheses** In the past, meat was preserved by packing it in salt. Explain how this technique might prevent the growth of microorganisms.

There would be a higher water concentration in microorganisms in the meat. Water would move from the

microorganism into the meat, resulting in death or inhibition of the microorganism's growth.

Going Further

Propose an experiment to determine the concentration of syrup or another solution that would be isotonic for an egg. If resources are available and you have the permission of your teacher, perform the experiment.

Chapter 8   Photosynthesis

Measuring the Effect of Light Intensity on Photosynthesis

You may want to refer students to Section 8–3 in the textbook for a discussion of the relationship between light intensity and photosynthesis.
Time required: 40 minutes

Introduction

Photosynthesis captures energy from sunlight. Plants, algae, and some bacteria use the energy captured during photosynthesis for their metabolic reactions. During photosynthesis in plants, chlorophyll and enzymes in leaves convert certain wavelengths of light into chemical energy. A simple equation can be used to represent photosynthesis.

$$\text{light energy} + CO_2 + H_2O \xrightarrow{\text{Enzymes and Chlorophyll}} \text{carbohydrate} + O_2$$

In this investigation you will examine the relationship between the amount of light energy available and the rate of use of carbon dioxide by a plant in the process of photosynthesis.

Problem

What is the relationship between light intensity and the rate of photosynthesis?

Pre-Lab Discussion

Read the entire investigation. Then, work with a partner to answer the following questions.

1. What are the variables in this experiment? Identify the manipulated and responding variables and two controlled variables.

   The manipulated variable is light intensity. The responding variable is pH. Controlled variables include

   the initial pH, the size of the plant sprigs, and time.

2. How will you provide carbon dioxide to the evergreen sprigs?

   Carbon dioxide is provided by blowing into the BTB solution.

3. How will you know whether the carbon dioxide has disappeared from the solutions in the test tubes?

   When the carbon dioxide disappears, the BTB solution changes from yellow to blue.

4. If the carbon dioxide does disappear from the solutions in the test tubes, how will you know whether it was consumed by photosynthesis or simply evaporated into the air?

   Greater loss of carbon dioxide from test tubes closer to the light and containing sprigs supports the

   idea that photosynthesis is removing the carbon dioxide.

5. How do you expect the intensity of light to affect the color of the BTB indicator? Predict the result you expect for this experiment.

   In test tubes that contain sprigs, the color should change to blue most quickly closer to the light.

Materials *(per group)*

8 large test tubes
4 test-tube racks
250-mL beaker
distilled water
bromthymol
   blue indicator solution
   or carbon dioxide probe

Dissolve 0.5 g bromthymol blue in 500 mL distilled water. If necessary, add 0.1% ammonium hydroxide by drops until the solution turns blue. Read all the information on chemical safety from any Materials Safety Data Sheet that accompanies a chemical.

dropper
straw
4 sprigs of an evergreen (such as yew)
paper towel
scalpel or single-edged razor blade
meter stick
floodlight

Safety 🔥🦺🧪🔪✋🔥

Use caution when working with chemicals, as they may irritate the skin or stain skin or clothing. Put on a laboratory apron and plastic gloves and wear safety goggles. Be careful to avoid breakage when working with glassware. Be careful when handling sharp instruments. Return or dispose of all materials according to the instructions of your teacher. Note all safety symbols next to the steps in the Procedure and review the meaning of each symbol by referring to Safety Symbols on page 8.

Procedure

1. Work in groups of two or four students. **CAUTION:** *Wear safety goggles, gloves, and a lab apron.* Obtain eight large test tubes and four test-tube racks. Place two test tubes in each test-tube rack.

2. Using a beaker, fill each of the eight test tubes with distilled water to about 4 cm from the top.

3. If you are using a carbon dioxide probe, see your teacher for instructions. Bromthymol blue indicator solution (BTB) indicates the presence of carbon dioxide by turning yellow. Add BTB to one test tube, one drop at a time, stirring with a straw. Count the drops you add. Stop when the water changes color to a pale blue. Then add the same amount of BTB to each of the other seven test tubes. Stir each test tube with a straw.

4. Using a straw, blow gently into each test tube of BTB-water solution to add carbon dioxide to the solution. Continue blowing until the color changes to a pale yellow color. **CAUTION:** *Be careful not to inhale any of the BTB solution.*

5. Obtain four sprigs of an evergreen plant and place them on a paper towel. Using a scalpel or razor blade, carefully cut and remove about 0.5 cm from the base (blunt) end of each sprig. Cut more if necessary to ensure that all four sprigs are the same size. **CAUTION:** *Be careful when using sharp tools.* In each of the four test-tube racks, place one sprig, cut end down, into one of the two test tubes of BTB-water solution.

6. Place one test-tube rack 50 cm from the floodlight or other light source provided by your teacher. Place the second rack 40 cm from the light source, the third rack 20 cm from the light source, and the fourth rack 10 cm from the light source. Record the time you place each rack in front of the light source in the Data Table.

Name_____ Class_____ Date_____

7. Observe the test tubes for the remainder of your lab period. Record in the Data Table the time required for a color change to occur in each test tube.

8. Compare the results in your Data Table with those of other groups in your class, according to your teacher's instructions.

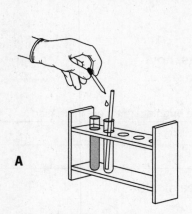

A

Add BTB solution to test tube, one drop at a time. Stir with a straw until the water changes to a pale blue.

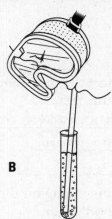

B

With a straw, blow gently into each test tube until the solution changes to a pale yellow color.

C

With a razor blade, carefully cut off about 0.5 cm from the base end of each sprig.

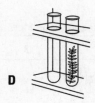

D

Place a sprig, cut end down, into one test tube in each test-tube rack.

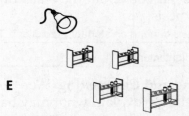

E

Place test-tube racks at specified distances from the light source. Observe any color changes and note the time.

Figure 1

Data Table

Distance from Light	Contents of Test Tube	Time Placed in Light	Time of Color Change	Elapsed Time before Change
50 cm	no plant			no change
50 cm	sprig of evergreen			fourth change
40 cm	no plant			no change
40 cm	sprig of evergreen			third change
20 cm	no plant			no change
20 cm	sprig of evergreen			second change
10 cm	no plant			no change
10 cm	sprig of evergreen			first change

9. Make a graph of the observations that you recorded in the Data Table. On the horizontal axis, plot distance from the light source. On the vertical axis, plot the time required for the color of the BTB solution to change. Use two different colors or symbols to graph the results from the test tubes that contained sprigs and those that did not contain sprigs.

Analysis and Conclusions

1. **Analyzing Data** In the test tubes that contained plant sprigs, how did distance from the light source affect the time required to see a color change? How can you explain this result?

   Test tubes closer to the light source changed color more quickly because the brighter light there increased

   the rate at which photosynthesis consumed carbon dioxide.

2. **Inferring** Were there any test tubes in which you did not see a color change? How can you explain this observation?

   Test tubes that lacked a plant sprig did not change color because photosynthesis did not occur in

   those test tubes.

3. **Drawing Conclusions** Was your prediction correct? Explain what the results tell you about the effect of light intensity on photosynthesis.

   Responses will depend on student predictions. The results indicate that photosynthesis increases

   with greater light intensity.

4. **Comparing and Contrasting** Were results consistent throughout the class? If not, explain what may have affected the results.

   Variation within the class may reflect differences in plant quality, light, or judgement of BTB color.

5. **Predicting** Predict what would happen to the color of the BTB-water solution if you placed a tube with a plant sprig in darkness.

   The color would not change.

Going Further

Based on the results of this investigation, propose a hypothesis about whether or not a temperature change in the test tubes, caused by the light source, could be a factor affecting the results. Propose an experiment to test your hypothesis about the effect of temperature on photosynthesis. If the necessary resources are available and you have your teacher's permission, perform the experiment.

Name_____ Class_____ Date _____

Observing Respiration

You may want to refer students to Chapter 9 in the textbook for a discussion of cellular respiration and its reactants and products.
Time required: Part A: 40 minutes for set-up; 10 minutes to observe 24 hours later. Part B will depend on students' experiments

Introduction

Cellular respiration occurs in all living things. During this process, animals take in oxygen and release carbon dioxide by breathing. Is it possible to observe an animal release carbon dioxide? Plants are different from animals in that they do not breathe in the same way animals do. Do they carry out cellular respiration? How could the release of carbon dioxide by plants be observed? In this investigation, you will first observe the release of carbon dioxide by humans. Then you will design and conduct an experiment to investigate whether plants also release carbon dioxide.

Problem

How can you observe the release of carbon dioxide by an animal? Do plants also release carbon dioxide as a product of cellular respiration?

Pre-Lab Discussion

Read through the entire investigation. Then, work with a partner to answer the following questions.

1. Identify the manipulated and responding variables in Part A.

The manipulated variable will be exhaling into the test tube and the responding variable will be the color of

the indicator.

_____

_____

2. What is an acid indicator? How and why is one being used in this experiment?

An indicator is a substance that changes color with a change in acidity. When carbon dioxide is exhaled into the

test tube containing the cabbage indicator, a color change from purplish-blue to reddish-blue is observed,

indicating the presence of an acid. This is because of the presence of carbon dioxide, which forms a weak acid

called carbonic acid when combined with water.

_____

_____

_____

3. Apply your understanding of Part A to an experiment with a plant such as a radish or bean seedling instead of a person. Why couldn't an identical experiment be used to demonstrate the release of carbon dioxide by plants?

A plant seedling cannot blow through a straw into the test tube.

_____

_____

_____

4. How could a new experiment be designed to demonstrate the release of carbon dioxide by a seedling?

A seedling could be placed into the test tube of indicator, left over time, and compared to a control test tube of

indicator with no seedling.

5. Discuss the possible outcomes of an experiment with a seedling and explain the meaning of each.

If the indicator in the test tube containing the seedling turns reddish-blue, the seedling released carbon

dioxide. If the indicator in the test tube containing the seedling does not change color, the seedling did not

release carbon dioxide.

Suggested Materials *(per group)*

distilled water

hot plate

2 500-mL beakers

purple cabbage leaves

large slotted spoon

straw

10 radish seedlings   Pea or bean seedlings also can
be used.

test tubes

stoppers

cotton ball

forceps

Safety ⬡ 🔥 🧤 🥽 ⚗️ 🔥 ☠️ ⚠️ ✋ 🔥

Put on safety goggles. Put on a laboratory apron and plastic gloves. Be careful to avoid breakage when working with glassware. Use extreme care when working with heated equipment or materials to avoid burns. Observe proper laboratory procedures when using electrical equipment. Always use special caution when working with laboratory chemicals, as they may irritate the skin or stain skin or clothing. Never touch or taste any chemical unless instructed to do so. Note all safety alert symbols next to the steps in Design Your Experiment and review the meaning of each symbol by referring to Safety Symbols on page 8.

Design Your Experiment

Part A. Using Cabbage Indicator

🧤 1. Tear the purple cabbage leaves into small pieces. Place the cabbage pieces into one of the beakers.

⬡ 2. Pour about 250 mL of distilled water into the other beaker. Using
🔥 the hot plate, heat the water until it boils. **CAUTION:** *Put on safety*
🔥 *goggles. Be careful when working with the hot plate.*

🥽 3. Pour the hot distilled water into the bowl that contains the cabbage.
⚗️ **CAUTION:** *Be careful when working with heated materials to avoid*
✋ *burns.* Allow the water to cool. The water will turn purplish-blue in color when mixed with the cabbage.

4. Using the slotted spoon, scoop out the cabbage pieces. Discard the cabbage, saving the liquid. The liquid will serve as an acid indicator. The color of the cabbage indicator will change from purplish-blue to reddish-blue when the indicator is mixed with an acid. When carbon dioxide combines with water, it forms a weak acid called carbonic acid.

5. Pour the cabbage indicator into 2 test tubes so that they are half full. Put a rubber stopper into one test tube.

6. Exhale a few times into the uncovered test tube, as shown in Figure 1. **CAUTION:** *Be sure not to inhale any of the cabbage indicator.* Observe any changes in the color of the cabbage indicator in both test tubes. Record your observations.

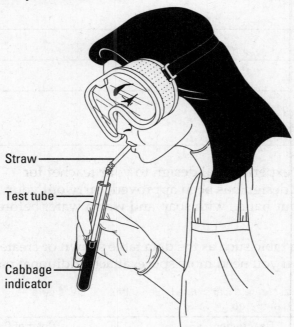

Straw

Test tube

Cabbage indicator

Design Your Experiment

It is vital that before students conduct their self-designed experiments, the procedure be carefully examined and approved by the instructor.

Part B. Carbon Dioxide and Plants

1. In the space provided below, design an experiment to determine whether plants release carbon dioxide. Write your hypothesis, identify the variables, and write out the procedure in the space below. Be sure to include a control in your experimental plan.

Hypothesis:

Acceptable hypotheses: Plants release carbon dioxide as a product of cellular respiration or Plants do

not release carbon dioxide.

Manipulated variables:

Addition of radish seedlings to test tube

Responding variables:

Presence of carbon dioxide as indicated by color of indicator in test tube.

Controlled variables:

Time, volume of indicator, size of seedlings, temperature, etc.

Procedure:

1. Make indicator as described in Part A.

2. Add cabbage indicator to two test tubes so they are one quarter full.

3. Place a cotton ball and 10 radish seedlings in one test tube.

4. Put a rubber stopper in each of the two test tubes.

5. Wait 1 day.

6. Make observations after 1 day and record.

7. _____

Safety Precautions:

_____

2. Submit your written experimental design to your teacher for approval. Once your design has been approved, carry out your experiment. Wash your hands with soap and warm water before leaving the lab.

If students struggle in designing this experiment, ask leading questions about photosynthesis and nutrition in adult plants and seedlings.

3. Record your data in a table such as the data table shown or create your own data table. If you need more space, attach additional paper.

Data Table

You may choose to create a class data table so that the class data can be posted and analyzed.

Test Tube	Description	Color of Cabbage Indicator
1	Test tube with human breath	Reddish-blue
2	Test tube covered with foil	Purplish-blue
3	Test tube with radish seedlings	Reddish-blue
4	Test tube with no radish seedlings	Purplish-blue

Analysis and Conclusions

1. **Analyzing Data** Describe the color change after exhalation into the test tube of cabbage indicator as compared to the test tube of indicator that was left alone? How can you explain what occurred?

The indicator that was exhaled into changed from purplish-blue to reddish-blue while the test tube that was left alone remained purplish-blue. This indicates that carbon dioxide was exhaled and when it combined with water, it formed carbonic acid.

2. Analyzing Data In the experiment that you designed, describe any color changes that occurred and provide an explanation. What happened in the "control" test tube and what does it mean?

Answers will depend on student designs and results. For the test tube containing radish seedlings, the

indicator turned to reddish-blue indicating that carbon dioxide was available to combine with water to form

carbonic acid. The test tube with no radish seedlings was the "control" because it had no source of carbon

dioxide and it did not change color.

3. Drawing Conclusions What conclusions can be drawn from the data collected in both experiments?

Humans and plant seedlings both produce carbon dioxide. Since carbon dioxide is a product of cellular

respiration, both must be undergoing cellular respiration.

4. Designing Experiments What argument could be made against your conclusions if a control had not been used?

If controls had not been used in either case, it could be argued that the cabbage indicator turns from

purplish-blue to reddish-blue spontaneously as a function of time.

5. Predicting If the experiment is done again but more seedlings are placed in one of the test tubes, what do you predict would occur? Explain the reason for your prediction.

The color of the water would change more rapidly with more seedlings because more cellular respiration

would have occurred and more carbon dioxide produced as a result.

6. Drawing Conclusions Did the color of the cabbage indicator change when you exhaled into the test tube? Explain your answer.

Yes. The carbon dioxide that was exhaled formed carbonic acid when it combined with the water in

the cabbage indicator.

Going Further

What question(s) did the results of your experiment raise? Design an experiment that would address one such question or that would logically follow this experiment.

Observing Specialized Cells

You may want to refer students to Section 7–4 in the textbook for a discussion of the relationship between cell structure and function.
Time required: 50 minutes

Introduction

The cell is the basic unit of structure and function in all living things. All of the processes necessary for life occur in cells. In single-celled organisms, all of the life functions of the organism take place within one cell. Multicellular organisms, such as humans and plants, are made up of many cells with different structures and functions. The cells of multicellular organisms take on special functions.

In this investigation, you will observe several types of cells and relate their structural differences to their functions.

Problem

How are the structures of specialized cells adapted to fit their particular functions?

Pre-Lab Discussion

Read the entire investigation. Then, work with a partner to answer the following questions.

1. What kinds of cells will you observe in this investigation? Which of these cells belong to plants? Which belong to animals?
   Cells from lettuce and water plant leaves are plant cells. Cells from human tissues are animal cells.

2. In this investigation, you will prepare two wet mounts of specimens and examine three prepared slides. Why is it not practical for you to examine all of your specimens as wet mounts?
   It is not possible to obtain and prepare human tissues in the school laboratory.

3. Why is an oak leaf probably not a good specimen for this investigation?
   In general, oak leaves are too thick to for light to pass through them, making it hard to see the individual cells.

4. What structures do you expect to find in all five cell samples?
   The cells will all have a cell membrane, cytoplasm, and a nucleus.

5. In what ways do the cells you will observe in this investigation differ from one another in function? Based on the differences in function, predict how the cells are likely to differ in structure.
   Unlike animal cells, plant cells carry out photosynthesis; thus, plant cells, such as those found in lettuce
   and water plant leaves, will contain chloroplasts.

Materials *(per group)*

microscope	3 coverslips
lettuce leaf	forceps
water plant leaf	dissecting probe
dropper pipette	prepared slides of 3 types of human tissues
3 microscope slides	Skeletal muscle, blood, nerve, bone, or skin

Safety

Put on a laboratory apron. Plant parts and their juices can irritate your eyes and skin. Use forceps or wear gloves when handling plants. Handle all glassware carefully. Always handle the microscope with extreme care. You are responsible for its proper care and use. Use caution when handling microscope slides as they can break easily and cut you. Note all safety alert symbols in the Procedure and review the meaning of each symbol by referring to Safety Symbols on page 8.

Procedure

1. Obtain a microscope and place it about 10 cm from the edge of the laboratory table.

2. Carefully clean the eyepiece and the objective lenses with lens paper.

3. Locate a rib in the lettuce leaf. As shown in Figure 1, bend the lettuce leaf against the curve until it snaps.

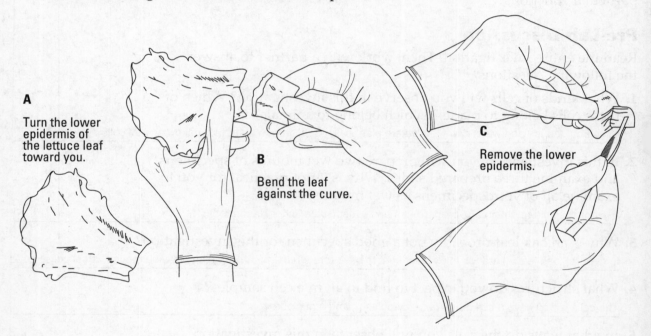

A
Turn the lower epidermis of the lettuce leaf toward you.

B
Bend the leaf against the curve.

C
Remove the lower epidermis.

Figure 1

4. **CAUTION:** *Be careful when handling sharp instruments. Handle all glassware carefully. Use forceps or wear gloves when collecting plant specimens.* With the forceps, carefully remove the thin layer of surface tissue called the epidermis from the piece of lettuce. Spread out the epidermis as smoothly as possible on a microscope slide. **Note:** *If the epidermis becomes folded on the slide, use a dissecting probe to gently unfold and flatten it.*

5. To prepare a wet-mount slide, place a drop of water in the center of the slide. Using the dissecting probe, gently lower the coverslip onto the lettuce epidermis as shown in Figure 2.

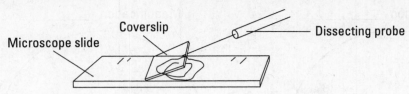

Coverslip

Microscope slide

Dissecting probe

Figure 2

6. **CAUTION:** *Always handle the microscope with extreme care and do not use it around water or with wet hands. Never use direct sunlight as the light source for the microscope.* Observe the lettuce epidermis under the low-power objective of the microscope. **Note:** *It may be necessary to adjust the diaphragm so there is sufficient light passing through the cells.* Notice the shapes of the epidermal cells.

7. Switch to the high-power objective. **CAUTION:** *When turning to the high-power objective, look at the objective from the side of your microscope so that the objective lens does not hit or damage the slide.*

8. In the Data Table, write the type of cell that you examined. Describe its general shape and place a check mark in the columns below the structures that you are able to observe under the high-power objective.

9. In the space provided on the next page, draw and label what you see under the high-power objective. Record the magnification of the microscope.

10. Repeat steps 5 to 9 using the water plant leaf.

11. Repeat steps 6 to 9 using the 3 prepared slides of human cells and/or tissues.

12. Wash your hands with soap and warm water before leaving the lab.

Data Table

Cell Type	Shape	Cell Structures						
		Cell wall	Cell membrane	Nucleus	Nuclear envelope	Cytoplasm	Vacuoles	Plastids
Answers will vary depending on slides available.								

Magnification _____

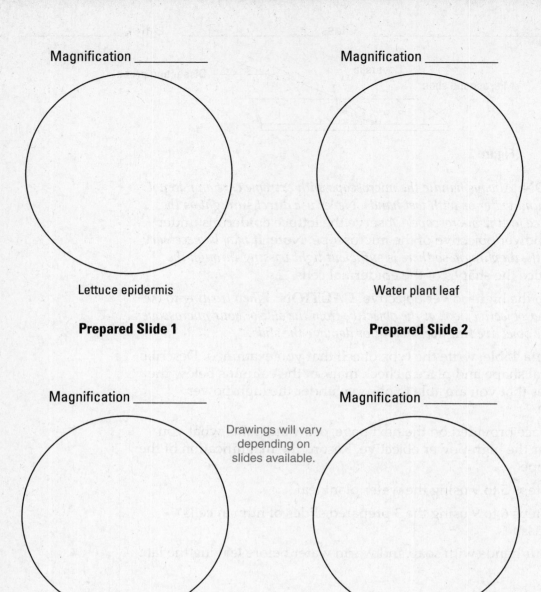

Lettuce epidermis

Prepared Slide 1

Magnification _____

Water plant leaf

Prepared Slide 2

Magnification _____

Drawings will vary
depending on
slides available.

Magnification _____

Name_____ Class_____ Date _____

Prepared Slide 3

Magnification _____

_____

Analysis and Conclusions

1. **Evaluating and Revising** Did your observations support your
   initial prediction about the structures common to all the cells? List
   the structures all the cells you observed have in common.

   Students should observe a cell membrane, a nucleus, and cytoplasm in all of the cells.
   _____

   _____

2. **Comparing and Contrasting** Compare and contrast the shapes of
   the different cells you observed. Describe any similarities or
   differences.

   Answers should be supported by the data collected. The lettuce and water plant cells will be uniform and

   cuboidal in shape. The human cells will vary in shape depending on the types of tissues observed.

   _____

3. **Analyzing Data** For each type of human tissue you observed,
   describe one feature that is not found in any of the other tissues you
   observed.

   Answers should be supported by the data collected and will depend on the tissues students observe. For

   example, bone tissue has individual cells embedded in layers of mineral material; epithelial tissue is flat,

   blood tissue contains disk-shaped cells that lack a nucleus and large irregularly shaped nucleated cells;

   skeletal muscle is striated.

4. **Drawing Conclusions** How is each tissue you observed adapted to
   perform its function?

   Answers should be supported by the data and will depend on the tissues students observe. For example, the

   water plant cells contain chloroplasts, which help the plant carry out photosynthesis. Epithelial tissue is flat,

   which enables it to serve as a good layered covering.

Going Further

Write a short report on the types of tissues found in humans and
plants. Include the general characteristics and functions of each type.

Chapter 11   Introduction to Genetics

Investigating Inherited Traits

You may want to refer students to Chapter 11 in the textbook for a discussion of the basic principles of heredity.
Time required: 40 minutes

Introduction

Heredity is the passing on of traits from parent to offspring. The genetic makeup of an individual is known as its genotype. The physical characteristics of an individual, which are the result of its genotype and its environment, are known as its phenotype.

Some alleles are expressed only when the genotype is homozygous. These alleles are said to produce recessive phenotypes. Alleles that are expressed whether the genotype is homozygous or heterozygous produce dominant phenotypes. An allele that codes for a dominant trait is represented by a capital letter, while an allele that codes for a recessive trait is represented by a lowercase letter. Sometimes when the genotype is heterozygous, neither the dominant nor the recessive phenotype occurs. In this situation, called incomplete dominance, an intermediate phenotype is produced.

In humans, the sex of an individual is determined by the particular combination of two chromosomes called the sex chromosomes. Individuals who have two X chromosomes (XX) are females, whereas those who have an X and a Y chromosome (XY) are males. In this investigation, you will observe how the results of different allele combinations produce certain traits.

Problem

How are traits inherited?

Explain to the students that the actual combination of genes is much more complicated than is indicated by this investigation. Some of the traits result from multiple alleles. In order to simplify the investigation, assume that all of the traits used are the result of the combination of two alleles, or an allele pair.

Pre-Lab Discussion

Read the entire investigation. Then, work with a partner to answer the following questions.

1. What does a single side of a double-sided coin or disk represent?

   Each single side of a coin or disk represents one of two possible alleles.

2. What is the probability, in percent, that a single coin toss will result in heads? In tails?

   The probability that a single coin toss will result in either heads or tails is 50 percent.

3. Why is a coin toss a good way to represent allele combinations that occur in nature?

The combination of alleles in nature occurs by chance, as does the result of a coin toss.

4. For the traits explored in this lab, do all heterozygous pairs of alleles produce an intermediate phenotype?

No; for some of the traits listed, heterozygous pairs produce only the dominant phenotype.

5. Can you accurately determine an organism's genotype by observing its phenotype? Explain your answer.

Although knowing an organism's genotype would allow one to predict its phenotype, some phenotypic traits can

be the result of either homozygous or heterozygous combinations of alleles. This source of uncertainty could

prevent the determination of genotype from phenotype.

Materials *(per group)*

3 textbooks
2 coins

To reduce the noise produced by flipping coins, have students use plastic disks used for bingo or tiddly-winks (available at toy or hobby shops). Have students place a small piece of masking tape on each side of the two disks. Mark one side of each disk "H" (heads) and the other side of each disk "T" (tails). Remind students that the pieces of masking tape should be the same size so that both sides of the disk are the same weight.

Procedure

1. Place the textbooks on the laboratory table so that they form a triangular well.

2. Determine which partner will toss for the female and which will toss for the male. Remember that there are two genes per trait.

3. Have the partner who is representing the male flip a coin into the well to determine the sex of the offspring. If the coin lands heads up, the offspring is a female. If the coin lands tails up, the offspring is a male. Record the sex of the offspring in the blank at the top of page 111.

4. For all the coin tosses you will now make, heads will represent the dominant allele and tails will represent the recessive allele.

5. You and your partner should now flip your coins into the well at the same time to determine the phenotype of the first trait, the shape of the face. Note: *The coins should be flipped only once for each trait.*

6. Continue to flip the coins for each trait listed in the table in Figure 1. After each flip, record the trait of your offspring by placing a check in the appropriate box in the table. (Note: Some information in Figure 1 has been simplified. Some listed traits are actually produced by two or more genes.)

7. Using the recorded traits, draw the facial features for your offspring in the space on page 111.

Name________________________ Class________________ Date ____________

Traits	Dominant (both heads)	Hybrid (one head, one tail)	Recessive (both tails)
Shape of face	round *RR*	round *Rr*	Square *rr*
Cleft in chin	present *CC*	present *Cc*	absent *cc*
Texture of hair	curly *HH*	wavy *Hh*	straight *hh*
Widow's peak	present *WW*	present *Ww*	absent *ww*
Spacing of eyes	close together *EE*	medium distance *Ee*	far apart *ee*
Shape of eyes	almond *AA*	almond *Aa*	round *aa*
Position of eyes	straight *SS*	straight *Ss*	slant upward *ss*
Size of eyes	large *LL*	medium *Ll*	small *ll*

Figure 1

Traits	Dominant (both heads)	Hybrid (one head, one tail)	Recessive (both tails)
Length of eyelashes	long LL	long Ll	short ll
Shape of eyebrows	bushy BB	bushy Bb	fine bb
Position of eyebrows	not connected NN	not connected Nn	connected nn
Size of nose	large LL	medium Ll	small ll
Shape of lips	thick TT	medium Tt	thin tt
Size of ears	large LL	medium Ll	small ll
Size of mouth	large LL	medium Ll	small ll
Freckles	present FF	present Ff	absent ff
Dimples	present DD	present Dd	absent dd

Figure 1 *continued*

Sex of offspring

       Answers will vary.

_____

Drawing of Offspring

Answers will depend on student data and should be consistent with the information provided in Figure 1.

Analysis and Conclusions

1. **Inferring** What are the possible genotypes of the parents of an offspring who has wavy (*Hh*) hair?

   HH and *Hh*; *Hh* and *Hh*; *Hh* and *hh*; *HH* and *hh*

2. **Predicting** Would you predict that another pair of students in your class would have an offspring genetically identical to yours? Support your answer.

   Because the genotype of each trait is determined by chance, and because there are so many traits considered, the probability of two genetically identical offspring within a single class is highly unlikely.

3. **Drawing Conclusions** Do you think anyone in your class has all the same genetic traits that you have? Explain your answer.

   No. Each person has a unique combination of many genetic traits passed on to them by their parents. (Identical twins, however, do share all of their genetic traits.)

4. **Comparing and Contrasting** How is this coin-toss model similar to the way in which traits are inherited in living things? How is the model different?

   Like the model, alleles are independent of one another, and inheritance of one allele does not influence the inheritance of another. Moreover, inheritance of a particular allele occurs by chance. Unlike this simplified model, many traits are coded for by several genes.

Going Further

Some inherited diseases cause an individual to die before reaching reproductive age. Using library or Internet resources, read about one of these diseases, and write a brief report about what is understood about its transmission, and in what types of populations it tends to occur. Some examples of inherited diseases that cause early death include Duchenne muscular dystrophy, Tay-Sachs disease, and Krabbe's disease.

Inherited diseases that cause early death are nearly always recessive disorders, and some are concentrated in populations with a common ethnic origin. The metabolic disorder Tay-Sachs disease tends to occur in Jewish families of Eastern European origin, for example.

Chapter 12   DNA and RNA

Extracting DNA

You may want to refer students to Chapter 12 in the textbook for a discussion of DNA.
Time required: 50 minutes

Introduction

It was not until 1944, through an experiment with bacteria, that DNA—deoxyribonucleic acid—was found to be the carrier of genetic information within a cell. Since that time, much has been learned about the molecular structure of DNA, how it codes and replicates information, and how that information is ultimately expressed as an organism's phenotype. In this investigation, you will use a laboratory detergent and specific laboratory techniques to extract DNA from eukaryotic cells.

Problem

What laboratory procedures can be used to extract DNA from liver cells?

Pre-Lab Discussion

Read the entire investigation. Then, work with a partner to answer the following questions.

1. After making a suspension of liver cells, you will examine a drop of this suspension under a microscope. Why will you add methylene blue stain before using the microscope?

   The stain will make the liver cells more visible, especially the nucleus containing the DNA.

2. SDS (sodium dodecylsulfate) is a laboratory detergent. What is the purpose of adding SDS to the liver cell suspension?

   SDS will dissolve the cell membranes so that DNA can be extracted from the cells.

3. The liver cells in this experiment will undergo lysis, a dissolving of the cell membranes. How will you know when lysis has occurred?

   Students will use the microscope to observe the changing condition of the liver cells as more and more

   SDS is added to the suspension. They will be able to see when lysis occurs.

4. Near the end of this experiment you will layer ethanol on top of the liver cell/SDS mixture in order to precipitate out the DNA. Why is it important to add the ethanol very slowly and carefully?

   If ethanol is added too quickly, it will mix in with the solution instead of floating on top.

5. What will you do with the liver DNA after you have extracted it?

   Examine it under a microscope, with and without blue stain.

Materials *(per pair)*

fresh liver (beef or pork)

scalpel or dissecting scissors

mortar and pestle

25-mL graduated cylinder

salt solution (0.9% NaCl)

cheesecloth

250-mL beaker

dropper pipette

microscope slide

methylene blue stain (0.25%)

coverslips

compound microscope

1-mL pipette with safety pipetting bulb

10% SDS solution (sodium dodecylsulfate)

95% ethanol

glass stirring rod

0.9% salt solution
Dissolve 9 g of salt (NaCl) in enough warm distilled water to make a total of 1 L of solution.

10% SDS solution
Add 90 mL of distilled water to 10 g of SDS (sodium dodecylsulfate). Stir until thoroughly mixed.

Read all the information on chemical safety from any Materials Safety Data Sheet that accompanies a chemical.

Safety

Always use special caution when working with laboratory chemicals. They may irritate skin or stain skin and clothing. Put on a laboratory apron and plastic gloves, and use safety goggles except when viewing through the microscope. If you are using a microscope with a lamp, follow all safety rules related to electrical equipment. Be careful to avoid breakage when working with glassware. Be careful when handling sharp instruments. Never touch or taste any laboratory chemical unless instructed to do so. Make sure that there are no flames, sparks, or open heating sources present when using ethanol. Treat all solutions containing liver cells as if they were hazardous. Return or dispose of all materials according to the instructions of your teacher. Note all safety symbols in the Procedure and review the meaning of each symbol by referring to Safety Symbols on page 8.

Procedure

1. Work with a partner. **CAUTION:** *Wear your safety goggles, plastic gloves, and laboratory apron.* Cut a piece of liver about 2 cm long and place it in the mortar. Use a scalpel or scissors to cut the liver into very tiny pieces. **CAUTION:** *Always be careful when using sharp objects.*

2. Use a graduated cylinder to pour 10 mL of salt solution into the mortar. Use a pestle to mash the pieces of liver into the saline solution until a suspension of liver cells has been formed. See Figure 1.

3. Fold two layers of cheesecloth in half. Use the resulting four layers to strain the liver suspension into a beaker.

4. Use a dropper pipette to remove a drop of the liver-cell suspension. Place the drop on a microscope slide.

5. Add a small drop of methylene blue stain to the cells. Add a coverslip and observe the liver cells in a microscope at both low and high power. Draw some liver cells and their nuclei in the space provided on page 116.

The SDS solution is a laboratory detergent that dissolves the lipid-based cell membranes allowing for the extraction of DNA. Making a series of wet mounts helps students to see when the cells have lysed. The extracted DNA can be spooled onto a glass rod.

The amount of SDS needed to dissolve the membranes will differ with the type and freshness of the liver. Fresh pork or beef liver from a butcher will give better results than liver purchased from a supermarket.

6. Use the 1-mL pipette to mix 0.5 mL of the SDS solution with the liver-cell suspension remaining in the beaker.

7. Prepare and stain a wet mount of the mixture. Make observations under high and low power. Describe the appearance of the cells in Data Table 1. Rinse your microscope slide and coverslip.

Dry yeast may be substituted for liver in this experiment, but lysis will not be as easily observed.

8. Repeat steps 6 and 7 approximately five times or until all the cell membranes have been broken down and no longer appear to surround the cell or the nucleus. At this point, the cells have undergone lysis. After each amount of SDS is added, observe the appearance of the cells. Record your observations in the Data Table. Then use the spaces provided on page 117 to draw cells that have undergone lysis.

9. Note the volume of liver-cell suspension/SDS mixture remaining in the beaker. Multiply this volume by 2. The result is the volume of ethanol you must add to the mixture.

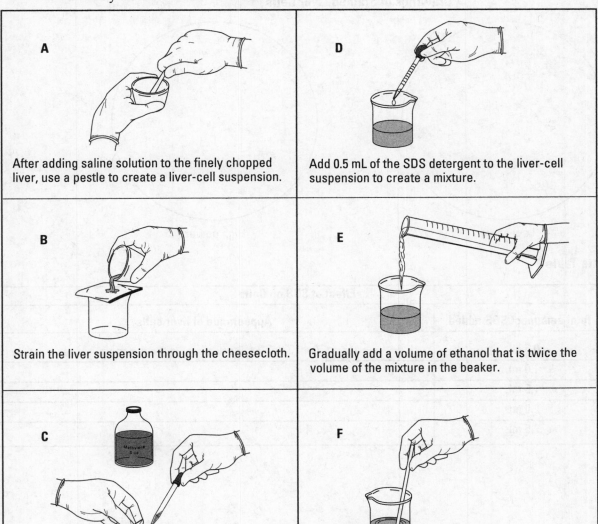

A
After adding saline solution to the finely chopped liver, use a pestle to create a liver-cell suspension.

D
Add 0.5 mL of the SDS detergent to the liver-cell suspension to create a mixture.

B
Strain the liver suspension through the cheesecloth.

E
Gradually add a volume of ethanol that is twice the volume of the mixture in the beaker.

C
Make a wet mount of the liver suspension and observe it under high- and low-power objectives.

F
Very slowly spool the mucuslike strands of DNA onto a glass rod.

Figure 1

10. *Gradually* and gently pour the ethanol on top of the liver/SDS mixture. (If you add the ethanol too quickly, the materials will mix together.) Use the glass rod to *slowly* stir the mixture. You will observe that a white substance begins to form where the two solutions meet. The substance consists of strands of DNA. Twirl the glass rod slowly in order to spool out the DNA. Describe what this substance looks like in Data Table 2. **CAUTION:** *Avoid flames when using ethanol.*

Students will probably find this procedure easier to do if they are seated.

11. Prepare a wet mount of a small piece of your spooled DNA. Stain with methylene blue. In Data Table 2 and the space provided on page 117, record your description of the stained DNA and draw a picture of the stained DNA.

Show students how to use a paper towel to draw the stain under the coverslip of a wet mount slide.

12. Wash your hands with soap and warm water before leaving the lab.

Drawings of Stained Liver Cells

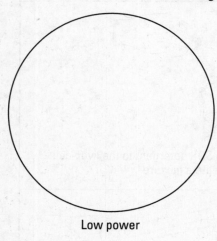

Low power

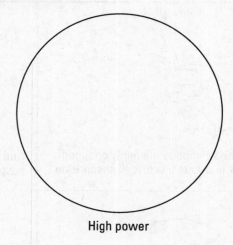

High power

Data Table 1

Effect of SDS on Cells	
Total amount of SDS added	**Appearance of liver cells**
0.5 mL	At some point, the SDS will dissolve the cell membranes.
1.0 mL	
1.5 mL	
2.0 mL	
2.5 mL	

Name_____ Class_____ Date _____

Drawings of Cells That Have Undergone Lysis

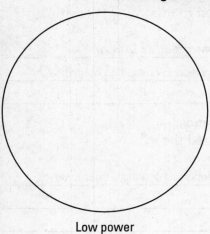

Low power

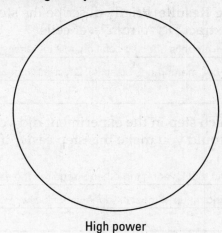

High power

Data Table 2

Observations of DNA	
Specimen	**Description**
Spooled DNA	
Stained DNA	

Drawings of Stained DNA

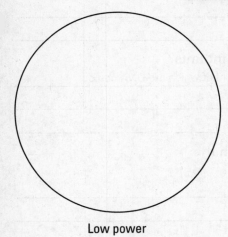

Low power

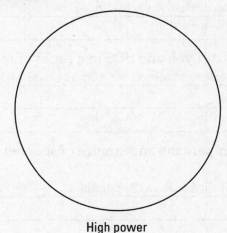

High power

Analysis and Conclusions

1. **Communicating Results** Briefly describe the steps you used in this experiment to extract DNA from liver cells.

   Make suspension of liver cells and salt solution. Mix increasing amounts of the detergent SDS into the

   suspension until the cell membranes dissolve. Layer ethanol on top of the solution to precipitate out the DNA.

2. **Evaluating** Which step in the experiment did you find the most difficult? How could you make this step easier if you repeated the experiment?

   Most students will find that layering the ethanol requires the most care. Students will find this easier to do

   sitting down than standing up. It must be done very slowly.

3. **Comparing and Contrasting** Compare the amount of SDS you used with others in your class. Was it the same or different? Explain your answer.

   Each group probably used a slightly different amount of liver and thus needed a different amount of SDS to

   dissolve the membranes.

4. **Inferring** Review the descriptions you wrote in the Data Table. How did the cells change as you added more and more SDS?

   Adding more SDS caused more cells to lyse.

5. **Inferring** Why did you add SDS in a series of measured amounts?

   It allowed for precise determination of the moment of lysis and thus the point at which the DNA could

   be extracted.

6. **Observing** Compare the appearance of spooled DNA with the stained DNA.

   Spooled DNA was whitish. Stained DNA was blue.

Going Further

Based on the results of this investigation, develop a hypothesis about whether or not the material you extracted was actually DNA. Propose an experiment to test your hypothesis. If the necessary resources are available and you have your teacher's permission, perform the experiment.

Investigating Gel Electrophoresis

You may want to refer students to Section 13–2 in the textbook for a discussion of genetic engineering techniques.

Time required: 30 to 90 minutes for electrophoresis, 30-minute observation period

Introduction

Gel electrophoresis is a method of separating molecules such as DNA and RNA by charge, size, and shape. When an electric voltage is applied to the gel, negatively charged molecules move toward the positive electrode, and positively charged molecules move toward the negative electrode. The charge, size, and shape of a particular molecule all affect the rate at which it moves through the gel.

In this investigation, you will run a gel to compare the movement of several molecules. You also will design and conduct an experiment to determine the sizes of DNA fragments in an unknown mixture using a DNA ladder (a mixture of DNA fragments of known size).

Problem

How can gel electrophoresis be used to separate a mixture of different molecules? How could this technique be used to determine the sizes of unknown molecules?

Pre-Lab Discussion

Read the entire investigation. Then, work with a partner to answer the following questions.

1. For what purposes do scientists use gel electrophoresis?

Scientists use electrophoresis to separate charged molecules of DNA and RNA.

2. What properties of molecules affect how they migrate (or move) through the gel? Predict what types of molecules will move closer to the negative electrode and what types will move closer to the positive electrode.

The charge, size, and shape of molecules affect migration of molecules through the gel. Positively charged

molecules will move closer to the negative electrode, and negatively charged molecules will move closer to

the positive electrode. The larger a molecule is, the more slowly it will move.

3. The gel used in electrophoresis has microscopic pores that act like a sieve. Why would a small, compact molecule move farther through such a gel than a larger, less compact one?

Smaller, more compact molecules can move more easily through the pores of the gel. Larger, less compact

molecules will move more slowly than smaller ones.

4. In your own words, summarize the procedure for gel electrophoresis.

Load the samples into the wells, close the cover of the apparatus, connect the power source, run the

electrophoresis for the appropriate time, turn off the power source and disconnect the gel, carefully remove

the gel and observe the DNA bands.

5. How could gel electrophoresis be used to determine the size of DNA fragments in an unknown mixture?

The distance that the molecules of known sizes migrate can be compared to the distance that those

of unknown sizes migrate.

Suggested Materials *(per group)*

gel electrophoresis apparatus
direct current power source
transfer pipettes
DNA samples

Electrophoresis kits containing DNA samples are available from biological supply companies. (Introductory kits that use prepared dyes instead of DNA are also available.) Follow the directions provided in the kit. Some directions may tell you to store the kits in the refrigerator. To save time, you may decide to prepare the gel and buffer beforehand and have the gel apparatus set up for students at the beginning of the lab period. If so, be sure to explain to students how this was done.

Safety 🔬🦺✋🔥☠️🔱

Put on safety goggles. Put on plastic gloves and a laboratory apron. Observe proper laboratory procedures when using electrical equipment. Never touch or taste any chemical unless instructed to do so. Note all safety alert symbols next to the steps in Design Your Experiment and review the meanings of each symbol by referring to Safety Symbols on page 8.

Design Your Experiment

Part A. Electrophoresis Technique

1. Using a transfer pipette, carefully load each of the DNA samples into the wells in the middle of the gel in consecutive order. Load each well until it is full. **Note:** *Do not move the apparatus after samples have been loaded.* **CAUTION:** *Wear safety goggles, plastic gloves, and a laboratory apron.* Demonstrate how to load samples into the wells.

2. After loading the samples, carefully close the cover of the apparatus.

3. Insert the plug of the negative (black) wire into the negative (black) input of the power source. Insert the plug of the positive (red) wire into the positive (red) input of the power source. See Figure 1.

Follow instructions accompanying kit to prepare the gel and buffer and to set up the gel apparatus. If there is time, it may be worthwhile for students to help with this process. It is recommended that students practice loading samples before beginning experiment; some kits provide samples for this purpose.

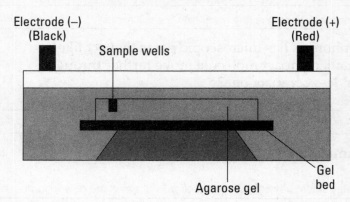

Electrode (−) (Black)   Electrode (+) (Red)

Sample wells

Agarose gel   Gel bed

Figure 1

4. Set the power source at the voltage determined by your teacher.

5. Run the electrophoresis for the appropriate length of time based on the voltage you are using, as determined by your teacher. Look for bubbles forming on the electrodes to be sure that current is flowing properly.

6. When the electrophoresis is completed, turn off the power, unplug the power source, disconnect the wires, and remove the cover from the apparatus.

7. Carefully remove the gel on its bed, holding each end of the gel to prevent it from slipping off the bed. **CAUTION:** *Make sure that power is disconnected before removing the gel.*

8. In Figure 2, indicate the relative positions of the bands of DNA.

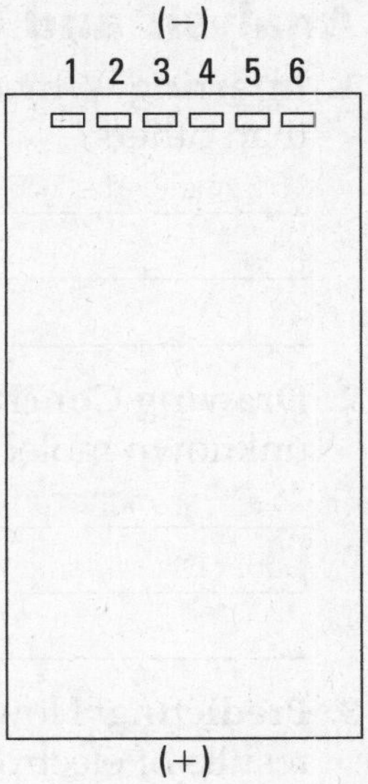

(−)

1 2 3 4 5 6

(+)

Figure 2

Part B. Your Own Experiment

1. In the spaces that follow, design an experiment to determine the size of DNA fragments in an unknown mixture using a DNA ladder (a mixture of DNA fragments of known size).

2. Submit a written experimental design to your teacher for approval using the space below. Once your teacher has approved your design, you may carry out your experiment.

Hypothesis:

Sample: The relative position of the DNA samples on a gel can be used to

determine the size of unknown molecules.

Manipulated variables:

Sizes of DNA molecules

Responding variables:

Positions of the bands on the gel

Procedure:

Procedure will be the same as the previous experiment; however, migration

distances on the gel will be measured and compared to molecules of known size.

See instructions included in kit for recommended voltage and running time.

Students should visually represent their results as accurately as possible in Figure 2. (See kit instructions for position of bands.)

Provide students with a list of the sizes of the DNA fragments in the ladder mixture. The procedure should be carefully examined and approved by the instructor before students begin. A process similar to the one used in the first part of the lab should be followed. Refer to the instructions provided with the DNA samples in the kit.

See kit instructions for more detailed instructions. Provide students with sizes of "known" molecules.

3. **Communicating Results** When you have finished running the gel, draw your results as accurately as possible on a separate sheet of paper. Number the lanes and show the relative positions of the bands. Measure and record the distance each band traveled on your drawing. Your teacher will provide you with the sizes of the DNA molecules in the ladder. Use this information to determine the sizes of the unknown DNA molecules.

Analysis and Conclusions

1. Inferring Why did some of the samples migrate greater distances than others?

The smaller the DNA molecules are, the farther they migrate.

_____

_____

2. Drawing Conclusions How did you determine the sizes of the unknown molecules?

The sizes of the "unknowns" were determined by comparing each migration distance to those of the

ladder DNA fragments.

_____

3. Predicting How would the concentration of the gel used affect the results of electrophoresis?

A more concentrated gel would be a denser sieve. DNA molecules would move more slowly through the gel, and it

would take longer to run the gel at the same voltage.

_____

Going Further

Research a genetic engineering technique that uses gel electrophoresis such as DNA fingerprinting (for determination of genetic diseases), recombinant DNA, or DNA sequencing. Write a short essay to explain the steps carried out in the technique and present your findings.

Chapter 14   The Human Genome

Making Karyotypes

You may want to refer students to Chapter 14 in the textbook for a discussion of genes, chromosomes, and mutations.
Time required: 40 minutes

Introduction

Several human genetic disorders are caused by extra, missing, or damaged chromosomes. In order to study these disorders, cells from a person are grown with a chemical that stops cell division at the metaphase stage. During metaphase, a chromosome exists as two chromatids attached at the centromere.

The cells are stained to reveal banding patterns and placed on glass slides. The chromosomes are observed under the microscope, where they are counted, checked for abnormalities, and photographed. The photograph is then enlarged, and the images of the chromosomes are individually cut out. The chromosomes are identified and arranged in homologous pairs. The arrangement of homologous pairs is called a karyotype. In this investigation, you will use a sketch of chromosomes to make a karyotype. You will also examine the karyotype to determine the presence of any chromosomal abnormalities.

Problem

How can chromosomes be observed?

Pre-Lab Discussion

Read the entire investigation. Then work with a partner to answer the following questions.

1. What clues to the presence of certain genetic disorders can be seen in a karyotype?

   Karyotypes can reveal missing, damaged, or extra chromosomes.

2. Why might a laboratory worker attempting to diagnose a genetic disorder prefer to work with photographs of chromosomes rather than the chromosomes themselves?

   Chromosomes are very small and fragile, and photographs of them can provide a great deal of information

   about the presence and structure of specific chromosomes in an individual's cells.

3. Why would it be much more difficult to construct a karyotype of unstained chromosomes?

   Stained bands on the chromosomes help workers distinguish one from the other.

4. Which pair of chromosomes can contain two very different chromosomes and still be considered normal? Explain your answer.

   Members of chromosome pair 23, the sex chromosomes, are very different in a normal male, including

   an X chromosome and a Y chromosome.

5. How do autosomes differ from sex chromosomes?

   Autosomes do not carry information about the sex of the individual, while sex chromosomes determine

   the individual's sex.

Materials *(per student)*

scissors   glue or transparent tape

Safety ✂

Be careful when handling sharp instruments. Note all safety alert
symbols next to the steps in the Procedure and review the meaning of
each symbol by referring to Safety Symbols on page 8.

Procedures

Part A. Analyzing a Karyotype

1. Observe the normal human karyotype in Figure 1. Notice that the
   two sex chromosomes, pair number 23, do not look alike. They are
   different because this karyotype is of a male, and a male has an X
   and a Y chromosome.

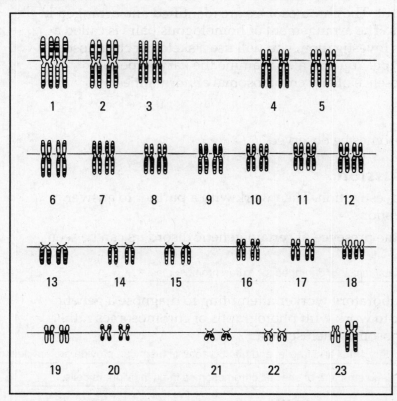

Figure 1

2. Identify the centromere in each pair of chromosomes. The
   centromere is the area where each chromosome narrows.

Part B. Using a Karyotype to Identify a Genetic Disorder

1. Study the human chromosomes in Figure 2 on page 125. Notice that
   23 chromosomes are numbered 1 through 23.

2. To match the homologous chromosomes, look carefully at the
   unnumbered chromosomes. Note their overall size, the position of the
   centromere, and the pattern of the light and dark bands. Next to the
   unnumbered chromosome that is most similar to chromosome 1, write 1.

3. Repeat step 2 for chromosomes 2 through 23.

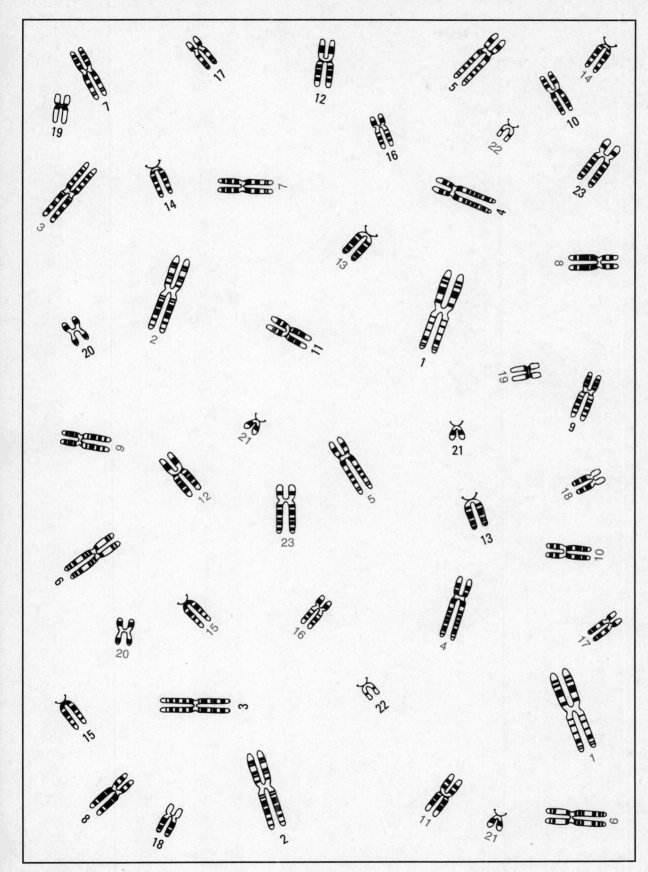

Figure 2

Name________________________________ Class____________________ Date______________

4. Use scissors to cut out all the chromosomes from Figure 2. Tape them in their appropriate places in Figure 3. Note any chromosomal abnormalities. **CAUTION:** *Be careful when handling sharp instruments.*

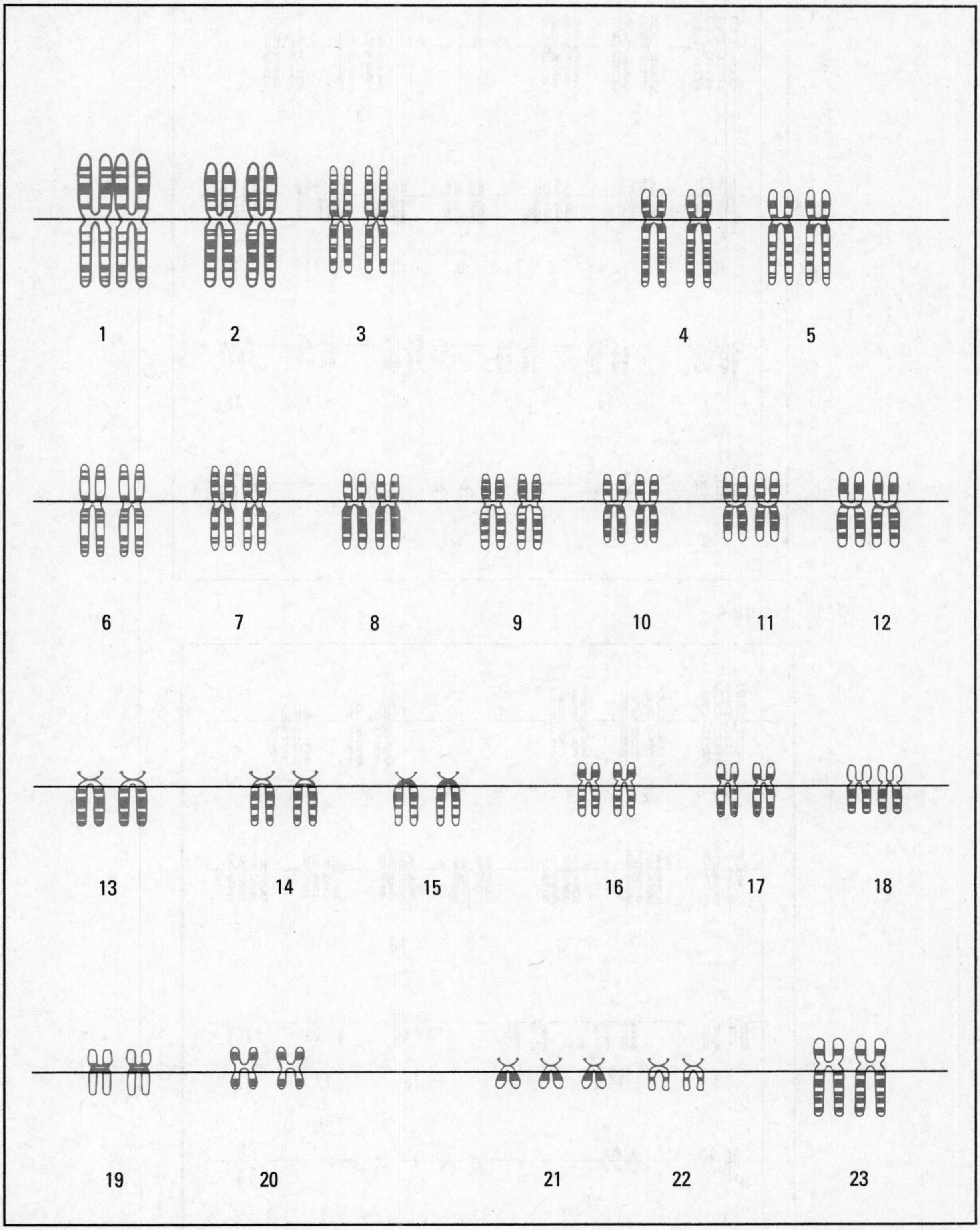

Figure 3

5. Observe the karyotypes in Figures 4 and 5. Note the presence of any chromosomal abnormalities.

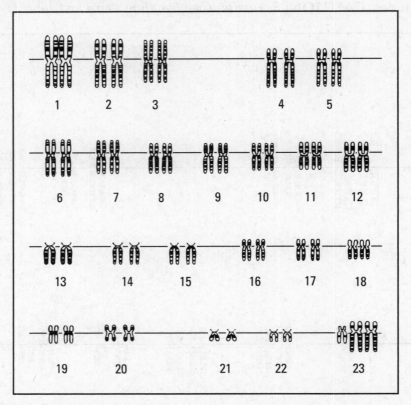

Figure 4

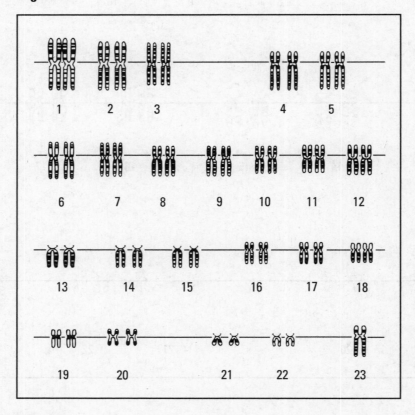

Figure 5

6. Draw a data table in the space below in which to record your observations of the karyotypes shown in Figures 1, 3, 4, and 5. Record any evidence of chromosomal abnormalities present in each karyotype. Record the genetic defect, if you know it, associated with each type of chromosomal abnormality present.

Students' data tables should show that the karyotype in Figure 1 is normal and not associated with a genetic defect. The karyotype in Figure 3 (which was constructed by the students) has an extra X chromosome 21 which produces trisomy 21—Down syndrome. The karyotype in Figure 4 has an extra X chromosome 23, which is associated with Klinefelter syndrome. The karyotype in Figure 5 has only one X chromosome, which is associated with Turner syndrome.

Analysis and Conclusions

1. **Comparing and Contrasting** Of the four karyotypes that you observed, which was normal? Which showed evidence of an extra chromosome? An absent chromosome?

   The karyotype in Figure 1 is normal. The karyotypes in Figures 3 and 4 show evidence of an extra

   chromosome, while the karyotype in Figure 5 shows that a chromosome is missing.

2. **Formulating Hypotheses** What chromosomal abnormality appears in the karyotype in Figure 4? Can you tell from which parent this abnormality originated? Explain your answer.

   Chromosome 23 has an extra X chromosome. Of these three chromosomes, the Y originated from the father,

   and one of the X chromosomes originated from the mother. The second X chromosome, however, could have

   come from either parent.

3. **Inferring** Are chromosomal abnormalities such as the ones shown confined only to certain parts of the body? Explain your answer.

   No; because all chromosomes occur in every cell in the body, these abnormalities would pervade the body.

4. **Drawing Conclusions** Are genetic defects associated with abnormalities of autosomes or of sex chromosomes? Explain your answer.

   Genetic defects can be associated with abnormalities of either autosomes or sex chromosomes,

   for example, the extra autosome at 21 in Figure 3, and the missing sex chromosome in Figure 5.

5. **Posing Questions** Formulate a question that could be answered by observing chromosomes of different species of animals.

   Students' questions might center on comparisons of the number and appearance of chromosomes of

   different animal species.

Going Further

Using library materials or the Internet, research one type of deletion syndrome (a syndrome that results from loss of parts of chromosomes). Write a short paragraph describing the chromosomal abnormality involved and the characteristics of the disorder.

Well-known deletion syndromes include *cri du chat* syndrome (5p-deletion) and Wolf-Hirschhorn syndrome (4p-deletion). In addition to these, several deletion syndromes result from deletions of very small parts of genes. Students might encounter Alagille syndrome, Angelman syndrome, DiGeorge syndrome, Prader-Willi syndrome, Miller-Dieker syndrome, and Williams syndrome, among others. Most produce severe mental retardation and anatomical abnormalities.

Chapter 15   Darwin's Theory of Evolution

Comparing Adaptations of Birds

You may want to refer students to Section 15–3 in the textbook for a discussion of adaptations.
Time required: 50 minutes

Introduction

When Charles Darwin explored the Galápagos Islands, he noted the great variety of beak shapes on the finches there. It was later determined that Darwin's finches made up 13 separate species. The similarities among the species suggested a common ancestor: A single species of finch that came from the mainland of South America. How did these birds evolve into genetically unique groups? With few native competitors and a wide variety of food sources, the newcomers were able to establish niches based on variations in beak shape and size. Finches with beaks that could exploit a particular food source—insects in the bark of trees, for example—established their own niche in the new habitat. Natural selection thus favored beak specialization because it enabled many birds to coexist within the same ecosystem. Many birds also show specialization of other body parts, including legs, feet, wings, and eyes. In this investigation, you will examine some bird characteristics. What are the survival benefits of each bird's adaptations?

Problem

What adaptations have evolved among modern birds that enable them to survive in diverse habitats?

Pre-Lab Discussion

Read the entire investigation. Then, work with a partner to answer the following questions.

1. What can you learn from observing and comparing specific physical traits of different birds?

   The physical traits constitute evidence that can be used to make inferences about the behaviors and habitats of

   the birds.

2. What are some terms you can use to describe the size and shape of a bird's beak?

   Size can be described using terms such as long, short, large, or small. Shape can be described using

   straight, curved, hooked, pointed, flat, narrow, or broad.

3. How does a bird's beak help you identify its habitat?

   The size and shape indicate the types of foods the bird eats. The bird must live, or at least hunt, in a

   habitat that includes those foods.

4. A certain bird ordinarily lives in or near water and spends much of its time swimming. Based on Data Table 1, what type of feet would you expect this bird to have?

   Webbed and paddlelike feet that enable the bird to swim well.

5. Birds that spend much time perching have three front toes and one back toe. Based on Data Table 1, how is this different from the feet of birds that are better adapted for climbing than for perching?

The feet of climbing birds have two front toes and two back toes. The back toes help keep the bird from falling

when climbing upward.

Materials *(per group)*

specimens or illustrations of birds detailing their physical adaptations, field guides to birds

Procedure

1. Look carefully at the diagrams of birds in Figure 1. Notice the details of each bird's feet and beak. Using the diagrams, complete Data Table 1 by filling in one or more examples of birds that exhibit each of the beak and foot adaptations described.

2. **Inferring** In Data Table 2 on page 134 consider the adaptations of the birds listed and then describe their likely habitat. Check your answers using a field guide.

It might be helpful to have several different types of field guides for students to use as references if they are having difficulty with the lab or wish to check their responses. Mounted specimens may be available on loan from local nature centers, museums, or colleges.

If time permits, suggest that students use field guides or other sources to compare wing length and shape, and have students discuss the adaptive benefit of these features.

Woodpecker

Cardinal

Great horned owl

Common snipe

Purple martin

Osprey

Figure 1 (Diagrams are drawn in approximate, not exact, scale.)

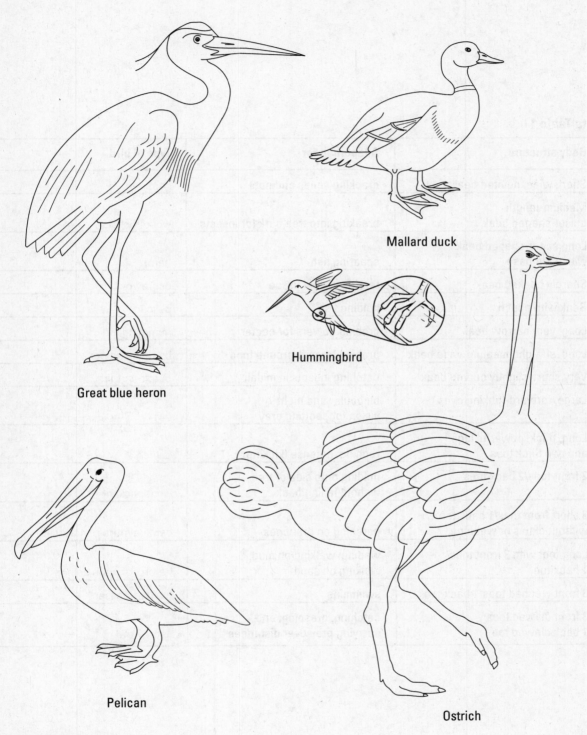

Great blue heron

Mallard duck

Hummingbird

Pelican

Ostrich

Figure 1 *continued*

Make sure students understand that
a particular bird may be listed more
than once in Data Table 1.

Data Table 1

Body structure	Adaptation for	Type of bird
Short, wide, pointed beak	cracking seeds and nuts	cardinal
Medium-length, chisel-shaped beak	breaking into tree bark for insects	woodpecker
Long spear-shaped beak with wide base	spearing fish	heron
Sharply hooked beak	tearing animal tissue	osprey/owl
Beak with pouch	holding fish	pelican
Long, very narrow beak	probing flowers for nectar	hummingbird
Long, straight, medium-wide beak	probing for soft-ground food	common snipe
Very short, slightly curved beak	catching insects in midair	purple martin
Large, forward-looking eyes	binocular and night vision for spotting prey	owl
Long, thick, powerful legs and two thick toes	running; defense (kicking)	ostrich
2 front toes/2 back toes	holding onto side of tree without falling back	woodpecker
3 short front toes/1 back toe without claws or webbing	perching on branches	cardinal/purple martin
Long foot with 3 front toes/ 1 back toe	wading; walking on mud; walking on sand	heron/common snipe
3 front webbed toes/1 back toe	swimming	mallard/pelican
3 front clawed toes/ 1 back clawed toe	catching, grasping, and carrying prey over distances	osprey/owl

Accept inferences that students can
justify with evidence and logic.

Data Table 2

Bird	Habitat
Osprey	shorelines
Great horned owl	coniferous woods near open fields
Woodpecker	forests; parks; suburban areas
Purple martin	fields near streams/rivers
Great blue heron	marshes; shores of lakes, ponds, and rivers
Common snipe	bogs; marshes; shorelines
Mallard duck	creeks; rivers; ponds; lakes
Pelican	shorelines; estuaries
Cardinal	wooded and suburban areas
Hummingbird	wherever appropriate plants are found, including suburban areas
Ostrich	savanna; grassy plain

Analysis and Conclusions

1. **Comparing and Contrasting** Each pair of birds mentioned below shares some characteristics. Yet they each have their own niche; they do not compete directly for the same resources. For each pair, describe how the birds are similar and how they are different. How might their differences enable them to occupy different niches?

   a. osprey and great horned owl
   Both have similar beaks and claws adapted for hunting; the owl has large eyes that enable it to hunt at night.

   b. woodpecker and purple martin
   Both eat insects. The woodpecker has a longer beak that can probe. The purple martin's beak helps it

   catch and trap insects as it flies.

   c. great blue heron and common snipe
   Both have feet adapted for wading; the heron has longer legs, enabling it to wade more deeply.

2. **Inferring** Birds have hollow bones. Explain how this is adaptive.

It is a structural adaptation that lessens their weight and enables them to fly.

3. **Observing** The hummingbird's beak is adapted to getting its food. Describe another adaptation of the hummingbird that enables it to get the food it needs.

Its tiny, lightweight body and its ability to beat its wings rapidly for hovering over flowers assist the

hummingbird in obtaining nectar.

4. **Inferring** Birds such as Darwin's finches are adapted to occupy highly specific niches. Would this adaptation make it easy or difficult for such birds to adapt to environmental change? Explain your answer.

It would be difficult for them to adapt because they are so specialized. For example, they might not be able

to adjust to an environmental change such as loss of a food source.

5. **Formulating Hypotheses** Why might a particular bird be found in more than one habitat?

Birds might hunt or feed in one habitat but nest or seek shelter in another.

6. **Inferring** Birds are well-adapted to their habitats, yet some birds are considered members of endangered species. Infer why certain birds are endangered.

Students may infer that certain birds are now endangered because their habitats are being destroyed.

Going Further

Based on the results of this investigation, develop a hypothesis about the physical characteristics and habitat requirements of birds that live in hot, dry climates such as the desert. When developing a hypothesis, consider sources of food, water, shelter, nesting materials, and other factors. To test your hypothesis, with your teacher's permission, use various resources to learn about the physical characteristics and the habitat of one or more desert-dwelling birds.

Modeling a Gene Pool

You may want to refer students to Chapter 16 in the textbook for a discussion of population genetics and the Hardy-Weinberg principle.
Time required: 50 minutes

Introduction

A population is a group of organisms of the same species that live together in a particular location. Each population is normally isolated from other populations of the same species. Populations can be observed for many characteristics.

Before assigning this activity, determine how you want groups to share their data in Procedure, Step 13, and which comparison(s) they will make.

Population genetics is the study of genes in a population of organisms. Biologists who study population genetics are interested in how frequently alleles of a gene appear in a population. Biologists are also interested in any changes in gene frequencies that may be occurring.

In this investigation beans will be used to represent individuals in a simulated population of organisms. Red beans will be symbols for homozygous dominant individuals RR. Pink (pinto) beans will be symbols for heterozygous individuals Rr. White beans will be symbols for homozygous recessive individuals rr. You will study various crosses using the beans and analyze frequencies and frequency changes as they appear in a simulated population in which a harmful phenotype occurs. In addition to this, you will be able to see how a potentially lethal genetic disorder affects allele frequency in the population over generations.

Problem

How does gene frequency change in a population of organisms?

Pre-Lab Discussion

Read the entire investigation. Then work with a partner to answer the following questions.

1. Why are you asked to set aside and not use some of the white beans at the start of the experiment?

   They represent those individuals that display the recessive phenotype and die before they attain

   reproductive age.

2. If the initial breeding population (the parent generation) is composed of 16 RR individuals, 32 Rr individuals, and 8 rr individuals, how many R alleles are present in the parent generation? How many r alleles are present in the parent generation?

   There are 64 R alleles and 48 r alleles present.

3. For the individuals in this lab, can the genotype of each be determined from the phenotype? Explain your answer.

   Yes. Because heterozygous individuals have an intermediate phenotype, genotype can be determined

   from phenotype.

4. Is the population represented by this lab in genetic equilibrium? Why or why not?

No. Evolution is occurring because the frequency of recessive alleles is being reduced, violating

the conditions necessary for genetic equilibrium.

5. Predicting How would you expect the gene pool of this population to change over time?

The proportion of the recessive allele *r* would decrease over time.

Materials *(per group)*   You may wish to have students bring calculators to help with analyzing data.

paper bag   pink (pinto) beans
red beans   white beans

Procedure

1. Work in pairs. Obtain an opaque container such as a paper bag. Place into it 16 red beans (*RR*), 32 pink beans (*Rr*), and 16 white beans (*rr*). The white beans represent individuals having the potentially lethal phenotype (*rr*). To represent the early deaths in the parent generation, remove half of the white beans and set them aside.

2. Mix the beans. Then, without looking into the container, remove the beans in pairs. Each pair will be one of the six possible combinations, as shown in Figure 1. Count the number of pairs of each of the six combinations. These six combinations will represent the parent pairs that will produce the first generation of offspring. To help count the pairs, you may wish to divide a sheet of paper into six columns with labels. See Figure 2 A and B on page 139. **Note:** *You will not necessarily have a pair of each type.*

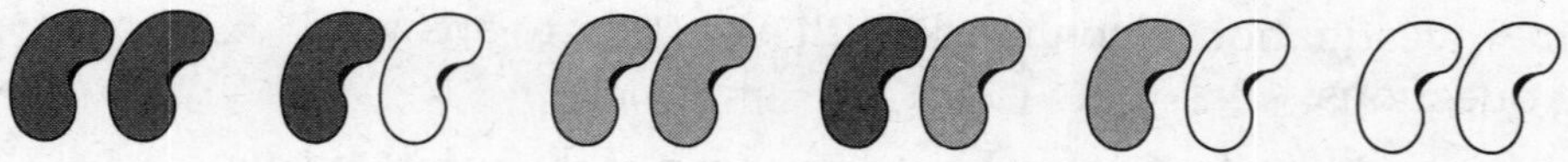

RR × RR   RR × rr   Rr × Rr   RR × Rr   Rr × rr   rr × rr

Figure 1

3. Record the number of parent pairs for each combination in Data Table 1 on p. 140.

4. Assume that each pair of parents will have four offspring. Calculate the expected number of offspring for each category of parent pairs. Record these numbers in Data Table 1. For example, if you counted six *Rr* × *Rr* parent pairs, and each pair has four offspring, there will be 24 offspring for that combination. Recall from your study of genetics that the expected ratio of genotypes for the cross of two heterozygous parents is 1 *RR* : 2 *Rr* : 1 *rr*. The expected ratio of genotypes for 24 offspring would be 6 *RR* : 12 *Rr* : 6 *rr*. Record the numbers that reflect your data in Data Table 1.

5. Calculate the total of each expected genotype from this first generation of offspring and record the totals in Data Table 1.

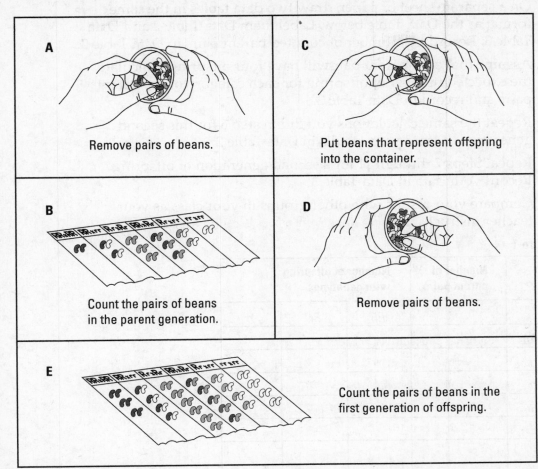

Figure 2

6. Using these totals, count the total number of *R*'s and *r*'s in the offspring population. Remember that each *RR* individual has 2 *R*'s, and each *Rr* individual has 1 *R* and 1 *r*. Record the data in the bottom row of Data Table 1. Then calculate the frequency of each allele by using the following formulas:

$$\text{Frequency of } R = \frac{\text{Total } R}{\text{Total } R + \text{Total } r}$$

Frequency of *r* = 1 − Frequency of *R*

Record your calculated gene frequencies in Data Table 1.

7. Based on the totals in Data Table 1, put enough beans to represent all the first generation offspring into your container. You will need to obtain more beans since each parent pair had four offspring. As before, remove one-half of the total number of white beans (*rr* offspring) to represent individuals that die before reproducing.

8. Mix the beans. Then, without looking into the container, pull out pairs of beans until you have removed all the beans. Arrange these pairs into the six possible combinations as you did in Figure 2 E. These six combinations will represent the first generation parents that will produce the second generation of offspring.

9. On a separate sheet of paper, draw two data tables in the same format as the Data Table below. Label them Data Table 2 and Data Table 3. Record the number of counted parent pairs in Data Table 2.

10. Assume that each parent pair will have four offspring. Calculate the expected number of offspring for each category of the parent pairs and record in Data Table 2.

11. Repeat the same calculations you did in step 6 for this second generation. Record your results in Data Table 2.

12. Repeat Steps 7 through 11 for a second generation of offspring. Record your data in Data Table 3.

13. Compare your results with other groups in your class as your teacher instructs. Explain how you want groups to compare results.

Data Table 1

Parent pairs	Number of parent pairs	Number of offspring with genotypes		
		RR	*Rr*	*rr*
RR × *RR*	Students' data sets will vary due to chance.			
RR × *rr*	Approximate probabilities for the six possible			
Rr × *Rr*	parent allele pairs are as follows: *RR* × *RR*:			
RR × *Rr*	0.078; *RR* × *rr*: 0.083; *Rr* × *Rr*: 0.322; *RR* × *Rr*:			
Rr × *rr*	0.332; *Rr* × *rr*: 0.167; *rr* × *rr*: 0.018.			
rr × *rr*				
	Totals:			

Total of *R's* _____ in offspring   Total of *r's* _____ in offspring

Frequency of *R* = _____   Frequency of *r* = _____

Analysis and Conclusions

1. **Calculating** Which of the six parent pairs of the first parent set (*RR* × *RR*, *RR* × *rr*, *Rr* × *Rr*, *RR* × *Rr*, *Rr* × *rr*, or *rr* × *rr*) is least likely to occur? Why is this so?

   rr × *rr*; The first parent set began with a reduced proportion of the *r* allele, and the probability of two

   occurring together was then much reduced.

2. **Predicting** Would you predict that another group of students in your class would have data identical to yours? Explain your answer.

   Because the actual combinations of alleles are determined by chance, the occurrence of two identical sets

   of data within a single class is possible but highly unlikely.

3. Drawing Conclusions Can a single factor that affects the reproductive success of only some individuals in a population result in evolution? Explain your answer.

Yes; a change in reproductive success of certain individuals will ultimately change the relative frequencies

of certain alleles.

4. Using Models Can you use this activity as it is to model all patterns of inheritance in a population? Explain your answer.

No; this model is complicated by a harmful phenotype and reduction of a recessive allele in a small

population over generations.

5. Forming Operational Definitions Evolution is change of a population over generations. Form an operational definition of evolution as it occurs in this model.

Sample: Evolution is evidenced by the reduction of the relative frequency of the recessive allele *r* over generations.

Going Further

Sometimes the relationship between a certain phenotype and overall reproductive success is not a simple one. Using library or Internet resources, research the incidence of sickle cell anemia, an inherited disorder, and its relationship to malaria, a disease due to a pathogen. Use this example to explain how natural selection can work to keep a harmful allele in a population.

Although individuals who are homozygous for the sickle-cell allele usually die, the heterozygous condition confers immunity. This incidental advantage tends to preserve the sickle-cell allele in populations where malaria is a health problem.

Making Coacervates

You may want to refer students to Section 17–2 in the textbook for a discussion of how life began, as well as Section 7–3 to review selective permeability.
Time required: 45 minutes

Introduction

How did life on Earth begin? According to a hypothesis by Russian scientist Alexander Oparin, all life developed gradually from materials found in the oceans on primitive Earth. According to Oparin, prehistoric oceans probably consisted of a rich mixture of organic chemicals, including proteins and carbohydrates. If certain kinds of proteins and carbohydrates are mixed together with water, coacervates, or droplets showing lifelike characteristics, may form. Coacervates are not alive. However, in a manner similar to cells, coacervates appear to ingest materials, grow, and reproduce. Because of this, scientists have hypothesized that coacervates may have been among the precursors of cells. In this investigation, you will produce coacervates and observe their behavior.

Problem

How do coacervates act like living organisms?

Pre-Lab Discussion

Read the entire investigation. Then, work with a partner to answer the following questions.

1. What mixture will you prepare at the beginning of the investigation?
   A mixture of gelatin and gum arabic

2. Why does the investigation ask you to gradually increase the acidity of the mixture?
   Coacervates will form only under certain conditions of acidity. The goal is to find the correct pH so that
   the coacervates will form.

3. What will you do with the coacervates once you have made them?
   Examine them under the microscope, looking for characteristics they share with living cells, and test them
   for selective permeability.

4. What characteristics of living organisms do you predict coacervates will show?
   Sample: The ability to absorb materials selectively, grow, and reproduce.

5. How will this investigation help you understand scientific hypotheses about how life on Earth first began?
   The coacervates will probably show some characteristics of living structures. This indicates how the first
   forms of life might have arisen from a mixture of inorganic materials.

Suggested Materials (per group)

1 medium-sized test tube

1 rubber stopper that fits the test tube

1% gelatin solution

1% gum arabic solution

1% hydrochloric acid solution

pH test paper

2 dropper pipettes

microscope

microscope slide

coverslip

10-mL graduated cylinder

glass stirring rod

water-soluble dye   Use red food coloring or Congo red stain.

oil-soluble dye   Sudan III stain.

Read all the information on chemical safety from any Materials Safety Data Sheet that accompanies a chemical.

Dissolve 3.5 g gelatin in 346.5 mL distilled hot water. Refrigerate until needed.

Dissolve 0.75 g gum arabic in 74 mL distilled hot water.

Slowly stir 1 mL concentrated hydrochloric acid into 99 mL distilled water.

If gelatin or gum arabic is unavailable, these substitutes may work: alcohol added to gelatin in water; dilute sodium sulfate added to gelatin in water; sugar added to egg yolk in water; gum arabic, sucrose, or alcohol added to egg albumin in water. First put the protein in water, and then add the carbohydrate to it.

Safety

Put on a laboratory apron. Put on safety goggles and plastic gloves. Handle all glassware carefully. Always use special caution when working with laboratory chemicals as they may irritate the skin or cause staining of the skin or clothing. Never touch or taste any chemical unless you are instructed to do so. Always handle the microscope with extreme care. You are responsible for its proper care and use. Use caution when handling microscope slides as they can break easily and cut you. Note all safety alert symbols next to the steps in Design Your Experiment and review the meaning of each symbol by referring to Safety Symbols on page 8.

Design Your Experiment

Part A. Making Coacervates

1. Obtain a test tube and a rubber stopper that fits the test tube. Use the graduated cylinder to pour 6 mL of gelatin solution into the test tube. Next add 4 mL of gum arabic solution to the test tube. Mix the two solutions by inserting a stopper and gently inverting the test tube several times. **Note:** *Mix the solutions gently. Do not shake the test tube, as this will hinder the formation of coacervates.* **CAUTION:** *Wear your safety goggles, plastic gloves, and laboratory apron.*

2. Coacervates will form only under specific environmental conditions. One important condition is the acidity of the environment. Unstopper the test tube and dip a glass stirring rod into the mixture. Touch a drop of the mixture onto a piece of pH paper. Compare the color of your pH paper to information given on the package of test papers or information supplied by your teacher. Record the pH under Trial 1 in the Data Table.

Name_____ Class_____ Date _____

3. The cloudiness or clearness of the mixture may indicate the presence or absence of coacervates. Hold the test tube up to a light source. Record if the mixture is cloudy or clear under Trial 1 in the Data Table.

4. Use a dropper pipette to put 2 drops of the mixture on a clean microscope slide. Place a coverslip over the mixture and examine it under low power. Coacervates, as shown in Figure 1, look like droplets of material with tiny bubbles inside. **Note:** *You may not see coacervates until the pH (acidity) is adjusted, so do not get discouraged.* Observe the number, size, and movement of any coacervates present and record this information under Trial 1 in the Data Table. Clean the slide and coverslip.

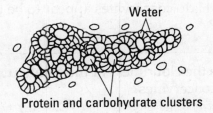

Water

Protein and carbohydrate clusters

Figure 1

5. Use a second dropper pipette to change the pH of the mixture by adding 3 drops of weak hydrochloric acid solution. **CAUTION:** *Hydrochloric acid can cause burns. If the acid touches your skin or clothes, immediately wash the area with water and notify your teacher.* Stopper the test tube and gently invert it once or twice to mix the solution.

6. Repeat steps 2 through 4, recording all information under Trial 2 in the Data Table.

7. Repeat step 5 four more times, adding 3 drops of weak hydrochloric acid each time. Test the pH of the mixture, observe and record the degree of cloudiness, and make observations of coacervates under the microscope. Record this information under Trials 3 through 6 in the Data Table.

Data Table

	Observation of Coacervates					
	Trial					
	1	2	3	4	5	6
pH			pH should become more acidic.			
Cloudy/clear	Mixture should be cloudy at a pH of approximately 4; solution will otherwise remain fairly clear.					
Microscopic observations	Coacervates should be the largest and most abundant at a pH of approximately 4.					

Part B. Your Own Experiment

1. One characteristic of living cells is selective permeability. Now that you have determined the best pH for making coacervates, write a design for an experiment to determine whether coacervates are equally permeable to water-soluble substances and oil-soluble substances. You can use water-soluble and oil-soluble dyes in your experiment.

2. With your teacher's approval, carry out your experiment.

3. Wash your hands with soap and warm water before leaving the lab.

Analysis and Conclusions

1. **Analyzing Data** At what pH do coacervates appear to be the largest and most abundant?

   4

2. **Analyzing Data** How does the cloudiness of the solution relate to the presence or absence of coacervates?

   The cloudier the material in the test tube, the larger and more abundant the coacervates.

3. **Drawing Conclusions** Did the results of your experiment in Part B support the hypothesis that coacervates are selectively permeable? Explain your answer.

   Answers will depend on the student experiments. In general, the water-soluble materials used to make the

   coacervates will absorb water-soluble dyes, but not oil-soluble dyes.

4. **Comparing and Contrasting** How are coacervates similar to living organisms? How are they different?

   They may appear to move, reproduce, absorb materials, and associate with one another. Accept various

   other student observations that indicate lifelike activity. Observed differences may include the lack of nuclei

   and/or other cell organelles, inability to carry on metabolism, and inability to produce wastes.

5. **Formulating Hypotheses** Do you think your coacervate investigation would have worked if you had substituted other proteins and carbohydrates? How could you test your hypothesis?

   Students will most likely answer that other raw materials could probably be used to produce coacervates.

   An investigation similar to the one just conducted could be set up to test other substances.

Going Further

Use resources in the library or on the Internet to learn about Sidney Fox's experiments on proteinoid microspheres. Design an experiment to make microspheres and compare their characteristics to living cells. If the necessary resources are available and you have your teacher's permission, perform the experiment.

Using and Constructing a Dichotomous Key

You may want to refer students to Chapter 18 in the textbook for a discussion of the classification system used in biology. Time required: 45 minutes

Introduction

All cultures have developed names for the living things found in their environments. When various everyday names are used for the same organism, confusion is possible. So, scientists have developed an international system for naming and classifying all organisms. Identification guides, called keys, have been developed to help all peoples recognize and identify organisms according to their scientific names.

The word *dichotomous* comes from the word *dichotomy,* meaning "two opposite parts or categories." A dichotomous key gives the reader a series of opposing descriptions of basic features of an organism. The reader studies the specimen and selects the descriptions that apply to it until reaching a statement that characterizes only one species and names it. In this investigation, you will use a typical dichotomous key to identify the genus and species of several different salamanders. Then, you will create your own dichotomous key to categorize a diverse group of wildflowers.

Problem

How is a dichotomous key used to distinguish among similar organisms?

Pre-Lab Discussion   Students may work alone or with a partner, depending on your preference.

Read the entire investigation. Then, work with a partner to answer the following questions.

1. How many choices does a dichotomous key provide at each step?

   There are two choices at each step.

2. What are some of the apparent differences among the salamanders illustrated?

   The size, color, shape, numbers and patterns of spots, and the presence or absence of external

   gills are differences.

3. Based on the information in Figure 2, what is a distinguishing characteristic of the members of the genus *Ambystoma*?

   They all have a body coloring pattern with a black background and variable white spots.

4. What might be a good strategy for beginning to create a dichotomous key for the six types of wildflowers shown in the diagram?

   Find a broad difference between them such as the number of petals in the flower or the number of

   divisions in the leaf.

5. If you were to use live flowers instead of diagrams, what other characteristics could you use to identify the flowers?

   The color, scent, leaf size, and flower size could be compared.

Procedure

Part A: Using a Dichotomous Key

1. Examine the drawings of the salamanders in Figure 1. Choose one salamander to identify by using the key.

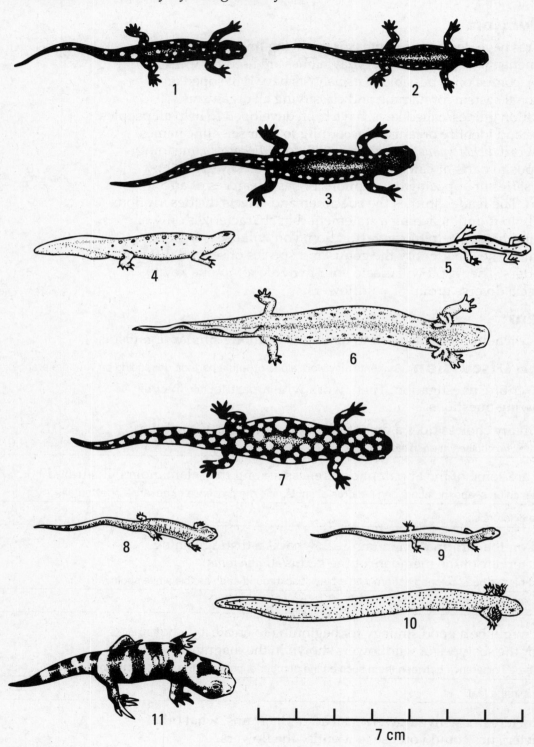

Figure 1

7 cm

2. Use the dichotomous key (Figure 2) to determine the genus and species of that salamander. Begin by reading statements 1a and 1b. One of the statements describes the salamander; the other statement does not. Follow the directions for the statement that applies to that salamander and continue following the correct statements until you have identified it. Record the scientific and common name of the salamander in the Data Table on page 150.

3. Repeat step 2 for each of the other salamanders in Figure 1.

1	a	Hind limbs absent	*Siren intermedia*, siren
	b	Hind limbs present	Go to 2
2	a	External gills present in adults	*Necturus maculosus*, mud puppy
	b	External gills absent in adults	Go to 3
3	a	Large size (over 7 cm long in Figure 1)	Go to 4
	b	Small size (under 7 cm long in Figure 1)	Go to 5
4	a	Body background black, large white spots variable in size completely covering body and tail	*Ambystoma tigrinum*, tiger salamander
	b	Body background black, small round white spots in a row along each side from eye to tip of tail	*Ambystoma maculatum*, spotted salamander
5	a	Body background black with white spots	Go to 6
	b	Body background light color with dark spots and/or lines on body	Go to 7
6	a	Small white spots on black background in a row along each side from head to tip of tail	*Ambystoma jeffersonianum*, Jefferson salamander
	b	Small white spots scattered throughout a black background from head to tip of tail	*Plethodon glutinosus*, slimy salamander
7	a	Large irregular white spots on a black background extending from head to tip of tail	*Ambystoma opacum*, marbled salamander
	b	No large irregular black spots on a light background	Go to 8
8	a	Round spots scattered along back and sides of body, tail flattened like a tadpole	*Triturus viridescens*, newt
	b	Without round spots and tail not flattened like a tadpole	Go to 9
9	a	Two dark lines bordering a broad light middorsal stripe with a narrow median dark line extending from the head onto the tail	*Eurycea bislineata*, two-lined salamander
	b	Without two dark lines running the length of the body	Go to 10
10	a	A light stripe running the length of the body and bordered by dark pigment extending downward on the sides	*Plethodon cinereus*, red-backed salamander
	b	A light stripe extending the length of the body without dark pigment on the sides	*Hemidactylium scutatum*, four-toed salamander

Figure 2

Data Table

Number	Genus and species	Common name
1	*Plethodon glutinosus*	slimy salamander
2	*Ambystoma jeffersonianum*	Jefferson salamander
3	*Ambystoma maculatum*	spotted salamander
4	*Triturus viridescens*	newt
5	*Eurycea bislineata*	two-lined salamander
6	*Necturus maculosus*	mud puppy
7	*Ambystoma tigrinum*	tiger salamander
8	*Plethodon cinereus*	red-backed salamander
9	*Hemidactylium scutatum*	four-toed salamander
10	*Siren intermedia*	siren
11	*Ambystoma opacum*	marbled salamander

Part B. Constructing a Dichotomous Key

1. Examine Figure 3, which shows some common North American wildflowers. Note different characteristics in flower shape, number of petals, and leaf number and shape.

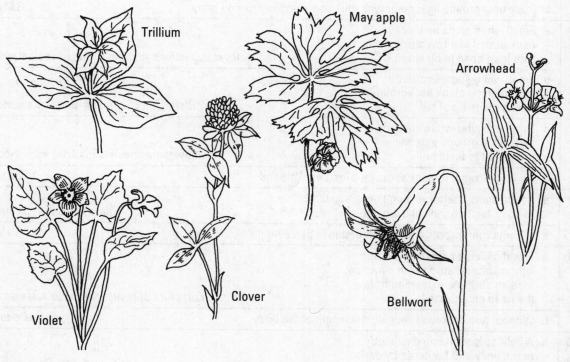

Figure 3

2. Use the space below to construct a dichotomous key for the wildflowers in Figure 3. Be sure to use enough pairs of statements to have a final positive statement for each to identify each of the six flowers shown. Use the key to salamanders as a model for developing your wildflower key.

3. Check the usefulness of your wildflower key by letting another student see if he or she can use it to identify each pictured flower.

Wildflower Dichotomous Key

A possible key follows:

1a Having numerous small petals .... Clover
1b Lacking numerous small petals........................... Go to 2

2a Having 3 separate petals only .... Arrowhead
2b Having more than 3 separate petals .... Go to 3

3a Having 3 inner petals surrounded by 3 leaflike structures .... Trillium
3b Having 5 or 6 petals .... Go to 4

4a Having 5 petals .... Violet
4b Having 6 petals .... Go to 5

5a Having 6 petals that form a bell-like shape .... Bellwort
5b Having 6 petals arranged in a flat circular shape .... May apple

Analysis and Conclusions

1. Analyzing Data What are some examples of basic differences among the salamanders pictured?

Adults with external gills and salamanders with hind limbs absent are two of the most basic differences.

2. **Drawing Conclusions** Do the dichotomous keys you have just
worked with have any limitations in distinguishing between
species?

Yes, they are based only on appearance. There may be other important traits that distinguish species.

3. **Comparing and Contrasting** Do any of the wildflowers shown in
Figure 3 appear to be similar enough to be in the same genus?

No, the structures of the wildflowers are too different from each other.

4. **Evaluating** What characteristics should be very similar in order to
support an inference that two plants are closely related?

They should share strong similiarities in several basic structures such as flowers, leaves, and seeds

to be closely related. However, similar traits may be due to convergent evolution instead of a shared ancestry.

5. **Drawing Conclusions** Could the three salamanders from the genus
Ambystoma be more closely related than *Necturus*, the mud puppy,
and *Triturus*, the newt?

Yes, but anatomical features are only one indicator of possible evolutionary relationships. Scientists would

have to compare the DNA of the five species to determine how closely they are related to one another.

Going Further

Construct an evolutionary tree diagram based on the physical
similarities and differences of the salamanders shown in Figure 1.
Assume that those most similar share a recent ancestor and those that
are most different had a common ancestor long ago. Explain why your
evolutionary tree is a hypothesis, and describe what kind of evidence
might show whether your hypothesis is correct.

Controlling Bacterial Growth

You may want to refer students to Section 19–2 in the textbook for a review of the methods of controlling bacterial growth before performing this investigation.

Time required:
50 minutes, plus a
15-minute observation
period after 48 hours
of incubation

Introduction

Chemical substances that either kill bacteria or inhibit bacterial growth are called antimicrobial agents. Antimicrobial agents are of three basic types: antiseptics, or chemicals used to inhibit the growth of or kill bacteria on living tissues; disinfectants, or chemicals used to inhibit the growth of or kill bacteria on nonliving things; and antibiotics, or compounds that block the growth and reproduction of bacteria.

   The effectiveness of each type of antimicrobial agent is influenced by many factors. Some of these factors include the environmental conditions in which the agent is applied, the chemical properties of the agent, how long the agent has been stored, and the rate of deterioration of the agent.

   In this investigation, you will test the effectiveness of disinfectants and antibiotics in inhibiting the growth of bacteria.

Problem

How can the growth of bacteria be controlled?

Pre-Lab Discussion

Read the entire investigation. Then, work with a partner to answer the following questions.

1. Why is it important not to open sterile agar plates?

   To prevent the plates from becoming contaminated by airborne microorganisms.

2. Why do you think it is so important to write only near the edges of the petri dish?

   So that the writing will not obstruct the view of the bacteria growing in the petri dish.

3. Why is it important to use sterile techniques while inoculating the agar plates?

   Sterile techniques should always be used when working with bacteria to prevent contamination

   of the environment and of the bacteria being studied.

4. What is the purpose of the disk soaked in distilled water in each inoculated petri dish?

   The disk serves as a control.

5. What is the purpose of taping closed the lids of the petri dishes?

   To keep the lids from coming open and allowing contamination of the inoculated plates.

Materials *(per group)*

Annotations for the preparation of cultures are found after Going Further.

glass-marking pencil
Bunsen burner
matches
2 sterile cotton swabs
beaker of water
test-tube rack
sterile filter-paper disks
forceps
distilled water
metric ruler
transparent tape

Read all the information on chemical safety from any Materials Safety Data Sheet that accompanies a chemical.

culture of *Escherichia coli* B
2 sterile nutrient agar plates
3 disinfectants chosen from the following: chlorine bleach, household cleaner, household disinfectant, phenol
3 antibiotic disks chosen from the following: aureomycin, chloromycetin, penicillin, streptomycin, tetracycline, terramycin

Annotations for preparation of agar plates are found after Going Further.

Antibiotic disks are available from biological supply houses.

Safety 🥽🧤🧫💧🌡🧪☠🔥🗑🔪

Never culture pathogenic bacteria. However, treat all bacterial cultures as if they are pathogenic. Firmly seal with transparent tape any bacterial plates that are used for student inspection. For sterilization, use a high-temperature gas flame rather than an alcohol burner or candle flame. Cultures should be killed before disposal. Autoclave or pressure-cook all cultures and contaminated glassware at 15 pounds pressure per square inch (103.4 Pa) for 20 minutes. Disposable plates should be incinerated.

If your immune system has been weakened, you should not be present when this experiment is being performed. Put on safety goggles, a laboratory apron, and plastic gloves. Be careful to avoid breakage when working with glassware. Tie back loose hair when working with flames. Do not reach over an open flame. Always follow your teacher's directions and use special caution when working with bacterial cultures. Wash your hands thoroughly after carrying out this investigation. Return or dispose of all materials according to the instructions of your teacher. Review the meaning of each safety symbol by referring to Safety Symbols on page 8.

Procedure

Part A. Inoculating a Sterile Nutrient Agar Plate

1. Put on your laboratory apron. Obtain two sterile nutrient agar plates. Carefully turn over each plate and lay it on your worktable. **CAUTION:** *Be very careful not to open the petri dishes of sterile agar while handling them.*

2. With a glass-marking pencil, mark the bottom of each petri dish shown in Figure 1. Draw two lines at right angles to each other so that the dish is divided into four equal areas, or quadrants. Number the quadrants on each dish 1 through 4. **Note:** *Place the numbers near the edges of the dishes.* Write your initials near the top center of each dish. Carefully turn the petri dishes right side up.

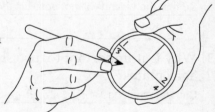

Figure 1

3. Put on your plastic gloves. Obtain a test tube containing a bacterial culture of *Escherichia coli* B. Place the test tube in a test-tube rack. **CAUTION:** *Use extreme care when working with bacterial cultures. Avoid spills. If a spill does occur, immediately call your teacher for assistance.* Obtain two sterile cotton swabs. Carefully read steps 4 through 8 and study Figure 2 before you proceed. Remove your plastic gloves.

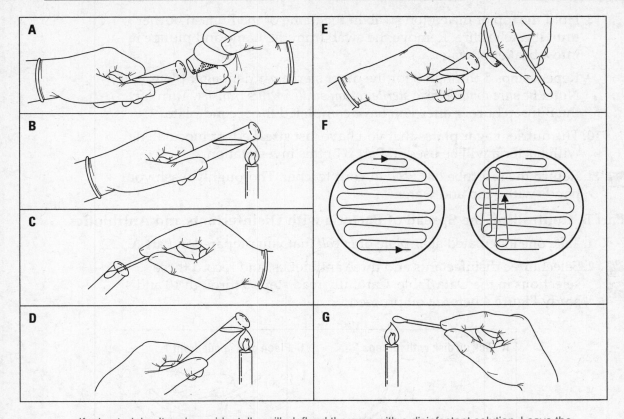

Figure 2 If a bacterial culture is accidentally spilled, flood the area with a disinfectant solution. Leave the disinfectant on the affected area and any broken glassware for at least 30 minutes before carefully wiping the area with moist paper towels. A clearly marked bottle of disinfectant should be placed on each worktable in case such accidents occur. Make sure students are supervised when using the burner.

4. Put on your safety goggles and light the Bunsen burner.
   CAUTION: *Use extreme care when working with or near an open flame. Tie back loose hair and clothing.*

5. Pick up the test tube of *E. coli*. Remove the cotton plug. **Note:** *Do not let the cotton plug come in contact with any other object.* Pass the mouth of the tube back and forth through the burner flame.

6. Insert a sterile cotton swab into the bacterial culture. **Note:** *Shake any excess liquid into the test tube.* Remove the cotton swab. **Note:** *Do not let the cotton swab come in contact with any other object.* Pass the mouth of the tube back and forth through the burner flame. Replace the cotton plug and return the test tube to the rack.

7. Slightly open a sterile nutrient agar plate. Place the tip of the cotton swab near the top center of the agar. Streak the agar as shown in Figure 3A. Lift the swab off the plate and turn the petri dish 90° to the right. Streak the agar again, as shown in Figure 3B. Close the petri dish.

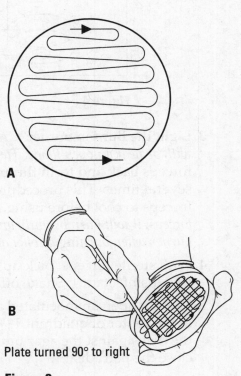

Plate turned 90° to right

Figure 3

8. Hold the top of the cotton swab in the flame of the Bunsen burner until it catches fire. Remove the swab from the flame and plunge it into a beaker of water.

9. Repeat steps 5 through 8 for the other sterile nutrient agar plate. **Note:** *Be sure to use a new sterile cotton swab for this transfer.* Turn off the Bunsen burner after you have completed the second plate.

10. The nutrient agar plates that you have just streaked, or inoculated, with bacteria will be used in Part B of this investigation.

11. Return the test tube of *E. coli* to your teacher. Thoroughly wash your hands with soap and water.

Part B. Controlling the Spread of Bacteria with Disinfectants and Antibiotics

1. Take one inoculated agar plate of *E. coli* that you prepared in Part A.

2. Select three disinfectants and three antibiotics, and record these selections in the Data Table. Carefully read steps 3 through 10 and study Figure 4 before you proceed.

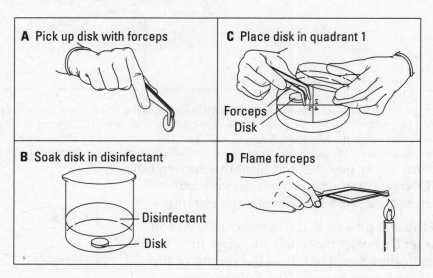

A Pick up disk with forceps

C Place disk in quadrant 1

Forceps
Disk

B Soak disk in disinfectant

Disinfectant
Disk

D Flame forceps

Figure 4

3. Light the Bunsen burner. **CAUTION:** *Use extreme care when working with or near an open flame. Tie back loose hair and clothing.* Pass the forceps back and forth through the flame of the Bunsen burner several times. This procedure sterilizes the forceps. Allow the forceps to cool before using. **CAUTION:** *If there is alcohol on the forceps, it will burn brightly and quickly. Stand back from the Bunsen burner when burning alcohol off the forceps.*

4. With sterile forceps, pick up a disk of filter paper. Insert the disk into disinfectant 1. Shake off any excess liquid.

5. Slightly open an inoculated agar plate. Position the filter-paper disk in the center of quadrant 1. With the tip of the forceps, gently press the disk against the agar until it sticks. Remove the forceps and close the petri dish.

6. Repeat steps 4 and 5 with the remaining disinfectant-soaked disks in quadrants 2 and 3 of the inoculated plate of *E. coli*. **Note:** *Remember to sterilize the forceps after each use.*

7. In quadrant 4, place a filter-paper disk soaked in distilled water.

8. Repeat steps 4 through 7 with the other inoculated agar plate using antibiotic disks instead of disinfectants. You should have two inoculated agar plates as shown in Figure 5.

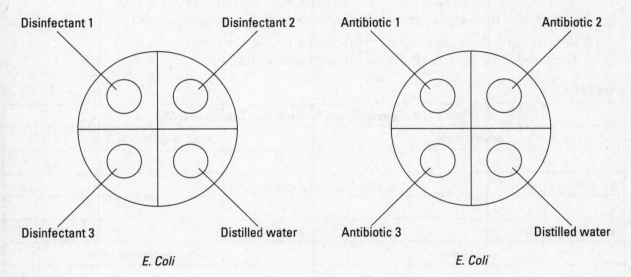

Figure 5

9. With transparent tape, tape the petri dishes closed, as shown in Figure 6. Turn the dishes upside down. Incubate the dishes for 48 hours at 37°C.

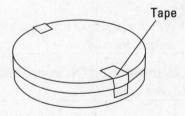

Figure 6

10. Observe the petri dishes after 48 hours. White or cloudy areas of the agar indicate bacterial growth. Notice any clear areas, called *zones of inhibition*, surrounding the filter-paper disks. A clear area indicates that the disinfectant or antibiotic inhibited bacterial growth. A lightly cloudy area surrounding a disk indicates that bacterial growth was slowed down. **Note:** *You may want to hold the petri dishes to the light to see the zones of inhibition more clearly.*

11. With a metric ruler, measure to the nearest millimeter the size of the clear zone surrounding each disk. Record your measurements in the Data Table. If no clear zone is present, record the measurement as 0.

12. Return the petri dishes to your teacher for proper disposal. Thoroughly wash your hands with soap and water.

Data Table

Effects of Disinfectants and Antibiotics on Growth of *E. Coli*	
Disinfectant	**Zone of inhibition** (mm)
1	
2	Answers will depend on disinfectants used.
3	
4 distilled water	
Antibiotic	**Zone of inhibition** (mm)
1	
2	Answers will depend on antibiotics used.
3	
4 distilled water	

Analysis and Conclusions

1. **Observing** Which disinfectant was most effective in preventing the growth of *E. coli*?
   Answers will vary depending on the disinfectants used.

2. **Observing** Which antibiotic was most effective in preventing the growth of *E. coli*?
   Answers will vary depending on the antibiotics used.

3. **Controlling Variables** How do you know that any inhibition you have observed is due to the disinfectants and antibiotics on the disk?
   There should be no inhibition around the control disks.

4. **Analyzing Data** Pretend that a serious staphylococcus infection has developed in the locker room of your school's gym. Assume that you are responsible for getting rid of the staph contamination. How would you do so?
   Use a sterile inoculating loop to collect a sample of suspected sources of the bacteria. Culture the bacteria

   with disinfectant disks. Scrub the area with the most effective disinfectant.

5. Formulating Hypotheses Scientists have observed that an antibiotic seems to lose its effectiveness against a particular population of bacteria after a prolonged period of time. What do you think is responsible for this phenomenon?

The antibiotic kills the susceptible bacteria in the population. The surviving bacteria are immune to the

antibiotic and will produce offspring that will inherit this immunity.

6. Formulating Hypotheses Why are the different disinfectants not equally effective against all species of bacteria?

Species of bacteria differ from one another and therefore react differently to various disinfectants.

7. Inferring Suppose that your doctor diagnoses your condition as a bacterial infection and prescribes an antibiotic. Your doctor cautions you to take the antibiotic for 10 days even though you may feel fine after a few days. Explain why you should follow your doctor's orders.

After a few days, the antibiotic will probably have destroyed most of the bacteria. Thus, you will feel better.

However, some bacteria will remain and reproduce. The infection can then begin again. Taking the antibiotic

for 10 days helps ensure that all of the bacteria will be destroyed.

Going Further

Using the procedures presented in this investigation, test other species of bacteria—such as *B. subtilis*, *P. vulgaris*, and *S. lutea*—for their resistance or sensitivity to various disinfectants and antibiotics.

Pure cultures of *Escherichia coli* can be obtained from a biological supply house. Bacteria are easily cultured in tubes of nutrient broth. To prepare the nutrient broth, bring 350 mL distilled water to a boil in a 500-mL beaker. Slowly add 3 g dehydrated nutrient broth, stirring constantly. Pour the broth into small test tubes and insert a cotton plug into each tube. Sterilize the tubes of broth for 15 minutes at 15 pounds pressure in an autoclave or pressure cooker. The sterilized tubes can be stored in a refrigerator until they are needed. Transfer bacteria to the tubes of sterile nutrient broth using an inoculating loop and following sterile technique. Store inoculated tubes at room temperature for 2 or 3 days to allow the bacteria to grow. Tubes of bacteria can also be incubated at 37°C for 24 hours and then used immediately. Subcultures and dilutions of the cultures can be made at 2-week intervals. Cultures remain viable stored in a refrigerator for several weeks.

To prepare nutrient agar plates, mix 3 g beef extract, 5 g peptone, and 15 g agar in 1 L distilled water. Bring mixture to a boil, stirring constantly to avoid burning. Heat until liquid is clear. Sterilize in containers covered with cotton plugs in autoclave or pressure cooker for 15 minutes at 15 pounds pressure. Recipe makes about 50 petri dishes. Refrigerate. Nutrient agar can also be purchased from biological supply houses.

Investigating the Diversity of Protists

> You may want to refer students to Chapter 20 in the textbook for a discussion of the Kingdom Protista which includes animallike and plantlike species that are part of the food webs found in freshwater and marine environments. The concept of a food web is discussed in Section 3–2 in the textbook.
> Time required:
> Part A: 35 minutes;
> Part B: 40 minutes

Introduction

Protists are members of the Kingdom Protista which includes unicellular and colonial organisms. Protists are very diverse in the ways that they live and acquire energy. They include autotrophs that produce food using photosynthesis and heterotrophs that feed on a variety of prey. The kingdom also includes slime molds that live as decomposers on rotting wood and rich soil. The diversity of feeding behaviors contributes to the complex protist food webs found in terrestrial and aquatic habitats. In this investigation you will learn about the feeding strategies of several protists.

Problem

What are the ways that fresh water protists can acquire energy for survival and how well are they equipped to compete with other aquatic species?

Pre-Lab Discussion

Read the entire investigation. Then, work with a partner to answer the following questions.

1. What is the technique that you will use to determine the population density of each species of protist you will use in your experiment on predator/prey relationships? Why is it necessary to do this?

   Students will count the number of individuals in a drop of each culture contained within a 1-cm square area

   marked on a slide, to know the density of each species before they are mixed together.

   Why is it necessary to repeat the count several times?

   Since these are fast-moving species, a single counting may not be accurate.

2. What are some of the possible relationships that might exist between *Paramecia* and *Didinium*?

   They could be predator and prey species, with *Paramecium* the predator or the prey. They could a share a

   similar environment, but have separate food supplies and not be in competition. They could be autotrophs

   that make their own food, or they could compete for food.

3. What would a positive attraction to light suggest about how a protist gets energy?

   It may be that the species is an autotroph that uses photosynthesis to make its own food. It could also

   indicate that the species is a grazer and seeks brighter areas where autotrophs would be plentiful.

4. What would be a simple way to distinguish between an autotrophic protist and a predatory protist?

   An autotroph may contain chlorophyll and appear green.

5. What is the purpose of the card with the slit in the light sensitivity experiment?

The card provides an area of bright light as well as a dark area where the protists might avoid light.

Materials *(per group)*

living cultures of *Paramecium caudatum,*
   Didinium, Blepharisma, and *Euglena*

microscope slides

compound light microscope

dropper pipette

coverslips

glass-marking pencil

metric ruler

methyl cellulose

index cards

scissors

Vigorous cultures of *Paramecia, Didinium, Blepharisma,* and *Euglena* should be prepared several days before the experiment. Usually a wheat medium or hay infusion will produce enough bacteria to feed *Paramecia* and *Blepharisma.* A vigorous culture of *Paramecia* is needed to feed *Didinium. Didinium* will encyst if it does not eat at least 3 paramecia in 4–6 hours, so the culture will probably need to be fed with sufficient paramecia when it arrives.

Avoid storing *Blepharisma* in intense light. Doing so will cause the pink pigment to change into a poisonous colorless chemical that can dissolve the cytoplasm.

Euglena cultures are hardy as long as they are placed in indirect light.

Step seven of the procedure requires students to make a microscope slide size card with a slit in it. This can be done in advance during lab preparations to save time and avoid confusion.

Safety 🔳🔳🔳🔳🔳

Put on a laboratory apron. Handle all glassware carefully. Observe proper laboratory procedures when using electrical equipment. Use caution with sharp instruments. Return or dispose of all materials according to the instructions of your teacher. Wash your hands thoroughly after working with microorganisms. Note all safety symbols in the Procedure and review the meaning of each symbol by referring to Safety Symbols on page 8.

Procedure

Part A: A Study of a Predator–Prey Relationship

1. On two clean microscope slides, draw a 1-cm square using a glass-marking pencil. The square will make viewing of the organisms easier by preventing them from moving beyond its boundary.

2. Use a dropper pipette to place a drop of *Paramecium* culture on one of the slides. Add a drop of methyl cellulose to the slide to slow down the movement of the paramecia.

3. Using the low-power objective of the microscope, view the *Paramecium* culture. Count the number of paramecia that appear within the square. Record your observations in the Data Table. Wait 1 minute and then count the number of paramecia again. Wait another minute and count the number of paramecia a third time. Compute the average number of paramecia that appeared in the box at the three intervals of time.

Name_____ Class_____ Date _____

Data Table

	Number of *Paramecium*	**Number of *Didinium***
At start		
After 1 minute		
After 2 minutes		
Average		
After mixing species		
At start		
After 1 minute		
After 2 minutes		

4. Switch to the high-power objective. **CAUTION:** *When switching to the high-power objective, always look at the objective from the side of the microscope so that the objective does not hit or damage the slide.* Locate a single paramecium and observe its structure. Observe the method of movement the paramecium uses. Record your observations in the space below.

5. Repeat steps 2 through 4 using the *Didinium* culture. Record your results in the Data Table.

6. On a clean slide draw a 1-cm square using a glass-marking pencil. Add a drop of the *Paramecium* culture to the slide first and then a drop of the *Didinium* culture to the same square.

Students should make this slide without methyl cellulose so as not to interfere with the interaction of the two species.

7. Observe the mixed cultures of *Paramecia* and *Didinium* at the start, after one minute, and after two minutes and record your results in the Data Table.

Part B: A Study of the Light Sensitivity of *Euglena* and *Blepharisma*

 1. Trace the outline of a microscope slide onto an index card. Use scissors to cut out the outline. In the center of the cut-out piece, cut a slit about 2 cm long and 1 mm wide.

Students may find that folding the cut-out lengthwise makes it easier to cut the slit. This activity can also be done as part of the pre-lab work.

2. Place the card on the microscope stage with the slit over the opening of the microscope stage. Using the dropper pipette, place a drop of *Euglena* culture on a clean microscope slide. Add a drop of methyl cellulose to the slide to slow down the movement of the euglenas and apply a cover slip. Place the slide on top of the card on the microscope stage. Use the low-power objective on the microscope to locate several euglenas.

3. Observe the euglenas that are visible through the slit. Wait about 30 seconds, then quickly remove the card. Record your observations on the following page.

4. Increase the magnification to 100X or 400X and locate a single euglena. **CAUTION:** *When switching to the high-power objective, always look at the objective from the side of the microscope so that the objective does not hit or damage the slide.* Locate a single euglena and observe its structure and the way that it moves.

5. Repeat steps 1–4 using the *Blepharisma* culture. Return your materials and wash your hands before leaving the laboratory.

Analysis and Conclusions

1. Analyzing Data In Part A, which protist was the predator and which was the prey? Explain your answer.

The *Didinium* is the predator and the *Paramecium* is the prey. Students should see *Didinium* ingest the

Paramecium.

2. Inferring Based on your observations is a larger size a good indicator of a predatory species?

No, *Didinium* is actually smaller than *Paramecium*, but had no difficulty ingesting the larger protist.

3. Inferring Which of the species that you examined is likely to be an autotroph? Explain your answer.

Euglena is probably an autotroph because its green color implies that it contains chlorophyll, and because it

showed a strong attraction to light.

4. Drawing Conclusions Is *Euglena* a plantlike or animallike protist?

Euglena is often referred to as plantlike, but its ability to sense light and to swim toward it using a

flagellum is more animallike.

5. Comparing and Contrasting Three of the protists that you examined are called ciliates since they move by beating cilia. How would you categorize them according to their nutritional habits?

Didinium is a predator species and *Paramecium* and *Blepharisma* are most likely heterotrophs as well.

Going Further

Compare the sizes of *Didinium* and *Blepharisma*. If they have a predator-prey relationship how might it work? Mix a drop of the *Didinium* culture with a drop of the *Blepharisma* culture to determine whether they have a predator-prey relationship and if so, identify the predator.

Comparing the Characteristics of Molds

You may want to refer students to Section 21–2 in the textbook before performing this investigation. **CAUTION:** *Inquire in advance of this lab about allergies to molds among your students. Excuse any students who have allergic reactions to molds.*
Time required: 20 minutes; 30 minutes after 1 week; 15 minutes after 1 more week

Introduction

Although often associated with food spoilage and the deterioration of wood, cloth, and other materials, molds and other fungi can be useful too. People take advantage of molds, for example, to produce a variety of cheeses. Penicillin, an important antibiotic, was originally made from *Penicillium* mold. Even citric acid, which is used in lemon-flavored candies and foods, may be made from *Aspergillus niger*, a black mold.

In this investigation, you will design and carry out an experiment to determine which conditions are favorable for the growth of molds.

Problem

What conditions are favorable for the growth of molds?

Pre-Lab Discussion

Read the entire investigation. Then, work with a partner to answer the following questions.

1. What is the purpose of the moist paper towel shown in Figure 1?

   It provides moisture.

2. Have you ever found mold growing on food? Describe an environment where mold is likely to grow naturally on food.

   Students may suggest that mold grows on old bread that has been left in a warm, dark bread box for a while, food that has been left in a lunch sack, in their locker, or in a car—all potentially warm, moist places.

3. Write a hypothesis that you could test in this investigation.

   The hypothesis should be a testable statement about the growth of mold under specific conditions.

   For example, mold grows well in moist environments or mold does not grow well in cold environments.

4. Make one prediction based on the hypothesis you wrote in 3 above.

   Answers must be based on the hypothesis students wrote in question 3. Sample answer: A food source that

   is placed in a moist environment will show more mold growth than a food source placed in a dry environment,

   assuming all other variables are controlled.

5. How might you test your prediction using the suggested materials? What results would support the hypothesis you wrote in 3?

Answers will depend on the predictions. Sample answer: Prepare two clear plastic bags containing identical

food sources. Enclose a moist paper towel in one bag and a dry paper towel in the other. Place the bags in

the same environment and observe any mold growth. The hypothesis would be supported if the clear plastic

bag with the moist paper towel shows more growth than the bag with the dry paper towel.

Suggested Materials *(per group)*

paper towels
warm water
pieces of fruit, cheddar cheese, and bread
clear plastic bags
permanent marker
twist ties
hand lens

Citrus fruits, and bread and cheese without preservatives will give the best results.

Zipper-locking plastic sandwich bags will also work. If you use self-sealing bags, you do not need twist ties.

You may want to have on hand additional food sources, a fluorescent light source, dark cloths, ice and ice buckets or access to a refrigerator, and other equipment that students might want to include in their experiments.

Request additional materials from your teacher if you think you need them to carry out your experiment.

Safety 🔬🧤🧴📦🧪⚠️

Put on a laboratory apron, safety goggles, and plastic gloves. Never taste anything used in this laboratory investigation. Follow your teacher's directions and all appropriate safety procedures when handling microorganisms. Wash your hands thoroughly each time you finish working with the materials. Note all safety symbols in Design Your Experiment and review the meaning of each symbol by referring to the Safety Symbols on page 8.

CAUTION: *Do not allow students to open their sealed plastic bags. This will prevent fungal spores from circulating in the classroom. Treat all sealed bags as you would any other biohazard in the lab. Set up your disposal procedures in advance.*

Design Your Experiment

1. Figure 1 shows one method for growing mold: Seal a food source and a moist paper towel in a clear plastic bag and place the bag in the desired environment for at least one week. **CAUTION:** *Do not open the bag, once it has been sealed. Treat all growth as a biohazard. At the end of the investigation, dispose of all bags as instructed by your teacher. Wash your hands thoroughly after preparing the bags and after each time you touch them.*

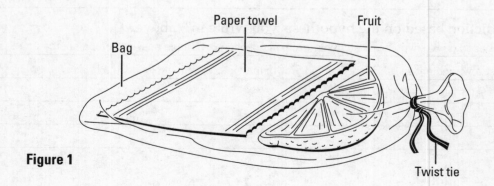

Figure 1

2. Choose at least one variable that you will test for its effect on mold growth. For example, you could examine the effects of temperature, moisture, light, or different food sources on mold growth.

You may want to let students know that a warm, moist environment is conducive to mold growth so

that they will know how to set up a proper control for their experiments.

3. Write a hypothesis about the variable(s) you will test for its effect on mold growth.

Answers will depend on the condition(s) students plan to test for mold growth. The hypothesis should be a

testable statement about mold growth. Examples include the following: (a) Molds grow under warm, moist

conditions or (b) well-lighted places are more conducive to mold growth than dark places are.

4. Design an experiment to test the hypothesis you wrote in step 3. On the lines provided, describe the variables you will include in your experiment and the procedure you will follow. **Note:** *Do not carry out your experiment until your teacher has instructed you to do so.*

Manipulated variable(s)

The manipulated variable(s) will depend on students' hypotheses and will be the condition(s) students are

testing for mold growth. For example, if students are testing the effect of temperature on mold growth, then

temperature will be the manipulated variable.

Responding variable

The responding variable will be mold growth. Students should include an operational definition or method

for assessing mold growth.

Controlled variables

The controlled variables will be all of the conditions that are not being tested. For example, if students are

testing the effect of temperature on mold growth, then exposure to light, moisture, and the type and size of

the food source should be identical for each sample. Moreover, the clear plastic bags, twist ties, and the

presence of a paper towel will all be controlled variables.

Procedure

The procedure will depend on the variable(s) students are testing for mold growth and may be similar to the procedure described in Step 1 and shown in Figure 1. For example, if students are testing for growth on different foods, then students will need to prepare one plastic bag for each food source under identical conditions—ideally warm, dark, and moist. If students wish to test the effects of temperature, then they should compare at least two identically prepared and maintained bags, one kept warm or at room temperature and one chilled.

5. What safety precautions should you follow as you conduct the experiment you describe above?

Answers should include all of the following and other precautions as needed: Do not touch, taste, or smell the contents of the bags or open the bags for any reason, once they are sealed. Wash your hands thoroughly after preparing the bags and after each time the bags are touched. Treat the contents of the bags, once sealed, as a biohazard, and dispose of them according to the teacher's directions.

6. Submit a written experimental plan to your teacher for approval. When your teacher has approved of your plan and given you permission to begin your experiment, carry out the experiment. **CAUTION:** *Put on a lab apron, safety goggles, and plastic gloves. Do not touch, taste, or smell the contents of the bags or open the bags for any reason, once they are sealed. Wash your hands thoroughly after preparing the bags and after each time the bags are touched. Treat the contents of the bags, once sealed, as a biohazard, and dispose of them according to your teacher's directions.*

CAUTION: *Make sure that students know to seal their plastic bags and not to open them. The bags are to be treated as biohazards. Instruct students about the method of disposal to follow. Students should understand that mold spores can cause disease*

7. Record your results in the Data Table provided or you may design your own data table. If you need more space, attach additional sheets of paper.

or severe allergic reactions in some individuals. Students should not touch, taste, or smell the contents of their bags, once they are sealed.

Data Table

Plastic bag	Type of food	Environment	Observations of growth (amount, color, texture)

Name_____ Class_____ Date_____

Analysis and Conclusions

1. **Controlling Variables** What was the control in your experiment? Explain your answer.

Answers will depend on students' experiments. Students should control for all of the relevant variables that they are not testing. A typical control for this experiment would be a bag that is kept in a moist, dark, warm environment.

2. **Evaluating and Revising** Look back at the hypothesis you tested in your experiment. Do your data support your hypothesis? Explain.

Answers will depend on students' hypothesis and data. Students should be able to explain whether or not their data support their hypothesis.

3. **Comparing and Contrasting** Based on the results of your experiment and those of your classmates, what conditions do you think are best for growing molds? Support your answer with data from the experiments.

Answers will depend on students' experiments and data. Most students will find that warm, dark, moist conditions are best for growing molds. Students may also comment on the best food source for growing molds based on their experiments.

4. **Drawing Conclusions** Based on the results of your experiment and those of your classmates, what can you do to inhibit the unwanted growth of molds on foods?

Answers will depend on students' experiments and data. Possible answers include keeping foods in the refrigerator, especially during warm, humid weather and lowering the temperature on the refrigerator.

5. **Inferring** Athlete's foot is a condition caused by a fungus growing on human feet. Describe the conditions that might encourage the growth of this fungus and what can be done to prevent athlete's foot.

Feet covered with shoes and/or socks produce a warm, moist, dark environment. Similarly, gym showers provide a warm, moist environment. Both are conducive to fungal growth. Keeping feet cool and dry by changing shoes and socks when they become damp and drying the feet and in between the toes after bathing can help prevent the condition.

6. Inferring Molds sometimes grow on basement walls and floors, causing odors and damage. How can these problems be prevented?

Basements are often moist and dark. Using a dehumidifier to remove moisture from the air can sometimes

lessen the problem. If possible, routinely open windows or doors to air out the area.

Going Further

Seeds are often soaked in a slightly acidic solution in order to prevent mold from growing on them. Design an experiment to test whether slightly acidic solutions retard fungal growth.

Students could test the effects of pH on fungal growth using an experimental design similar to the one used in this investigation.

Comparing Green Algae and Mosses

You may want to refer students to Section 22–2 in the textbook for a discussion of mosses.
Time required: Two 30-minute sessions

Introduction

Algae are photosynthetic protists. Algae can be classified by color—green algae, brown algae, and red algae. Green algae can be unicellular or multicellular. Several species of unicellular algae, for example, the green species *Chlamydomonas*, can provide an idea of how multicellular plants may have evolved.

In contrast to the algae, mosses are land-dwelling plants. They are usually found in moist environments because they lack the vascular tissue found in higher plants. Instead, water passes from cell by cell through osmosis and surface tension around the stems. Since this method of transport only works well over short distances, these plants never grow very tall.

The first multicellular organisms evolved in water. Algae living today can give us some idea of what these first organisms were like. Over time, some organisms adapted to life in drier environments and evolved structures to acquire, transport, and conserve water. The mosses may represent one stage in this process, as they live in moist environments on the land. Algae and mosses are alike in that they lack specialized vascular tissues to transport water and the products of photosynthesis, but they differ in many ways. In this investigation you will compare a brown alga with moss.

Problem

How are brown algae and mosses similar and different?

Pre-Lab Discussion

Read the entire investigation. Then, work with a partner to answer the following questions.

1. What is the major difference between the habitats of brown algae and mosses?
   Brown algae live in water; mosses live on land.

2. Which is closer to the ancestors of plants, algae or moss? Why do you think so?
   Algae are closer. Like the ancestors of modern plants, algae live in water. Some are unicellular.

   Most have simple structures.

3. Examine the illustrations in Figures 1 and 3. How are the holdfast and the rhizoids similar?
   Both anchor the organism.

4. What is shown in Figures 2 and 4?
   The life cycles of brown algae and moss.

5. Why is a water environment needed for sexual reproduction in both brown algae and mosses?

The sperm must swim to the eggs before fertilization can occur.

Materials *(per group)*

large shallow bowl

sea water

microscope

dissecting microscope

hand lens

dissecting tray

scissors

scalpel

microscope slide

coverslip

forceps

brown alga, *Fucus*

moss, *Polytrichum*

prepared slide of moss protonema

prepared slide of moss antheridia and archegonia

Fucus vesiculosus is also called rockweed. It can be purchased from biological supply houses. Other mosses such as *Funaria hygrometria*, *Mnium affine*, *Physcomitrium pyriforme*, or *Catharinea undulata* may be substituted.

Safety

Put on a laboratory apron. Always handle the microscope with extreme care. You are responsible for its proper care and use. Use caution when handling microscope slides, as they can break easily and cut you. Be careful when handling sharp instruments. Wear plastic gloves when handling plants. Note all safety alert symbols next to the steps in the Procedure and review the meaning of each symbol by referring to Safety Symbols on page 8.

Procedure

Part A. Adaptive Structures and Reproduction of *Fucus* Algae

1. Place the *Fucus* in a large shallow bowl. Cover the *Fucus* with sea water. **CAUTION:** *Wear plastic gloves.*

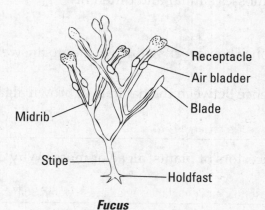

Figure 1

Fucus

2. Carefully remove a piece of *Fucus* from the bowl and place it on the dissecting tray.

3. Look for the main stem. At its base, notice a tough, fibrous pad of tissue called the holdfast.

4. Feel the stems in their midregions until you come across a small lump. This is the air bladder. Air bladders sometimes come in pairs on either side of the midrib.

5. Using the scissors, cut out a small section of the stem containing an air bladder. Place it back in the bowl and observe what happens.

6. Look at the leaflike structures on the seaweed. Find the flattened forked stem tips. Special cells called apical cells located at the tips divide by mitosis and produce the forked branching pattern.

7. Examine the stem tips for swollen areas called receptacles. Receptacles contain eggs and sperm.

8. Look for the most swollen receptacles because they are the most mature and are the best ones for examination. Orange-yellow receptacles contain gametes that are ready to be dispersed.

9. With a hand lens, notice the tiny bumps on the surface of a receptacle. For a closer look, use the dissecting microscope.

10. In order to examine the gametes, you will have to open the receptacles and look inside. Using a scalpel, carefully cut out a very thin cross section of the receptacle. See Figure 2. **CAUTION:** *Use extreme care when using a sharp instrument.*

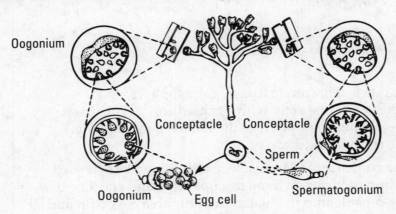

Life Cycle of *Fucus*

Figure 2

11. With the forceps, place the thin section of the receptacle on the microscope slide and prepare a wet mount.

12. Observe the section of the receptacle under the low power of the microscope. **Note:** *It may take a little practice to cut the section thin enough so that it can be viewed under the microscope.*

13. Inside the receptacle, look for several small, round chambers that come into contact with the receptacle. These chambers are called conceptacles. Notice whether a conceptacle has an opening to the outside wall. A female conceptacle has several round oogonial sacs, each of which contains 8 egg cells. A male conceptacle has spermatogonial sacs containing many orange dots. Each dot is a sperm cell. In *Fucus*, fertilization and development are external. In the space provided on page 175, sketch and label the conceptacle. Record the magnification.

If the students are having difficulties slicing the receptacle thin enough to prepare a wet mount, suggest that they try viewing it under the dissecting microscope without a coverslip.

Part B. Adaptive Structures and Reproduction of *Polytrichum* Moss

1. Examine a small clump of *Polytrichum* moss under the dissecting microscope. Use Figure 3 to identify the structures of a moss. **CAUTION:** *Handle the microscope with extreme care. Do not use electrical equipment near water or with wet hands. Never use direct sunlight as the light source for a microscope.*

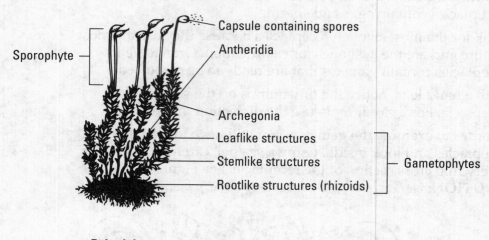

Polytrichum

Figure 3

2. Carefully separate a sporophyte from a gametophyte. A sporophyte consists of one stalk with a capsule on it. The green "leafy" part below the sporophyte is the female gametophyte. Notice that the capsule has a cap on it.

3. To examine the contents of the capsule, carefully remove the cap. Then place a drop of water on a microscope slide and squeeze the contents of the capsule into the water. Cover with a coverslip and locate the capsule's contents under low power. Then observe under high power. **CAUTION:** *When turning to the high-power objective lens, always look at the objective from the side of the microscope so that the objective lens does not hit or damage the slide.* In the space provided on page 175, sketch the spores. Record the magnification.

4. Examine a prepared slide of moss protonema. A protonema is a mass of tangled green filaments that grow from a spore.

5. Examine a prepared slide of moss antheridia and archegonia. These reproductive organs are found in the upper tips of the gametophytes.

6. Study Figure 4, which shows the life cycle of a moss. Compare the similarities and differences in the life cycles of *Fucus* and *Polytrichum*.

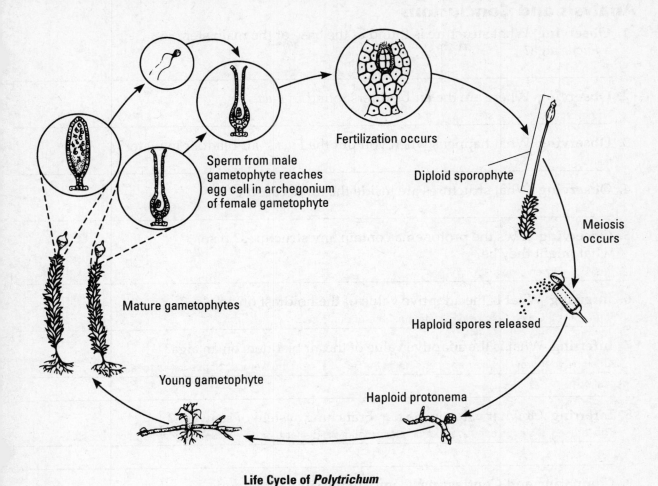

Fertilization occurs

Sperm from male
gametophyte reaches
egg cell in archegonium
of female gametophyte

Diploid sporophyte

Meiosis
occurs

Mature gametophytes

Haploid spores released

Young gametophyte

Haploid protonema

Life Cycle of *Polytrichum*

Figure 4

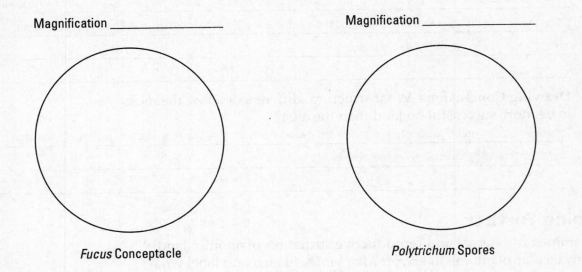

Magnification _____

Magnification _____

Fucus Conceptacle

Polytrichum Spores

Analysis and Conclusions

1. **Observing** What structure is found at the base of the main stem in a *Fucus* alga?

   The holdfast.

2. **Observing** Where are the air bladders found in *Fucus*?

   The midregions of the stems.

3. **Observing** What happens when you put the *Fucus'* air bladder in water?

   It floats.

4. **Observing** What structures are inside the moss capsule?

   Spores.

5. **Observing** Does the protonema contain any structures? If so, what might they be?

   Yes, possibly chloroplasts.

6. **Inferring** What is the adaptive value of the holdfast on an alga?

   It prevents the alga from being washed ashore or out to sea.

7. **Inferring** What is the adaptive value of the air bladders on an alga?

   An air bladder provides buoyancy and holds the "leaves" near the water's surface for increased light.

8. **Inferring** Of what value is the flat, branching system of seaweed?

   The larger, flat blades can receive a greater amount of light for a more efficient photosynthetic process.

9. **Comparing and Contrasting** Compare the similarities and differences in the life cycles of *Fucus* and *Polytrichum*.

   In *Fucus*, the female part forms an oogonium and the male part forms a spermatogonium. The egg and sperm unite externally and form the new organism. In the moss, however, there is a stage in which the spores divide by mitosis and grow into a gametophyte plant that develops gametes. They, in turn, develop into male and female portions that produce haploid gametes and then produce a zygote. The life cycle of a moss is more complex than the life cycle of an alga.

10. **Drawing Conclusions** What structural differences allow the moss to be more successful on land than the alga?

    The moss has an ability to absorb water through rhizoids and to store water in its storage tissues. The alga cannot do this and therefore is not adapted for life on land.

Going Further

Examine the external and reproductive structures of another land nonvascular plant, the liverwort *Marchantia*. Sketch and label what you see. Compare the structures of the liverwort with those you observed in the moss.

Observing Root and Stem Structures

You may want to refer students to Section 23–2 in the textbook for a discussion of roots and stems.
Time required: 45 minutes

Introduction

The first structures to appear on a germinating seed are the roots. The initial root to grow from a seed is the primary root, which is then followed by secondary roots that branch out from the primary root. In a taproot system, the primary root grows longer and thicker than the secondary roots. In a fibrous root system, the secondary roots continue to grow, and eventually all the roots are of equal or nearly equal size.

Roots anchor the plant in place, absorb water containing dissolved minerals from the environment, and act as storage areas for excess food. Adventitious roots grow from parts of the plant other than the roots. Aerial roots are roots that are suspended in the air.

Plant structures that grow between the roots and leaves are called stems. Although stems usually grow above the ground in vertical positions, they can also grow under the ground in horizontal positions. All stems begin growing as soft, tubelike structures. If the stem remains soft, and usually green, for the entire life of the plant, it is a herbaceous stem. A woody stem becomes hard and often turns brown.

Stems conduct water and dissolved minerals from the roots to the leaves, and food from the leaves to the rest of the plant. Stems may also function as food storage areas, supporting structures, and places for the growth of new plants.

In this investigation, you will examine the structures of roots and stems. You will also observe the structural differences between some monocot and dicot roots and stems.

Problem

What are some structures of roots and stems?

Pre-Lab Discussion

Read the entire investigation. Then, work with a partner to answer the following questions.

1. Why is methylene blue stain used when the cross section of the carrot is observed?

   Methylene blue stains some structures darker than others, allowing different parts of the carrot

   to be distinguished.

2. Why will you use a hand lens or a dissecting microscope rather than a compound light microscope to examine the cross section of carrot?

   Although the cross section is thin, it is not thin enough to allow examination under a light microscope.

3. If you are given a stained cross section on a slide, how can you tell whether it is a section of root or of stem?

Roots and stems have characteristic appearances. Root epidermal cells are large with respect to other cells;

roots may have root hairs; xylem and phloem are confined to the central area in roots. In stems, xylem and

phloem are organized into vascular bundles, which lie throughout or in a ring within the stem.

4. Do root hairs appear to significantly increase the volume or the surface area of a root? What benefit does this increase provide for the plant?

The surface area; increased surface area increases the plant's ability to absorb water from the soil.

5. Which root type is more likely to be a food source—a fibrous root or a tap root? Explain your answer.

The tap root is better adapted for food storage. It has much greater mass and volume than fibrous roots.

Materials (per group)

2-week-old radish seedlings

hand lens or dissecting microscope

microscope

carrot

dissecting tray

scalpel or single-edged razor blade

forceps

microscope slide

dropper pipette

150-mL beaker

methylene blue stain

ethyl alcohol

prepared slides of cross section of:
  Helianthus root, *Helianthus* stem,
  Zea root, *Zea* stem

To prepare the sprouting radish seedlings, soak seeds in water overnight and then place them in a moist paper towel for about 3 days.

Large old carrots are best for showing stele and cortex. It may be easiest for students to handle part of a carrot. A 10-cm piece would be a good size.

Read all the information on chemical safety from any Materials Safety Data Sheet that accompanies a chemical.

To make a 70% ethyl alcohol solution, add 70 mL 95% ethyl alcohol to a graduated cylinder. Fill to the 95-mL mark with distilled water.

Prepared slides are available from biological supply houses.

Safety 🖐️🥼🧤🔥🔪☢️☠️🚱🔥🧪

Put on safety goggles. Put on a laboratory apron. Be careful to avoid breakage when working with glassware. Observe proper laboratory procedures when using electrical equipment. Always handle the microscope with extreme care. You are responsible for its proper care and use. Be careful when handling sharp instruments. Use caution when handling microscope slides, as they can break easily and cut you. Always use special caution and wear disposable plastic gloves when working with laboratory chemicals, as they may irritate the skin or stain skin or clothing. Never touch or taste any chemical unless instructed to do so. Wash your hands with soap and warm water after carrying out this investigation. Note all safety alert symbols next to the steps in the Procedure and review the meanings of each symbol by referring to Safety Symbols on page 8.

Procedure

Part A. External and Internal Structures of a Root

1. Examine Figure 1 and identify each root as being taproot, fibrous, adventitious, or aerial. Write the correct root type in the blanks.

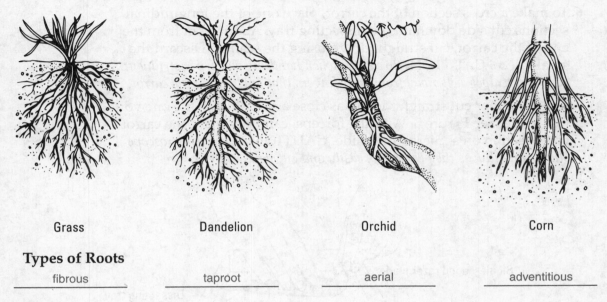

| Grass | Dandelion | Orchid | Corn |

Types of Roots

| fibrous | taproot | aerial | adventitious |

Figure 1

 2. Examine the radish seedling. Note the basic structures of the seedling: leaves, stem, and roots.

3. With a hand lens or dissecting microscope, examine the delicate root hairs extending from the root.

 4. Place the carrot in the dissecting tray. As shown in Figure 2, hold the carrot steady with one hand while you cut it in half lengthwise with the scalpel or single-edged razor blade. **CAUTION:** *Always cut in a direction away from yourself. Because the carrot is very hard, be careful not to let the scalpel or razor blade slip and cut you.*

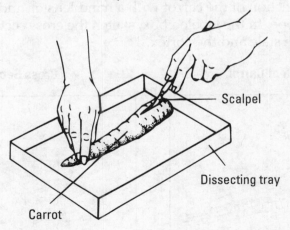

Scalpel

Dissecting tray

Carrot

Figure 2

5. Examine the two halves of the carrot. Each half is a longitudinal section. Notice the stele in the center. The stele contains the xylem and the phloem. Surrounding the stele is the food-storing cortex. In the labeled box, sketch a longitudinal section of the carrot. Label the stele and the cortex.

6. To make a cross section of the carrot, place one of the longitudinal sections cut side down on the dissecting tray. About 4 cm from the end of the carrot, cut straight down using the scalpel. Discard the small piece. **CAUTION:** *Be careful when handling a sharp instrument. Keep the scalpel well away from your fingers that are holding the carrot.*

7. Make another cut straight down, as close as possible to the one you just made. See Figure 3. With the forceps, carefully place the carrot cross section on a microscope slide. **CAUTION:** *Handle microscope slides carefully, as they can break easily and cut you.*

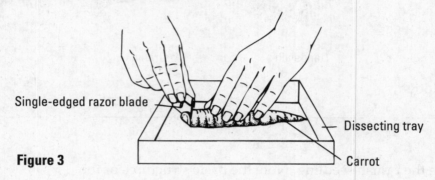

Single-edged razor blade

Dissecting tray

Carrot

Figure 3

8. Put on plastic gloves. Place the slide over the mouth of the beaker. Then using a dropper pipette, cover the carrot cross section completely with methylene blue stain. Allow the stain to set for 1 minute. **CAUTION:** *Methylene blue stain is a permanent stain. Be careful not to get it on your hands or clothing.*

9. After 1 minute, slowly pour alcohol over the carrot cross section until no more stain washes away. **CAUTION:** *Alcohol is flammable. Make sure there are no flames or heat sources present.*

10. Observe the cross section of the carrot with a hand lens or under a dissecting microscope. In the labeled box, sketch the cross section of the carrot. Label the stele and the cortex.

Longitudinal Section of Carrot

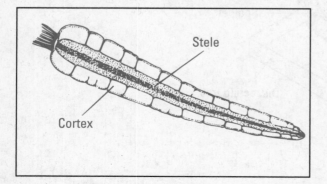

Stele

Cortex

Cross Section of Carrot

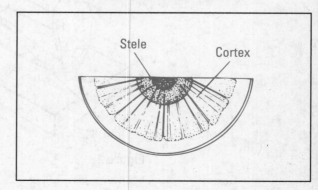

Stele

Cortex

11. Place the prepared slide of the sunflower (*Helianthus*) root cross section under the low power of the microscope. The sunflower is a dicot. Locate the epidermal cells that form the outer edge of the root. Examine different areas on the glass slide. Notice some root hairs, which are extensions of single epidermal cells. **CAUTION:** *Use the microscope with extreme care.*

12. Find the cortex, which is located within the epidermis. The cells of the cortex are large and thin-walled.

13. Locate the star-shaped pattern formed by xylem cells at the center of the root. Switch to the high-power objective and focus on one xylem cell. Note its thick cell wall. **CAUTION:** *When switching to the high-power objective, always watch the nosepiece from the side to make certain that the objective does not hit or damage the slide.*

14. Observe the smaller and thinner-walled phloem cells between the arms of the star. This distinctive pattern of xylem and phloem is typical of dicot roots. In Figure 4, label the xylem, phloem, cortex, epidermis, and root hair.

15. Examine the corn (*Zea*) root cross section under the low power of the microscope. Corn is a monocot.

16. Notice that groups of xylem cells are scattered within the central area of the root. Move the microscope slide around until you find the phloem cells, which are also scattered in bunches through the central area of the root.

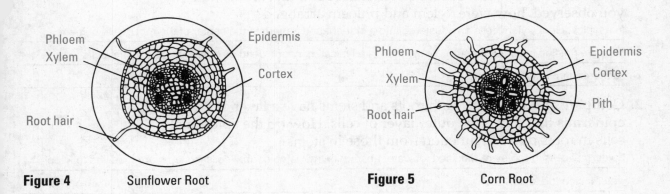

Figure 4   Sunflower Root   **Figure 5**   Corn Root

17. Notice that the cortex and epidermis are similar in both the sunflower root and the corn root. In Figure 5, label the xylem, phloem, cortex, epidermis, and root hair in the corn root.

Part B. Internal Structures of Stems

1. Observe the prepared slide of a cross section of a sunflower (*Helianthus*) stem under low power of the microscope. The sunflower has a herbaceous, or nonwoody, stem. Notice that the vascular bundles are arranged in a ring within the stem. Switch to the high-power objective and focus on a single vascular bundle. Observe the thick-walled xylem cells. Notice the smaller, thinner-walled phloem cells within the bundle.

2. Switch back to the low-power objective and observe the arrangement of cells within the stem cross section. The pith is the large area within the ring of vascular bundles. Surrounding the ring is the cortex. The outermost layers are epidermis. In Figure 6, label the vascular bundle, xylem, phloem, pith, cortex, and epidermis.

3. Observe the prepared slide of a cross section of a corn *(Zea)* stem under the low-power objective of the microscope. Note the general arrangement of the cell and the position of the xylem and phloem.

4. Examine the epidermis, cortex, and pith in the corn stem cross section. In Figure 7, label the vascular bundle, xylem, phloem, epidermis, cortex, and pith.

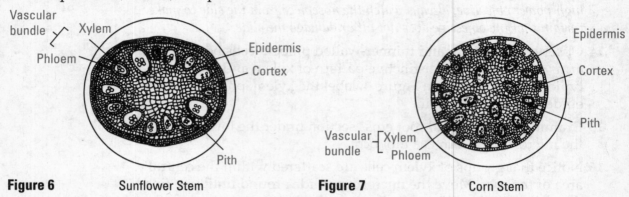

Figure 6   Sunflower Stem   **Figure 7**   Corn Stem

Analysis and Conclusions

1. **Observing** In the cross sections of monocot and dicot roots that you observed, how were xylem and phloem arranged?

In a typical dicot, xylem cells are clustered into a star-shaped pattern in the center of the root, while phloem

cells are nestled between the arms of the star. In a typical monocot, bundles of phloem and xylem cells are

scattered throughout the pith.

2. **Compare and Contrast** Both roots and stems have a layer of epidermis that forms the outer layer of cells. How do the epidermal cells in roots differ in function from those in stems?

Epidermal cells in roots are modified for water absorption, while epidermal cells in stems are modified to keep

water inside the stem.

3. **Inferring** Which kind of root system would more likely benefit a desert plant—a taproot or a fibrous root system? Explain your answer.

Because a fibrous root system has more surface area compared to its volume than a taproot, a fibrous root

system can better absorb water—a help to a plant in a dry soil.

Going Further

To observe how materials are transported up through a stem, cut the stem of a white carnation in half lengthwise. Measure out 50 mL of water into each of two beakers. Add 5 drops of red food coloring to one beaker and 5 drops of blue food coloring to the other beaker. Place the beakers side by side and carefully place one half of the carnation stem in each beaker. Allow the beakers to remain undisturbed for 24 hours. After 24 hours, observe the color of the carnation flower.

Half of the carnation should turn red and the other half should turn blue.

Investigating Germination and Seedling Development

You may want to refer students to Section 24–2 in the textbook for a discussion of seed formation, dormancy, and development.
Time required: Day 1: 20 minutes; Days 2 and 3: 35 minutes

Introduction

When conditions are suitable, a seed undergoes germination, or the development of an embryo into a seedling. For germination to occur, water, warmth, and oxygen must be available in the proper amounts. The amounts vary from species to species.

Germination can occur only in viable seeds, or seeds in which the embryo is alive. Not all viable seeds will germinate, even when given the proper amounts of water, warmth, and oxygen. Many seeds must go through a period of dormancy, during which the embryo is alive but not growing. Dormancy is an adaptation that prevents germination of the seed until conditions are suitable.

In this investigation, you will observe some of the processes associated with seed germination and seedling development.

Problem

What changes occur in a seed during germination and seedling development?

Pre-Lab Discussion

Read the entire investigation. Then, work with a partner to answer the following questions.

1. What are the major environmental requirements for the germination of seeds?
   Moisture, oxygen, and some warmth are required._____

   _____

2. Is a control needed for this study?
   No, this study is intended to allow us to observe seed germination under normal conditions._____

   _____

3. What is the advantage of using the *Brassica rapa* seeds for the study?
   Brassica rapa is a fast growing plant that should sprout quickly._____

   _____

4. What parts of a new seedling are the hypocotyl, epicotyl, and primary root?
   The hypocotyl is the lower portion of the stem below the attachment of the seedling to the cotyledons. The

   primary root is the radicle, or first root, adjacent to and below the hypocotyl. The epicotyl is the portion of the

   stem above the cotyledon attachment and is nearest the developing leaves._____

   _____

5. Why are no nutrients added to the water used to sprout the seeds?

The seeds contain all the nutrients necessary for germination. They were stored in the seed by the

parent plant during seed development.

Materials *(per pair)*

10 *Brassica rapa* seeds *Brassica rapa* is a fast-growing variant of wild mustard.

petri dish

forceps

hand lens

filter paper Filter paper circle should fit snugly into the petri dish.

fluorescent plant lamp (if available)

base of a 2-L soft-drink bottle The base of the plastic soft-drink bottle can be removed by filling the bottle with hot tap water and twisting off the base. The holes in the base should be covered with black electrical tape.

metric ruler

colored pencils

Safety 🖐️ 🧤 🔥

Handle all glassware carefully. Do not eat any materials such as the seeds provided by your teacher or the seedlings produced. Note all safety alert symbols next to the steps in the Procedure and review the meanings of each symbol by referring to Safety Symbols on page 8.

Procedure

1. As shown in Figure 1, use a metric ruler and pencil to draw a line across the filter paper about 3 cm from the top edge. Label the bottom edge of the filter paper with the seed type, date, and name of one member of your group. **Note:** *Be sure to use pencil to label the filter paper because ink will smear when water is added.*

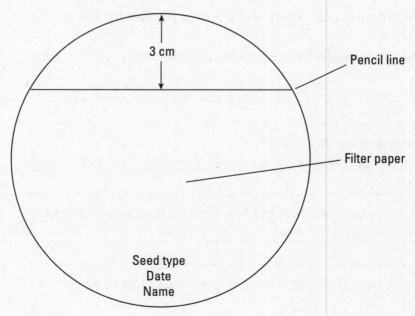

3 cm

Pencil line

Filter paper

Seed type
Date
Name

Figure 1

🖐️ 2. Place the filter paper in the top of a petri dish. Thoroughly wet the filter paper.

🧤 3. Use forceps to place 10 *Brassica rapa* seeds on the line you drew on the filter paper. Space the seeds out evenly across the line as shown in Figure 2.

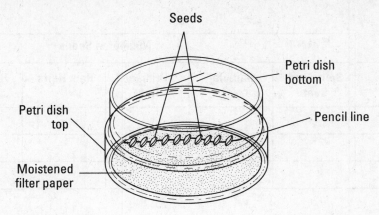

Figure 2

4. Cover the seeds by inserting the smaller bottom half of the petri dish into the top.

5. Carefully place the petri dish in the base of the 2-liter soft-drink bottle so that the seeds are at the top and the petri dish is tilted slightly. See Figure 3. Make sure that none of the seeds have fallen from their original positions. Slowly add water to the soft-drink bottle base from the side until the water reaches a depth of 2 cm.

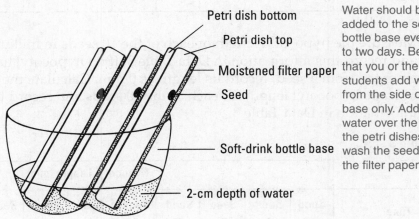

Water should be added to the soft-drink bottle base every one to two days. Be sure that you or the students add water from the side of the base only. Adding water over the tops of the petri dishes will wash the seeds from the filter paper.

Figure 3

6. Place the soft-drink-bottle base under a fluorescent plant lamp. If a fluorescent lamp is not available, place the base near the best source of light in the room.

7. After 24 hours, observe the germination of the seeds. If necessary, use the hand lens to observe the germinating seeds. Note the number of seeds that have a split seed coat, an emerging radicle, hypocotyl, or epicotyl, or the appearance of a primary root and root hairs. Record the information in Data Table 1 on p. 186.

A hand lens may be helpful in making these measurements.

8. Measure the primary root length of each of the 10 seeds in millimeters and record this information in Data Table 2 on p. 186. If no primary root has emerged from a seed, record its length as 0 mm. Calculate the average root length for each of the 10 seeds and record this information in Data Table 2.

Data Table 1

Time	Number of Seeds					
	Split Seed Coat	Radicle	Primary Root	Root Hairs	Hypocotyl	Epicotyl
After 24 hours						
After 48 hours						
After 72 hours						

Data Table 2

Time	Root Length (mm)										
	Seed 1	Seed 2	Seed 3	Seed 4	Seed 5	Seed 6	Seed 7	Seed 8	Seed 9	Seed 10	Average
After 24 hours											
After 48 hours											
After 72 hours											

9. Measure the hypocotyl length of each of the 10 seeds in millimeters and record this information in Data Table 3. If no hypocotyl has emerged from a seed, record its length as 0 mm. Calculate the average hypocotyl length for each of the 10 seeds and record this information in Data Table 3.

Data Table 3

Time	Hypocotyl Length (mm)										
	Seed 1	Seed 2	Seed 3	Seed 4	Seed 5	Seed 6	Seed 7	Seed 8	Seed 9	Seed 10	Average
After 24 hours											
After 48 hours											
After 72 hours											

10. Repeat steps 8 and 9 after two more 24-hour periods. Record the information in Data Tables 1, 2, and 3.

11. On the graph on page 187, construct a line graph showing the average root length over the 72-hour observation period. On the same graph, construct a line graph showing the average hypocotyl length over the 72-hour observation period. Use pencils of different colors to construct the two line graphs. Label each line graph.

12. In the box labeled 72-hour-old *Brassica* seedling below, sketch one of your 72-hour-old seedlings. Label the hypocotyl, primary root, root hairs, cotyledons, and true leaves.

13. Calculate the growth rate of the root over the three days by dividing the average length by the period of time. For example 30 mm/3 days = 10 mm/day

14. Calculate the growth rate of the hypocotyl using the same method as above.

72-hour-old *Brassica* Seedling

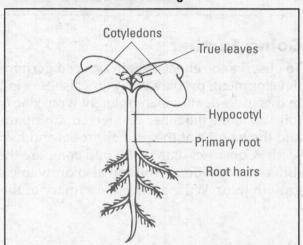

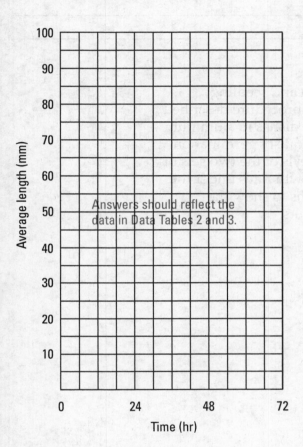

Answers should reflect the data in Data Tables 2 and 3.

Average length (mm) / Time (hr)

Analysis and Conclusions

1. Observing What is the first structure to emerge from inside the seed?

The radicle is the first structure to emerge from inside the seed.

2. Inferring What is the function of this structure?

The root anchors the plant to the soil and absorbs water and mineral nutrients needed for the growth

of the seedling.

3. Formulating Hypotheses Why is it important for the dry seed to take in water before it begins to germinate?

The seed absorbs water and swells. The increase in volume helps to weaken the seed coat. The water

also causes the growth of the radicle inside of the seed coat, causing the seed to break open.

4. Drawing Conclusions How does a seedling benefit from having its radicle emerge before its leaves?

Early growth of the radicle enables the seedling to absorb water needed for growth of the leaves and other parts.

5. Inferring As the seedling grows, what part turns green and photosynthesizes?

The cotyledons and the leaves turn green and photosynthesize.

Going Further

To observe the effect of light on seed germination and seedling development, prepare two petri dishes using the procedure described in this investigation. Completely wrap one of the dishes in aluminum foil and leave the other uncovered. Compare the rate of germination and the lengths of the primary roots and hypocotyls of the two sets of seeds. Construct data tables and compare the growth rates under the different conditions. You can also draw line graphs to show the growth rates. Write a simple summary of the results.

Investigating Germination Inhibitors

You may want to refer students to Section 32–3 in the textbook for a discussion of plant growth and development.
Time required: 40 minutes; brief observation period on each of 8 following days

Introduction

Tomato seeds will usually germinate when exposed to the proper amounts of moisture and oxygen and a fairly warm temperature. Yet inside the tomato, where these conditions are also met, tomato seeds do not germinate. Why? Plants contain certain hormones that control their metabolism and growth processes.

In this investigation, you will first observe the effect of a hormone that is a germination inhibitor on seeds. You will then design and conduct an experiment to investigate the effect of a germination inhibitor from one variety of tomatoes on a second variety of tomatoes.

Problem

What are the effects of a germination inhibitor on seeds? What effect does a germination inhibitor from one variety of plant have on seeds of a different variety of the same species?

Pre-Lab Discussion

Read through the entire investigation. Then, work with a partner to answer the following questions.

1. Identify the manipulated and responding variables in Part A of this lab.

   The manipulated variable will be presence of germination inhibitor (addition of tomato extract) and the

   responding variable will be germination of seeds.

2. What is the purpose of petri dish 1 in the first experiment? Should a similar petri dish be set up when you design your experiment? Explain.

   Petri dish 1 is the control; it is moistened with water only and will be compared with petri dish 2 that

   has tomato extract. Yes, a control (petri dish with no tomato extract) should be used in student designs. The

   number of seeds that germinate without the inhibitor will be compared to the number that germinate in the

   presence of the inhibitor.

3. Explain how you can determine whether or not a seed has germinated.

   Germination is the early growth of a new plant from a seed, usually the root. Once the root emerges,

   the plant has germinated.

4. Would it be possible to use a similar experiment to investigate the effect of a germination inhibitor from one variety of tomatoes on a second variety of tomatoes? How?

   The same procedure as in the first experiment could be used. Water should be added to one petri dish to

   serve as the control, and extract from the first variety of tomatoes should be prepared, as in the first experiment,

   and added to a second petri dish. The number of seeds that germinate in each dish over an 8-day period should

   be counted as before.

5. Discuss the possible outcomes of such an experiment (as discussed in Question 4) and explain the meaning of each.

If more seeds germinate in the control dish than in the other, then the extract from a second variety of

tomatoes inhibited germination of the first variety. If there is little difference in the number of seeds that

germinate, then the extract from a second variety of tomatoes did not inhibit germination of the first variety.

If fewer seeds germinate in the control dish than in the other, then the extract from a second variety of

tomatoes has a stimulatory effect on the first variety.

Suggested Materials *(per group)*

tomatoes (2 different varieties)
filter paper
strainer
mortar and pestle (or bowl and spoon)
funnel

250-mL beaker
4 petri dishes
2 dropper pipettes
plastic wrap
glass-marking pencil

Safety 🔲 🔲 ⚠️ 🔲

Put on a laboratory apron and plastic gloves. Be careful to avoid breakage when working with glassware. Never touch or taste any chemical unless instructed to do so. Note all safety alert symbols next to the steps in Design Your Experiment and review the meanings of each symbol by referring to Safety Symbols on page 8.

Design Your Experiment

Part A. Observing the Effects of a Germination Inhibitor

🔲 🔲 **1.** Put on your laboratory apron and plastic gloves. With the glass-marking pencil, label two petri dishes 1 and 2.

🔲 **2.** Using a mortar and pestle, crush one whole tomato (Variety A). Strain the crushed tomato and use the funnel to collect the extract in the beaker. With a glass-marking pencil, label the beaker "Extract A" and set it aside for now.

3. From the tomato pulp, remove 20 seeds and wash them.

4. Line petri dishes 1 and 2 with filter paper. Place 10 seeds in each dish.

5. Use separate dropper pipettes to moisten petri dish 1 with water and petri dish 2 with the tomato extract. Cover the petri dishes with plastic wrap. Observe the seeds for several days, adding more water or tomato extract as needed to keep the filter paper moist.

6. Record the total number of seeds that germinate daily in each petri dish in the appropriate place in the Data Table.

Data Table

Germination of Tomato Seeds								
Petri Dish	**Day 1**	**Day 2**	**Day 3**	**Day 4**	**Day 5**	**Day 6**	**Day 7**	**Day 8**
1 (Variety A with water)								
2 (Variety A with tomato extract)	More germinated seeds are expected in petri dish 1.							

Part B. Your Own Experiment Plan an experiment to investigate the effect of a germination inhibitor from one variety of tomatoes on the germination of seeds of a second variety of tomatoes.

1. Write your hypothesis, identify the variables, and write out the procedure in the spaces below. Be sure to include a control in your experimental plan. Prepare a data table to record your data on a separate sheet of paper.

It is vital that before students conduct their self-designed experiments, the procedure be carefully examined and approved by the teacher. Point out any safety issues to the students.

Hypothesis:

Acceptable hypotheses: Extract (containing germination inhibitor) from one variety of tomatoes will inhibit germination of the seeds from a second type of tomato. Extract (containing germination inhibitor) from one variety of tomatoes will not inhibit germination of the seeds from a second type of tomato. Extract (containing germination inhibitor) from one variety of tomatoes will have no effect on germination of the seeds from a second type of tomato.

Manipulated variables:

Addition of tomato extract to filter paper on petri dish.

Responding variables:

Germination of seeds.

Controlled variables:

Time, moistness of filter paper, seeds, temperature, etc.

Procedure:

Student designs should be similar to that described in previous experiment. Also see the answer to Question 4 in Pre-Lab Discussion.

_____

_____

_____

_____

_____

2. Submit your written experimental design to your teacher for approval. Once your design has been approved, carry out your experiment and record your data.

3. When you have finished your experiment, present the results of both experiments on the graph provided.

Data table should look similar to the one in the first experiment. You may choose to create a class data table so that the class data can be analyzed. Instruct students to plot four separate curves and to provide a legend on their graphs.

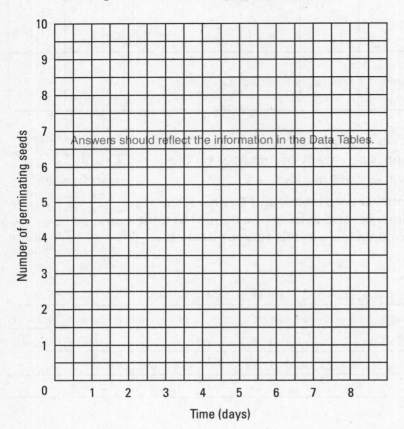

Answers should reflect the information in the Data Tables.

Number of germinating seeds (y-axis, 0–10)

Time (days) (x-axis, 0–8)

Analysis and Conclusions

1. Analyzing Data What were the results of Part A? How can you explain what occurred?

Answers will depend on student data. Very few or no seeds should germinate in the tomato extract, while

many should germinate in the water. The extract inhibits germination.

2. Evaluating and Revising Did the results of Part B support your hypothesis?

Answers will depend on student designs, hypothesis, and results. About the same number of seeds should

germinate in each of the two petri dishes indicating that the germination of seeds of one variety of tomato is

not inhibited by the extract of another tomato variety.

3. **Drawing Conclusions** What conclusions can be drawn from the data collected in both experiments?

Tomato extracts prevent germination of seeds, indicating that tomatoes contain germination inhibitors.

Answers may vary depending on varieties used. Extracts from one variety of tomatoes usually do not inhibit

the germination of seeds of a second variety, indicating that inhibitors are specific to (or "work" only in) the

variety from which they were collected.

4. **Formulating Hypotheses** Based upon your observations, what function might germination inhibitors have?

Preventing the germination of seeds until the time and conditions are likely to favor survival of seedlings.

5. **Inferring** The seeds of a particular type of desert plant contain a water-soluble germination inhibitor. Only heavy rainfall causes the plant to germinate. Explain why this plant is well adapted to life in the desert.

Light rain does not remove enough inhibitor to allow germination. The plant will only germinate after heavy

rain leaches out enough inhibitor, thus ensuring wet enough conditions for the seedling to survive.

Going Further

What question(s) did the results of your experiment raise? Design an experiment that would address one of your questions or one that would logically follow this experiment.

Comparing Sponges and Hydras

You may want to refer students to Sections 26–2 and 26–3 in the textbook for a discussion of sponges and cnidarians.
Time required: 45 minutes

Introduction

Sponges and cnidarians are simple invertebrates. Sponges make up the phylum Porifera, which means "pore-bearing." The phylum is named for the many pores that cover the body of a sponge. Cnidarians are members of the phylum Cnidaria. Hydras, jellyfishes, and sea corals are types of cnidarians.

Sponges have no true tissues or organs, no digestive tract, and no nervous system. Their bodies are loosely organized into two cell layers. Support comes from hard structures called spicules or from flexible material called spongin. Some sponges have both spicules and spongin.

Cnidarians have true tissues. Their bodies consist of two layers—an outer epidermis and an inner gastrodermis. Each cnidarian also has a body cavity in which food is digested. Cnidarians have a simple nerve net that allows them to respond to stimuli.

In this investigation, you will examine the characteristics of sponges and cnidarians.

Problem

What are some characteristics of a sponge and a hydra?

Pre-Lab Discussion

Read the entire investigation. Then, work with a partner to answer the following questions.

1. Sponges are filter feeders that consume microscopic particles of food. Since sponges do not have mouths, what body structures would you expect to find that enable them to feed?

   Some type of body openings or pores so that water and food can pass into the sponge.
   _____

2. Why were sponges once thought to be plants? How will you be able to use the results of this investigation to prove to someone that sponges are *not* plants?

   Sponges, like plants, are immobile. Microscopic examination should show that the cells of the sponges, unlike the

   cells of plants, have no cell walls. Also, none of the cells will have chloroplasts.
   _____

3. In Part A, why will you examine a longitudinal section as well as a whole sponge?

   By looking at a longitudinal section of sponge, you can see the internal structure of the sponge and the structure

   of its cells.
   _____

4. How are the habitats of sponges and hydras similar? Would this lead you to expect similar body structures? Explain your answer.

Both sponges and hydras live in water. Since a wide variety of animals live in water, this common habitat does not

necessarily imply similar body structures.

5. Like most cnidarians, hydras use stinging structures to capture small animals. Where would you expect to find these stinging structures?

The stinging structures should be on the tentacles.

Materials *(per group)*

preserved whole specimen of *Grantia*   Preserved specimens are available form biological supply houses.

prepared slide of *Grantia*, longitudinal section

hand lens

microscope

scalpel or single-edged razor blade

microscope slide

coverslip

chlorine bleach solution

toothpick

2 dropper pipettes

prepared slide of hydra, whole mount   Slides are available from biological supply houses.

prepared slide of hydra, longitudinal section

Safety ⬛🏠👓✂️🧪🧤🔥🗑️🔧

Put on a laboratory apron, safety goggles, and plastic gloves. Always use special caution when working with laboratory chemicals, as they may irritate the skin or cause staining of the skin or clothing. Never touch or taste any chemical unless instructed to do so. Always handle the microscope with extreme care. You are responsible for its proper care and use. Observe proper laboratoy procedures when using electrical equipment. Use caution when handling microscope slides, as they can break easily and cut you. Be careful when handling sharp instruments. Wash your hands with soap and warm water after carrying out this lab. Follow your teacher's instructions for disposing of materials. Note all safety symbols next to the steps in the Procedure and review the meanings of each symbol by referring to Safety Symbols on page 8.

Name_____ Class_____ Date _____

Procedure

Part A. Examining the Anatomy of a Sponge

1. With a hand lens, examine the external structure of the simple marine sponge *Grantia*. Find the osculum, which is a large opening at the top through which water flows out of the sponge. Locate several ostia (singular, ostium), or pores. Water flows into the sponge through the ostia. Note the long, straight spicules that encircle the osculum and project through the outer surface of the sponge. In the box labeled *Grantia*, sketch what you see. Label the osculum, ostia, and spicules.

2. Under the low-power objective of a microscope, examine a prepared slide of a longitudinal section of *Grantia*. **CAUTION:** *Use proper laboratory procedures when handling electrical equipment.* Note the two cell layers. The outer cell layer is called the ectoderm and the inner cell layer is called the endoderm. Look for the flagellated cells called choanocytes in the endoderm. Choanocytes collect food particles from the water that passes through the sponge's body cavity, or spongocoel. Between the ectoderm and the endoderm is mesenchyme, or a jellylike material containing some cells. Observe the spicules. In the circle labeled *Grantia*, Longitudinal Section, sketch what you observe. Label the ectoderm, mesenchyme, choanocyte, flagellum, spicules, and spongocoel. Record the magnification of the microscope.

Grantia

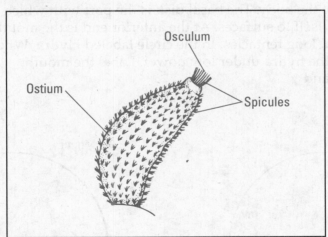

3. Using a scalpel or a single-edged razor blade, cut a small piece from the *Grantia* specimen. **CAUTION:** *Be very careful when handling sharp instruments. Always cut in a direction away from your hands and body.*

4. Put on safety goggles and plastic gloves. Place the piece of *Grantia* on a microscope slide. With a dropper pipette, add two drops of chlorine bleach solution to the piece of sponge. **CAUTION:** *Be very careful when using chlorine bleach. It may burn your skin or clothing.* Using a toothpick, gently stir the sponge and chlorine bleach solution.

5. Using another dropper pipette, add a drop of water to the slide. Then cover with a coverslip. Observe the *Grantia* spicules under the low-power objective of the microscope. In the circle labeled *Grantia* Spicules, sketch several spicules. Record the magnification of the microscope. Wash your hands thoroughly when you have finished.

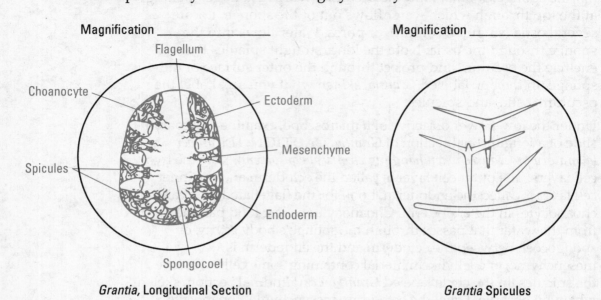

Magnification _____   Magnification _____

Grantia, Longitudinal Section   *Grantia* Spicules

Part B. Examining the Anatomy of a Hydra

1. Under the low-power objective of the microscope, examine a prepared, whole mount slide of a hydra. Locate the basal disk at the posterior end of the body. The basal disk is the part with which the hydra attaches itself to surfaces. At the anterior end is the mouth. Look for several long tentacles. In the circle labeled Hydra, Whole Mount, sketch the hydra under low power. Label the mouth, tentacle, body, and basal disk.

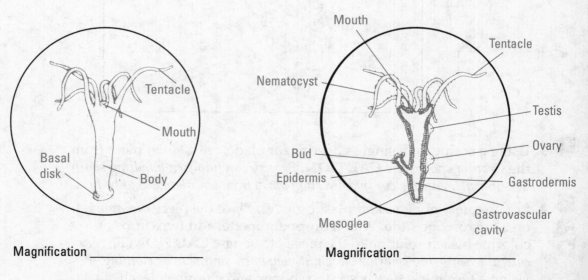

Magnification _____   Magnification _____

Hydra, Whole Mount   Hydra, Longitudinal Section

2. Under the low-power objective of the microscope, examine a prepared slide of a longitudinal section of a hydra. Locate the three layers: the outer epidermis, the inner gastrodermis, and the mesoglea, or thin layer of jellylike material between the epidermis and gastrodermis. Note the body cavity called the gastrovascular cavity.

3. Locate one of the hydra's tentacles. Notice the small bumps on the tentacle. They contain stinging structures called nematocysts.

4. Most species of hydra have separate male and female animals. However, in some species, individuals contain both male and female reproductive structures. Look for the testes, or cone-shaped structures found on the upper half of the body, and the ovary, found on the lower half of the body. Examine the hydra to see if it has testes or an ovary (or both). In the circle labeled Hydra, Longitudinal Section, sketch the hydra under low power. Label the mouth, tentacle, nematocyst, testis (if present), ovary (if present), bud (if present), epidermis, mesoglea, gastrodermis, and gastrovascular cavity.

Analysis and Conclusions

1. **Inferring** What is the function of the spicules of a sponge?
   They provide support for soft body tissue.

2. **Drawing Conclusions** What body structures make the sponge well adapted for living in water?
   The sponge has pores, an osculum, spicules for support, and flagella for creating water currents that bring needed materials into the sponge and carry wastes away.

3. **Inferring** What is the function of the gastrovascular cavity of a hydra?
   The gastrovascular cavity aids in the circulation of materials and the digestion of food.

4. **Comparing and Contrasting** Compare the sponge and the hydra in terms of body symmetry and tissue structure.
   The hydra has radial symmetry; the sponge is asymmetrical. The sponge does not have true tissues, whereas the hydra does.

5. **Comparing and Contrasting** How do sponges differ from flagellate protists?
   Protists are unicellular and many are motile. Their flagella appear on the exterior surfaces of their bodies.
   Sponges are multicellular and sessile, and their flagella are on the interior surfaces of their bodies.

6. **Inferring** Why do you think a *Grantia* sponge should not be used to wash cars or porcelain sinks?

The glasslike spicules in *Grantia* could easily scratch the paint on the car or the porcelain. Commercial

sponges contain spongin or are synthetic.

7. **Classifying** "Cnid" is the Greek word for nettle, or stinging hair. Is the phylum name Cnidaria appropriate to the group of organisms such as hydras and jellyfishes? Explain your answer.

The cnidocytes on the tentacles of hydras and jellyfishes are capable of stinging, making the phylum

name Cnidaria, to which these organisms belong, quite appropriate.

Going Further

To examine the feeding habits of the hydra, place several drops of hydra culture that has remained unfed for 24 hours in a watch glass. Add a drop of *Daphnia* culture to the watch glass. Place the watch glass under a dissecting microscope for observation. Describe what you see.

Observing the Structure of a Squid

You may want to refer students to Section 27–4 in the textbook for a discussion of mollusks.

To familiarize yourself with squid anatomy, you might do the dissection in advance.

Time required: 80 minutes

Introduction

You are probably familiar with clams, snails, slugs, squids, and octupuses, and you probably have noticed how very different they are. Nevertheless, all these are classified in the phylum Mollusca. You will be examining one type of mollusk—a squid. Squids have some characteristics in common with other mollusks, but they also have special features that make them unique. Squids are classified in the class Cephalopoda. In this investigation, you will be examining a squid to find out why squids are classified as mollusks. You will also determine what special adaptations make them different from other mollusks.

Problem

What evidence is there that squids are mollusks? What adaptations make them different from other mollusks?

Pre-Lab Discussion

Read through the entire investigation. Then, work with a partner to answer the following questions.

1. To what kingdom do mollusks belong?

   The animal kingdom.

2. Describe the characteristics that organisms classified in the phylum Mollusca share.

   Mollusks have a foot, a mantle, a radula, and a visceral mass. Most also have a shell.

3. Name some organisms that belong to the phylum Mollusca.

   Responses might include: clams, snails, slugs, squids, and octupuses.

4. Explain the characteristics that squids possess that lead to their classification as cephalopods.

   A cephalopod has its foot concentrated in the head region, tentacles with suction cups, a more advanced

   nervous system than other mollusks, a closed circulatory system, separate sexes, and an ink sac.

5. What other organisms belong to the cephalopod class and why?

   Octupuses, cuttlefishes, and chambered nautiluses. In these organisms, the foot is concentrated in the

   head region. All are free-swimming predators with tentacles extending from the head.

Materials *(per pair)*

squid
dissecting tray
dissecting pins
compound microscope
microscope slide
coverslip
dropper pipette

metric ruler
dissecting probe
scissors
hand lens
forceps
unlined white paper

A box of frozen squid can be obtained in many supermarkets. Keep frozen until the afternoon before students perform the investigation, and then rinse frozen specimens under cool water to thaw and separate them.

Safety 🥽👕🧤✋🔥🧪♨️🗑️

Put on a laboratory apron, safety goggles, and plastic gloves. Always handle the microscope with extreme care. You are responsible for its proper care and use. Use caution when handling microscope slides, as they can break easily and cut you. Observe proper laboratory procedures when using electrical equipment. Be careful when handling sharp instruments. Dispose of the squid specimen as instructed by your teacher. Wash your hands thoroughly when you are finished working with the materials. Note all safety symbols in the Procedure and review the meanings of each symbol by referring to Safety Symbols on page 8.

For a shorter laboratory period, omit the microscope section and the sketch of the eye.

Procedure

1. Put on a laboratory apron, plastic gloves and safety goggles. Obtain a squid specimen in a dissecting tray. Count the number of short arms and longer tentacles. Using a hand lens, examine the suckers on the arms.

A squid has eight arms and two long tentacles.

2. Study the two long, grasping tentacles and the sleek body with its pairs of fins and eyes. Place your squid on its dorsal surface. Locate the mantle, a loose edge of tissue near the eyes, and identify the siphon, noting it can be moved in any direction. In the space provided on page 203, make a careful sketch of the specimen, labeling the mantle, lateral fin, siphon, eye, tentacles, arms, and suckers.

3. Using the metric ruler, measure the length and width of your specimen in centimeters and record these measurements with your sketch.

Length of Squid _____

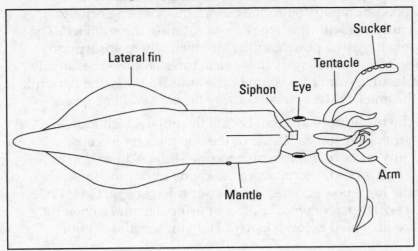

External Anatomy of a Squid

4. With forceps, lift the free end of the mantle just above the siphon, and using scissors, cut through the mantle in a straight line to the pointed end of the body. **CAUTION:** *Be careful when handling sharp instruments. Always cut in a direction away from your hands and body.* Spread the mantle, as shown in the illustration below, and with dissecting pins, secure it to the tray. As you examine the squid, refer to the illustration below to locate the internal organs. Trace the siphon backward, using a dissecting probe to move aside the muscles that are attached to and control the siphon. Wastes, ink, and gametes are carried out of the squid by a current of water that leaves through the muscular siphon.

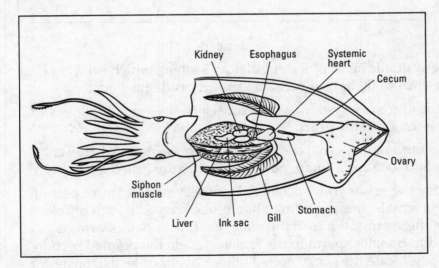

5. Examine the digestive system. Using scissors, start cutting at the neck and continue cutting through the head to a point midway between but just past the eyes, where you will reach a rough, muscular organ that surrounds the jaws. Push a probe between the jaws to locate the mouth.

6. Find the esophagus, a narrow tube below the jaws. Trace it to the stomach. Food moves through the esophagus, passing briefly through a junction with the liver before entering the stomach. The cecum is an elongated pouch off the stomach where absorption occurs. See if you can identify these structures. Follow the narrow tube, or intestine, from the cecum to the anus. Identify the dark ink sac near the anus. **Note:** *Do not puncture the ink sac at this time.*

7. Examine the respiratory system. Locate the gills, which look like curved feathers, one on each side of the body. Using forceps, transfer a tiny piece of gill to a microscope slide. Add a drop of water and a coverslip, and observe the tissue under the low-power and then the high-power objective of your microscope. **CAUTION:** *Observe proper laboratory procedures when using electrical equipment.* In the space provided below, sketch what you see under high power.

Squid Gill

8. Find the systemic heart of the circulatory system, which is located near the ends of the gills where they attach inside the body.

9. Locate the excretory system, which consists of two small kidneys that are anterior to the heart.

10. To locate the small internal shell, cut through the mantle between the eyes and look for a small, plasticlike structure called a pen.

11. Determine the sex of your specimen by observing the fourth pair of arms. In a female, there is a small horseshoe-shaped pouch or fold between these arms, while in the male, the fourth pair of arms is modified to transfer sperm to the female. Inside the pointed section of the body, locate the sticky gonad (either ovary or testis), posterior to the kidneys. Observe the specimen of another lab group so you have a chance to examine squids of both sexes. Identify the sex of your specimen and record your observations.

12. Squids have an excellent nervous system, which includes one pair of eyes. Using a hand lens, study one eye, noting the covering, or cornea. Record your observations.

13. Before completing the dissection, carefully puncture the ink sac with a dissecting probe and use the ink and the probe to write your name on an unlined piece of paper. Record your observations.

14. Discard your specimen as instructed by your teacher. Wash your hands thoroughly when you are finished with the materials.

At the end of the investigation, have students discard dissected parts of squid into a plastic bag and wash out dissecting trays with soapy water to remove fish smell.

Analysis and Conclusions

1. **Analyzing Data** Based upon your examination of the squid, what features explain its classification as a mollusk?

Presence of a foot (soft, muscular structure that contains the mouth and other feeding organs), visceral mass, and mantle. Students should provide descriptions of these features.

2. **Analyzing Data** What features did you observe that are unusual for a mollusk? What function does each serve?

The squid is unusual in that it does not have an external shell, the head is a modified foot, the foot contains arms and tentacles that enable it to capture prey, and it has an ink sac that releases ink to help it escape from predators.

3. **Drawing Conclusions** Often in biological systems, structure is said to be related to function. Describe the structure of the gills and explain how they are specialized for their function.

The gills are feathery in appearance. The large amount of surface area speeds up gas exchange (taking up oxygen and releasing carbon dioxide) that occurs there.

4. **Drawing Conclusions** Based upon your observations, what structures of a squid are specialized for movement?

Students may discuss its streamlined body design, which produces little resistance in moving through water; the absence of an external shell, making the squid lighter; and the muscular mantle, which pumps jets of water through an excurrent siphon.

5. Inferring How do the external and internal anatomy of a squid reflect its life as a predator?

Students may discuss the arms, circle of tentacles with suckers, jaws, advanced nervous system, and eyes.

6. Evaluating What part of this investigation did you find most challenging? Explain.

Students' responses will vary. Students may have difficulty locating specific organs. Students may also note that it is difficult to cut the squid without damaging internal organs.

Going Further

Examine the internal organs of a clam. See how many you can identify. Refer to the diagram in Section 27–4 of your textbook.

Obtain clams from a supermarket or seafood store. Ask a salesperson to open the clams for you. Refrigerate the clams and have students perform the dissection within 24 hours.

Investigating Insect Metamorphosis

Introduction

As insects develop from eggs to adults, they pass through complete or incomplete metamorphosis. Butterflies and beetles are examples of insects that have an active larval stage that does not resemble the adult insect. The mealworm beetle undergoes complete metamorphosis, as shown in Figure 1. The larvae (mealworms) and adult beetles eat different things. And like other insects, they do not maintain a constant internal body temperature. Instead, their body temperature usually depends on the temperature of their surroundings. As the seasons change, the foods available and the surrounding temperatures also change. It may be that the mealworm life cycle is controlled by the temperature and the food that is available during the year. In this investigation, you will design an experiment to determine how temperature affects the development of mealworms.

You may want to refer students to Sections 28–1 and 28–3 in the textbook for a discussion of arthropods and insect growth and development, including metamorphosis. Time required: Three 50 minute sessions for parts 1, 2 and 3. Then 15 minute observations, every other day for about 10–14 days

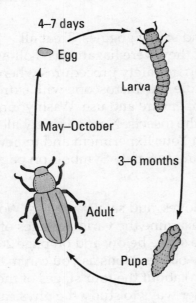

4–7 days

Egg

Larva

May–October

3–6 months

Adult

Pupa

Mealworm Life Cycle

Figure 1

Additional information on mealworms may be helpful. They are members of the genus *Tenebrio* and are called darkling beetles. They are considered pests of stored grain.

They can be found under bark, in rotten wood, or under logs, and they feed on decaying vegetation and seeds. Some feed on the roots and fruits in orchards.

Pre-Lab Discussion

Read the entire investigation. Then, work with a partner to answer the following questions.

1. What characteristic of mealworms makes it likely that temperature affects their rate of development?

Mealworms are ectothermic animals whose temperature varies with their environment.

_____

_____

2. What are some distinguishing anatomical characteristics of insects?

They have an exoskeleton that is divided into three parts: head, thorax, and abdomen. The head has the

eyes, antennae, and mouth parts. Three pairs of jointed appendages and wings are attached to the thorax.

3. At what time of year do the adult beetles usually appear?

They hatch from the pupae in the spring.

4. How do the adult beetles differ from the larvae?

The adults have wings and heavier body parts. Their legs are longer and sturdier.

Suggested Materials (per group)

A refrigerator and incubator (something as simple as a box with utility lamp can be used) are needed for step 3.

hand lens

mealworms in egg, larva, pupa, and adult stages

These can be purchased at a local pet store or from a biological supply company.

oatmeal

pieces of fresh apple or potato

plastic containers with loose-fitting lids for ventilation

small plastic cups for moving and observing animals

Quart-size containers are useful for classroom cultures. Student experiments could be done in pint-size containers.

Safety 🖐️🧤🥽🔬🐾✋⚠️

Wear a lab apron, plastic gloves, and safety goggles. Treat all containers of living organisms as if they were hazardous. Follow your teacher's directions and all appropriate safety procedures when handling live animals. Always handle the microscope with extreme care. You are responsible for its proper care and use. Wash your hands at the end of the lab if you handle the insects. Note all safety alert symbols next to the steps in Design Your Experiment and review the meanings of each symbol by referring to Safety Symbols on page 8.

Design Your Experiment

🖐️🧤🥽🔬🐾✋ **1.** Put on a lab apron, plastic gloves, and safety goggles. Working in teams, use the hand lens to examine the various stages of the mealworm life cycle. Use the space below and on page 209 to make drawings and to list as many observations as you can make (shape, senses, movement, and so on) about the four stages of the mealworm life cycle. Consider ways to study the physical and behavioral capacities of the larvae and adults. Use additional sheets of paper if necessary.

Be sure that students understand the implications of the variable body temperature of insects. Ask students to think about the consequences of being coldblooded.

Point out that newly formed pupae appear white but become yellowish brown as they develop.

Drawings of Mealworms in Different Stages

Check student diagrams for accuracy.

Mealworm Characteristics

_____

_____

_____

_____

_____

2. Use your textbook or other resources as references to label the parts of the insects in your drawings.

⚠ 3. Design an experiment to see if temperature affects the rate of metamorphosis from the mealworm stage to the beetle stage. Describe your experimental design in the spaces below and create any data tables that you may need. Your classmates may wish to pool their data and construct a graph of the results. Obtain your teacher's permission before performing your experiment.

Students can place their mealworms on a piece of paper for observation. Direct their inquiry with specific questions, such as asking how mealworms eat, move, feel to touch, smell, and so forth.

Hypothesis:

_____

_____

_____

_____

Independent Variable:

_____

Dependent Variable:

_____

Controlled Variables:

_____

Procedure:
Check students' procedures for safety and practicality.
_____

_____

_____

_____

_____

_____

Analyze and Conclude

1. Observing What are some anatomical characteristics of the larvae that show that they are arthropods and not annelid worms?

The larvae have segmented bodies, as do the annelid worms, but their mouthparts and three pairs of jointed appendages confirm that they are arthropods.

2. Analyzing Data Evaluate the class data on the effects of temperature on metamorphosis. At what temperature did the fastest insect metamorphosis occur? At which temperature did the slowest metamorphosis occur?

Answers will vary, but the fastest metamorphosis is likely to occur at the warmest temperature and the slowest rate in the coldest environment.

3. Inferring Propose an explanation for the effect of temperature on the rate of insect metamorphosis.

Insects are ectothermic (coldblooded) and their body processes usually occur at the temperature of their environment. Insects become dormant in winter. Warming usually speeds up the metabolic reactions that occur inside the larvae.

4. Interpreting Graphics Does the seasonal life cycle of the mealworm beetle seem consistent with the effects of temperature on metamorphosis that you observed?

The seasonal temperatures do appear to influence when a pupa can develop into an adult beetle. A warmer temperature favors metamorphosis and a colder one does not.

5. Predicting Would a very cold winter as opposed to a mild one make any difference in the number of insects observed the next summer? Explain your answer.

Yes, if the temperatures are too cold, the number of insects surviving in the larval and pupal stages may be less than in a mild winter. Fewer will develop into the adults in the spring.

Going Further

Test the effect of some other variable, such as light, on mealworm development. Obtain your teacher's permission before performing the experiment. Describe your results.

Comparing Invertebrate Body Plans

You may want to refer students to Section 29–1 in the textbook for a discussion of invertebrate body plans.
Time required: 45 minutes

Introduction

Invertebrates, like all other organisms, are divided into groups based on certain distinguishing characteristics. Two characteristics that are examined when grouping invertebrates are cell layers and body cavities.

The number of cell layers making up the body varies among invertebrates. Cnidarians—jellyfishes and sea anemones, for example—possess only two cell layers in their body wall: an inner gastroderm and an outer epidermis. Other invertebrates—worms, mollusks, arthropods, and echinoderms, to name a few—have three basic cell layers: an inner endoderm, a middle mesoderm, and an outer ectoderm.

The animals that possess three basic cell layers can be divided into groups based on the structure of their body cavity. The body cavity, if present, is a fluid-filled hollow in the body that is located between the endoderm and the ectoderm. Animals that lack a body cavity are called acoelomates. Animals that have a body cavity that is only partially lined with mesoderm are called pseudocoelomates. And animals that have a body cavity that is completely lined with mesoderm are called coelomates.

In this investigation, you will compare the body plans and structures of invertebrates from four different phyla.

The terms endoderm, mesoderm, and ectoderm are generally reserved for describing embryos. However, these terms are used here for the sake of simplicity and to avoid confusing students with additional terminology.

Problem

What are the differences in body plans and structures of the cnidarians, flatworms, roundworms, and annelids?

Pre-Lab Discussion

Read the entire investigation. Then, work with a partner to answer the following questions.

1. Which organisms will you observe in this investigation? Will you be observing live organisms?

   Students will observe prepared slides of a cnidarian *(Hydra)*, a flatworm *(Dugesia)*, a roundworm *(Ascaris*

   lumbrioides), and an earthworm *(Lumbricus terrestris)*. Students will not observe live specimens.

   _____

   _____

2. What should you do when switching from the low-power objective on the microscope to the high-power objective?

   Look at the objective from the side of the microscope to avoid damaging the slide.

   _____

   _____

3. Which organisms do you expect to have a coelom or a pseudocoelom?

Based on the diagrams and the information in the Procedure, students can predict that the roundworm

will have a pseudocoelom and the earthworm will have a coelom.

4. List two advantages a coelom might provide an organism.

A coelom provides a space in which organs can be suspended. The fluid-filled coelom also provides support for

the organism and allows for the development of more complex organs and organ systems.

5. Suppose a new phylum of invertebrates is discovered. These newly discovered invertebrates have a gastrovascular cavity and a very thin layer of mesodermal cells but show no organ development. Where would you place this new phylum on a phylogenetic tree with respect to the four phyla represented in this investigation?

Answers will vary. Because the organism has a mesodermal layer, it probably arose after cnidarians did.

However, because it lacks organs, it probably arose before flatworms did.

Materials *(per group)*

microscope
prepared slides of cross sections of: Prepared slides are available from biological supply houses.
   cnidarian *(Hydra)*
   flatworm *(Dugesia)*
   roundworm *(Ascaris lumbricoides)*
   earthworm *(Lumbricus terrestris)*

Safety 🔲🔳

Be careful to avoid breakage when working with glassware. Always handle the microscope with extreme care. You are responsible for its proper care and use. Observe proper laboratory procedures when using electrical equipment. Use caution when handling glass slides, as they can break easily and cut you. Note all safety symbols next to the steps in the Procedure and review the meanings of each symbol by referring to Safety Symbols on page 8.

Procedure

Part A. Examining the Body Plan and Structures of the Cnidarian

   1. Examine Figure 1 on page 213, which shows the basic body plans of the four invertebrates you will be examining.

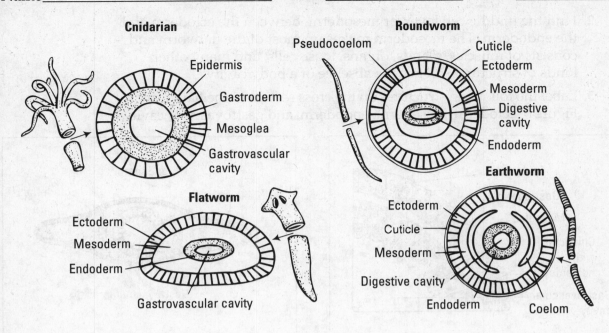

Figure 1

2. Examine a prepared slide of a cross section of a cnidarian under the low-power objective of a microscope. Look at the body layers. Switch to high-power to see the specific structures in greater detail. **Note:** *When switching to the high-power objective, always look at the objective from the side of the microscope so that the objective does not hit or damage the slide.* **CAUTION:** *Microscope slides have sharp edges and can break. Always handle the microscope with extreme care and do not use it around water or with wet hands. Never use direct sunlight as the light source for the microscope. Observe proper laboratory procedures when using electrical equipment.*

3. Locate the epidermis, or outer layer of cells. Try to find some barbed cells called cnidocytes, each of which contains a stinging structure called a nematocyst.

4. Locate the gastroderm, or inner cell layer. Notice how some of the cells in the gastroderm have flagella. These flagellated cells help to circulate food and other materials within the gastrovascular cavity.

5. Locate the gastrovascular cavity in the center of the cross section of the cnidarian. Food digestion occurs within the gastrovascular cavity.

6. Locate the mesoglea, which is a noncellular, jellylike material between the epidermis and the gastroderm.

7. Label the following structures on the cross section of the cnidarian (*Hydra*) in Figure 2 on page 214: epidermis, mesoglea, gastroderm, cnidocyte with nematocyst, and gastrovascular cavity.

Part B. Observing the Body Plan and Structures of the Flatworm

1. Examine a prepared slide of a cross section of a flatworm under low power. Locate the ectoderm, endoderm, and gastrovascular cavity.

2. Find the middle cell layer, or mesoderm, between the ectoderm and the endoderm. The mesoderm makes up most of the flatworm and consists of muscles, glands, organs, loose cells, and many other kinds of structures. Notice the absence of a body cavity.

3. Label the following structures on the cross section of the flatworm in Figure 3: ectoderm, mesoderm, endoderm, and gastrovascular cavity.

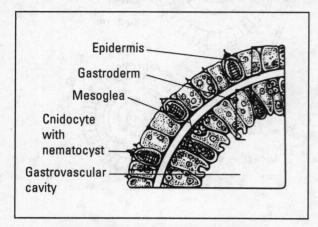

Cross Section of Cnidarian (Hydra)

Figure 2

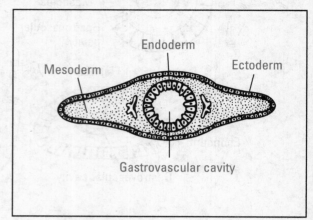

Cross Section of Flatworm (Dugesia)

Figure 3

Part C. Examining the Body Plan and Structures of the Roundworm

1. Examine a prepared slide of a cross section of a roundworm under low power. Locate the thick outer covering called the cuticle. This tough coating keeps a parasitic roundworm from being digested by its host. Just inside of the cuticle is the ectoderm, a thin layer of cells. Locate the mesoderm, the fiberlike layer just inside the epidermis.

2. Toward the center of the roundworm, look for the endoderm. The space inside the endoderm is the inside of the roundworm's digestive tract. The space between the endoderm and the mesoderm is called a pseudocoelom.

3. Label the following structures on the cross section of the roundworm in Figure 4 on page 215: ectoderm, mesoderm, endoderm, and pseudocoelom.

Part D. Examining the Body Plan and Structures of the Earthworm

1. Examine a prepared slide of a cross section of an earthworm. Find the thin protective outer layer called the cuticle. Just below the cuticle, look for the layer of cells of the ectoderm.

2. Inside the ectoderm are two muscle layers. The outer layer contains the circular muscles, which run circularly around the earthworm. The thick inner layer contains the longitudinal muscles, which run the length of the worm. These two layers of muscle are part of the mesoderm.

3. Examine the center of the cross section. You will see a round or horseshoe-shaped space that is the inside of the digestive tract. The layer of cells that surrounds the space is the endoderm.

4. Notice a relatively open space between the muscles surrounding the digestive tract and the muscles just inside the epidermis. This body cavity is called a coelom.

5. Locate a long, fiberlike structure inside the coelom. This structure, called a nephridium, is involved in excretion. There should be one nephridium on each side of the earthworm's body.

6. On the outer surface of the earthworm, find some bristly structures called setae. The earthworm uses the setae to help move its body through the soil.

7. Label the following structures on the cross section of the earthworm in Figure 5: ectoderm, circular and longitudinal muscles, endoderm, coelom, nephridium, and setae.

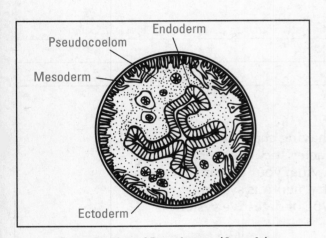

Cross Section of Roundworm (Ascaris)
Figure 4

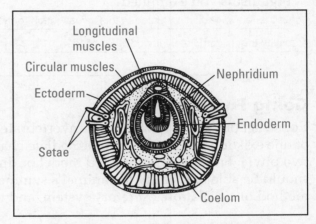

Cross Section of Earthworm (Lumbricus)
Figure 5

Analysis and Conclusions

1. **Inferring** What structures in the cnidarian correspond to the digestive cavity, ectoderm, and endoderm in the earthworm?

The gastrovascular cavity, epidermis, and gastroderm, respectively.

2. **Comparing and Contrasting** How is the body plan of the cnidarian different from the body plan of the flatworm?

Whereas the cnidarian has only two cell layers in its body, the flatworm has a third body layer (mesoderm).

3. **Comparing and Contrasting** How is the body plan of the flatworm similar to the body plan of the roundworm? How is the body plan of the flatworm different from the body plan of the roundworm?

Both the flatworm and the roundworm have three body layers: the ectoderm, the mesoderm, and the

endoderm. Whereas the flatworm has no body cavity (it is an acoelomate), the roundworm has a pseudocoelom.

4. **Classifying** Suppose a newly discovered organism is found to have three body layers. Scientists think that it is a worm but disagree as to the group in which it should be placed. How could they assign it to the proper group based on body structure?

Scientists could look at a cross section of the organism to determine if it is an acoelomate, a pseudocoelomate,

or a coelomate.

5. **Comparing and Contrasting** How is the body plan of the earthworm different from the body plans of the other three organisms you examined?

Of the four organisms studied in this investigation, only the earthworm has a true coelom, that is, a body

cavity that is completely lined with mesoderm.

Going Further

Construct or draw a new form of invertebrate having characteristics of one existing phylum or of intermediate characteristics between two phyla. From your completed model or drawing, your classmates should be able to identify the animal's symmetry, nervous system, method of circulation, excretory system, and type of digestive system.

Investigating Frog Anatomy

You may want to refer students to Section 30–3 in the textbook before performing this investigation.
Time required: Part A: 25 minutes;
Parts B–E: 75 minutes

Introduction

Frogs are typical amphibians, adapted to live in water and on land. The organization of an adult frog's internal organs is similar to the internal organization of other vertebrates that live on land. Its small size makes it easy to study. In this investigation you will dissect an adult frog and observe structures that make the frog adapted to its environment.

Problem

What are some features of a frog's anatomy that help it adapt to its environment?

Pre-Lab Discussion

Read the entire investigation. Then, work with a partner to answer the following questions.

1. What will you examine in Part A of this investigation?

   Students will examine the head and limbs of a frog.

2. Why is it important to make shallow cuts when cutting the skin around the frog's hindlimb?

   It is important to make shallow cuts because the frog's skin is very thin. Deep cuts may damage the

   muscles under the skin that students want to examine.

3. After you expose the internal organs in Part B, what two structures might you have to remove in order to examine the organs?

   If the frog is female, there may be a mass of black and white eggs that students should remove. The frog's

   organs may also be covered with fat bodies that must be removed.

4. Which organs of the digestive system will you identify in Part C?

   Students will identify the liver, the gallbladder, the small intestine, the stomach, the esophagus, the pancreas,

   the large intestine, and the cloaca.

5. Without the presence of eggs, how will you know whether your frog is male or female?

   A female frog will have ovaries, an oviduct, and an ovisac. A male frog will have testes.

Materials (per pair)

preserved frog
paper towels
dissecting tray
dissecting scissors
dissecting probes

forceps
plastic food bag
dissecting pins
waterproof marker

Preserved frogs may be purchased from a biological supply company. To reduce the number of frogs that need to be purchased, dissections can be done in groups rather than pairs, or you may wish to do a demonstration dissection.

Safety

Put on safety goggles, a laboratory apron, and disposable plastic gloves. Treat the preserved animal, preservation solution, and all equipment that touches the organism as potential hazards. Do not touch your eyes or your mouth with your hands. Be careful when handling sharp instruments. Return or dispose of all materials according to the instructions of your teacher. Wash your hands with soap and warm water after carrying out this investigation. Note all safety symbols next to the steps in the Procedure and review the meanings of each symbol by referring to Safety Symbols on page 8.

Read all the information on chemical safety from any Materials Safety Data Sheet that accompanies a chemical.

Procedure

Part A. The Head and Limbs

1. Work in pairs throughout this investigation. Wear your safety goggles, laboratory apron, and disposable gloves. Obtain a preserved frog from your teacher. Rinse the frog with water to wash off as much preservative as possible and then blot it dry with a paper towel. Place the frog in the dissecting tray and briefly examine it. **CAUTION:** *When working with preserved organisms, do not touch your eyes or mouth with your hands.*

2. Examine the frog's head. Notice the size and position of the eyes. The round, flattened areas of skin behind the eyes are the tympanic membranes, or eardrums. The two holes near the mouth are the nostrils, called the external nares.

3. To examine the interior of the mouth, pry open the mouth and use the scissors to cut the edges of the mouth at each hinge joint, as shown in Figure 1. **CAUTION**: *Handle sharp tools carefully.* Insert the dissecting probe into both external nares. The openings inside the mouth through which the probe emerges are the internal nares. Along the rim of the mouth you will find a row of small maxillary teeth. Farther back, attached to the roof of the mouth, are two sharp vomerine teeth.

4. Find the wide opening in the center of the mouth. This is the top of the esophagus—the tube that leads to the frog's stomach. Below the esophagus is a vertical slit called the glottis—the tube that leads to the lungs.

5. Use a dissecting probe to move the frog's tongue. Note where the tongue is attached to the jaw.

6. On page 222, label each part of the frog's mouth on the lines provided.

7. Examine the frog's forelimbs and hindlimbs. Observe the webbed toes. Compare the sizes of the muscles on the front and back limbs.

8. With the point of your scissors, carefully make an incision through the skin where one of the hindlimbs joins the body. If necessary, use the forceps to pull up the skin. Cut the skin around the hindlimb, as shown in Figure 2. **Note:** *The frog's skin is very thin. When cutting the skin, make shallow cuts to avoid damaging the muscles under the skin.* With the forceps, peel the skin off the hindlimb to expose the muscles underneath. Gently remove the thin, connective tissue covering the muscles. The muscles are connected to the bones with tough white cords called tendons. When a muscle contracts, the tendon moves and pulls the bone.

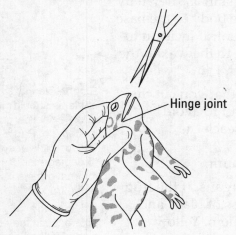

Carefully cut the edges of the mouth at each hinge joint.

Figure 1

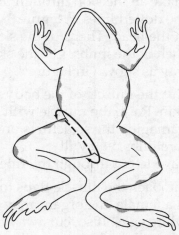

Carefully cut the skin around one hindlimb. Make shallow cuts to avoid damaging muscles.

Figure 2

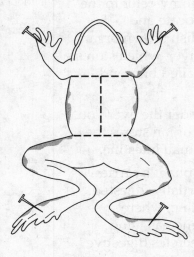

Gently lift the loose skin where the hindlimbs meet. Carefully make an incision through the raised skin.

Figure 3

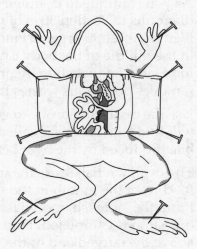

Lift the skin flaps and pin them to the wax.

Figure 4

9. At the end of the laboratory period, wrap the frog in a wet paper towel and put it in a plastic bag. Tie the bag closed and label it with your name and your partner's. **CAUTION:** *Wash your hands with soap and water after working with the preserved frog.*

Part B. The Frog's Internal Anatomy

1. Wear your safety goggles, laboratory apron, and disposable gloves. Lay the frog on its back in the tray. Use the dissecting pins to attach the limbs to the wax in the tray. With the forceps, gently lift the loose skin where the frog's hindlimbs meet. Use the scissors to make an incision through the raised skin. Cut the skin as shown by the dotted lines in Figure 3, along the center of the body to the base of the head. Then cut the skin laterally from the central incision to each of the limbs. Lift the skin flaps and pin them to the wax in the tray as shown in Figure 4.

2. Cut the muscle of the body wall in the same way that you cut the skin. Raise the muscle with your scissors as you cut to avoid damaging the structures underneath. When you reach the forelimbs, you will have to cut through the frog's breastbone, or sternum.

3. Pin back the muscle flaps to expose the internal organs. If the frog is a female, the organs may be covered with a mass of black and white eggs. If so, cut away the eggs and remove them. Yellow fingerlike structures, called fat bodies, may also be covering some organs. Remove those structures as well. Dispose of the eggs and fat bodies according to your teacher's instructions.

Part C. Digestive System

1. As you continue to examine the frog's internal anatomy, refer to the diagrams in Section 30–3 of your textbook to help locate and identify internal organs. Find the large, lobed, reddish brown organ in the middle of the body cavity. This organ is the liver, which stores food, aids fat digestion by producing a substance called bile, and removes poisonous wastes from the blood.

2. Use the dissecting probe to gently raise the liver. Under the liver you will find a greenish sac called the gall bladder. This organ stores the bile produced by the liver before it passes into the small intestine.

3. The oval, whitish sac is the frog's stomach. The esophagus carries food from the mouth to the stomach, where it is partially digested. From the stomach, food passes into the small intestine, where digestion is completed. Find the thin, ribbonlike pancreas lying above the curved end of the stomach. This organ secretes digestive enzymes into the small intestine.

Emphasize that students should make a shallow cut in step 2 of Part B because it is easy to damage the internal organs of the frog.

Point out the difference in the size of fat bodies in male and female frogs. Encourage students to suggest a reason for the difference. (Female frogs require larger fat reserves for their eggs.)

4. Notice that the small intestine is looped. With the dissecting probe, lift the small intestine. Using the forceps, carefully remove some of the connecting tissue that holds the small intestine in place. The small intestine leads to a wider tube called the large intestine. Food wastes pass from the large intestine to the cloaca, a large sac that passes wastes out of the frog's body.

5. Draw and label parts of the frog's digestive system in Figure 6 on page 222.

Part D. Circulatory and Respiratory Systems

1. Find the heart, a reddish triangular organ in the middle of the upper body. The heart has three chambers. The two upper atria collect blood from the veins and pass the blood to the lower chamber, the ventricle. The ventricle pumps the blood throughout the body through arteries.

2. The red, pea-shaped organ near the small intestine is the spleen. It produces white blood cells and removes dead red blood cells from the blood.

3. Locate the pair of spongy-textured lungs on either side of the heart. A frog takes in air through its external nares and enlarges its mouth by lowering the floor of the mouth. Then it closes its external nares and raises the floor of the mouth, forcing air through the glottis into the lungs.

Point out that the yellow, ribbonlike structure on each kidney is an adrenal gland, which is part of the frog's endocrine system.

4. Draw and label the heart, spleen, and lungs in Figure 6 on page 222.

Part E. Excretory and Reproductive Systems

1. Gently move the small intestines to the side with a dissecting probe. The two long, dark organs embedded in the back wall are the kidneys. The yellow, fingerlike projections above each kidney are fat bodies, which store fat. The kidneys filter chemical wastes from the blood. Find the tube, called the urinary duct, that leads from each kidney to the urinary bladder. The urinary bladder empties into the cloaca through which the urine, eggs, and sperm are eliminated from the body.

2. If your frog is filled with eggs, it is a female ready for breeding. If your frog is a female not ready for breeding, the egg-producing ovaries appear as thin-walled, gray, folded tissues attached to the kidneys. A coiled white tube, called an oviduct, leads from each ovary and carries eggs to an ovisac where the eggs are stored until a male squeezes the eggs from the female's body.

3. The yellow, bean-shaped testes of a male frog are attached to the kidneys. Sperm from the testes pass through the urinary duct into the cloaca.

4. Draw and label the excretory and reproductive structures of the male or female frog in Figure 7 below.

5. When you have finished your dissections, dispose of the frog as instructed by your teacher. Wash your hands with soap and water.

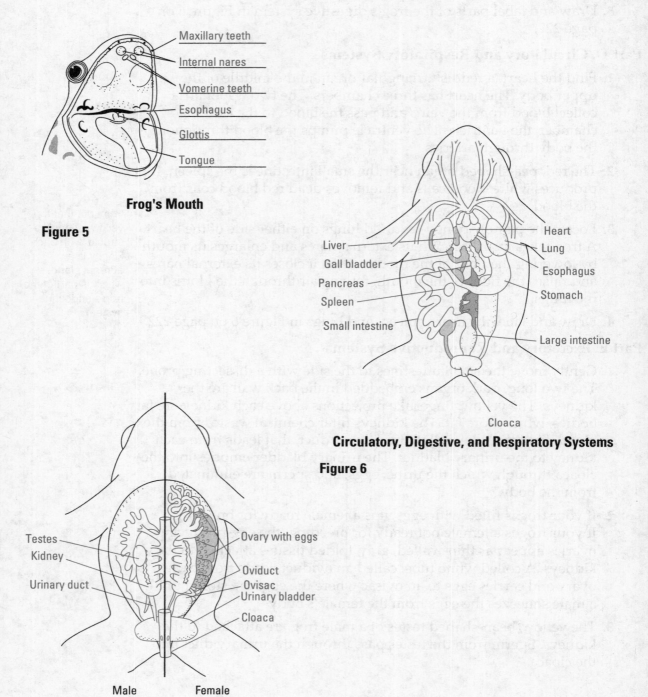

Maxillary teeth

Internal nares

Vomerine teeth

Esophagus

Glottis

Tongue

Frog's Mouth

Figure 5

Liver
Gall bladder
Pancreas
Spleen
Small intestine

Heart
Lung
Esophagus
Stomach

Large intestine

Cloaca

Circulatory, Digestive, and Respiratory Systems

Figure 6

Testes
Kidney
Urinary duct

Ovary with eggs

Oviduct
Ovisac
Urinary bladder

Cloaca

Male   Female

Reproductive and Excretory Systems

Figure 7

Analysis and Conclusions

1. Applying Concepts Identify three functions of a frog's cloaca.

The cloaca releases urine, food wastes, and reproductive cells (eggs and sperm) from the body.

2. Inferring Explain how the length of the small intestine relates to its function in absorbing nutrients.

Because the small intestine is so long, there is a great amount of surface area to absorb nutrients.

3. Drawing Conclusions Explain how the frog's hindlimbs are adapted for life on land and in water.

The webbed toes help the frog swim in water. The large leg muscles help the frog to leap long distances

on land and swim in water.

4. Inferring Describe a situation in which the location of the frog's external nares would be an advantage in breathing.

When the frog is partially submerged in water, it can breathe through its external nares because they are

on top of its head.

5. Inferring Infer how the attachment of the frog's tongue helps it to catch prey.

Because the tongue is attached to the front of the mouth, it can be extended farther to catch prey,

such as flying insects.

Going Further

Based on the results of this investigation, develop a hypothesis about whether or not the internal organs of frogs are similar to the internal organs of other amphibians. Propose an experiment to test your hypothesis. If the necessary resources are available and you have your teacher's permission, perform the experiment.

Examining Adaptations in Lizards

You may want to refer students to Section 31–1 in the textbook for a discussion of reptiles.
Time required: 50 minutes

Introduction

Reptiles are ectothermic, or coldblooded, vertebrates that are covered with dry scaly skin. They are adapted for reproduction on land. Most species are land dwelling, but some species spend much time in water. Turtles, snakes, lizards, crocodiles, and alligators are reptiles. Reptilian skin is dry, thick, and waterproof, protecting the body from drying out even in very dry climates. The skin is covered by tough scales that protect the animal from injury.

The anole, or American chameleon, is a common lizard found throughout the southern United States. It can be found on shrubs, trees, and fences, and on the ground. Often it is found around homes, and it seems to thrive in areas inhabited by humans. The anole is best known for the ability of its skin color to change from green to brown or gray. This change in skin color is thought to be stimulated by changes in light intensity, temperature, and emotional state.

In this investigation, you will observe the external structures of an anole. You will also design an experiment to observe its response to environmental change.

Problem

What are the external structures of a lizard? What changes occur in a lizard's coloration in different environments?

Pre-Lab Discussion

Read the entire investigation. Then, work with a partner to answer the following questions.

1. Anoles are found in dry environments. What type of skin would you predict anoles to have?

   A thick skin that would prevent water loss.

   _____

2. What evidence would indicate that anoles are land-dwelling rather than water-dwelling animals?

   The absence of webbing in feet; limbs better suited to walking or climbing than to swimming.

3. What is the difference between Part A and Part B of this investigation?

   A preserved anole is examined in Part A; a live animal in Part B. Part A has step-by-step instructions; Part B

   asks for an experimental design.

4. What kinds of things are easier to examine in a preserved anole than in a live animal? What can you learn from the live animal that you can't learn from the preserved specimen?

Body structures, particularly internal ones, are easier to study in a preserved specimen. A live animal is

needed to study behaviors.

5. What is the purpose of averaging the measurements and calculations you will make in Step 2 of Part A of the investigation?

To determine typical measurements for a group of animals.

Suggested Materials *(per group)*

preserved anole

live anole

6 sheets of construction paper
  (green, yellow, brown, red, black, and white)

metric ruler

dissecting tray

paper towels

Preserved anoles are available from biological supply houses. Live anoles are available from biological supply houses, or they can be collected in nature. Anoles will not drink water from a container. Set up a terrarium and each day spray the plants with water so that the anoles can lick the water droplets.

Safety 🛡️🧤⚗️🔥♻️🗑️🧪

Put on safety goggles, plastic gloves, and a laboratory apron. Always use special caution when working with laboratory chemicals, as they may irritate the skin or cause staining of the skin or clothing. Never touch or taste any chemical unless instructed to do so. Follow your teacher's instructions for storing or disposing of the preserved anoles. Follow your teacher's directions and all appropriate safety procedures when handling live animals. Wash your hands with soap and warm water after carrying out this investigation. Note all safety symbols next to the steps in Design Your Experiment and review the meanings of each symbol by referring to Safety Symbols on page 8.

Read all the information on chemical safety from any Materials Safety Data Sheet that accompanies a chemical.

Design Your Experiment

Part A. External Anatomy of the Anole

1. Put on safety goggles, plastic gloves, and a laboratory apron. Obtain a preserved anole. Rinse the anole with water to remove excess preservative. **CAUTION:** *The preservative used on the anole can irritate your skin. Avoid touching your eyes while working with the anole.* Dry the anole with paper towels and place it on a dissecting tray.

2. Measure the entire body length of the anole in centimeters. Record this measurement in Data Table 1. Also measure the length of the tail alone in centimeters. Record this measurement in Data Table 1. Obtain the measurements of four other groups of students and record this information in Data Table 1. Determine the average length of the five anoles and their tails and record this information in Data Table 1.

Data Table 1

Anole	Entire Body Length (cm)	Tail Length Only (cm)
1		
2		
3		
4		
5		
Average		

3. Observe the texture and color of the anole's skin. Answer questions 1 and 2 in Analysis and Conclusions.

4. Indentify the sex of your anole. Males are generally larger than females and have a dewlap, or fold of skin under the neck. Females have only a small, primitive dewlap. Answer question 3 in Analysis and Conclusions.

5. Locate the head, trunk, and tail of the anole.

6. Examine the head of the anole. Look for the presence of eyelids and external ear openings. Look for the presence of nostrils.

7. Open the mouth of the anole. Look for the presence of teeth.

8. Examine the feet of the anole.

9. In Figure 1 label the following external structures of the anole: head, trunk, tail, dewlap, foot, nostrils, and external ear opening.

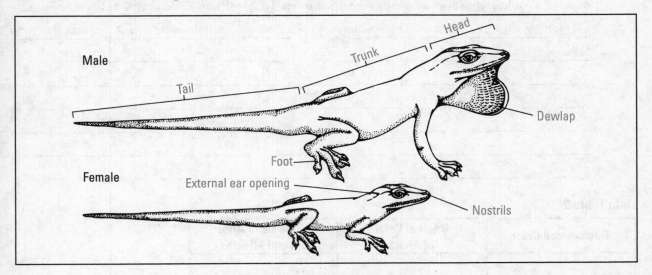

External Anatomy of the Anole

Figure 1

10. Follow your teacher's instructions for disposing of the anole or storing it for further use.

Part B. Your Own Experiment

1. Formulating Hypotheses Does an anole change color to adapt to changes in its environment? Record your hypothesis in the space provided.

2. Designing Experiments Obtain a live anole. Design an experiment to investigate how an anole responds to changes in the color of its environment. Outline the steps in your procedure in the space provided.

3. Obtain your teacher's approval for your experimental procedure. Then carry out the experiment.

4. Use Data Table 2 to record your observations.

Hypothesis:

Students' hypotheses will vary. Some may indicate the anole changes to lighter colors when placed on lighter

backgrounds, and to darker colors when placed on darker backgrounds. Others will hypothesize that the anole's

color will not change in response to background color.

Independent Variable:

Background color

Dependent Variable:

Color of anole

Controlled Variables:

Factors such as lighting, temperature, and container in which the anole is placed

Procedure:

Students' procedures should include placing the anole on different-colored backgrounds, observing any color change,

and recording the results. Tell students to allow the anole to calm down for several minutes after each change of

background color.

Data Table 2

Background Color	Original Color of Anole	Anole Color After Several Minutes

Analysis and Conclusions

1. **Observing** Describe the texture and appearance of the anole's skin.

   The anole's skin has a rough surface that is covered with horny epidermal scales.

   _____

2. **Observing** What is the color of your anole?

   The anole will probably be green or brown.

   _____

3. **Inferring** What is the sex of your anole? How can you tell?

   Students should look for the absence or presence of a dewlap, which occurs in males.

   _____

4. **Analyzing Data** How does the anole's average tail length compare to its average body length?

   Students should find that the tail is as long, if not longer, than the trunk and the head combined.

   _____

5. **Formulating Hypotheses** What is the possible function of the dewlap?

   Students might answer that it aids in courtship or mating behavior. They might also mention that when flared,

   its menacing appearance helps to frighten predators.

   _____

6. **Inferring** What is the function of the eyelids on the anole?

   Because anoles live in hot, dry climates, the eyelids function to shield the eyes from the sun, much as our

   eyelids do.

   _____

7. **Inferring** What is the function of the teeth of the anole?

   The teeth are used to grind insects or other food for the anole.

   _____

8. **Inferring** How are the anole's feet adapted for life on land?

   The anole does not have webbed feet. This aids the anole in running and climbing on land.

   _____

9. **Analyzing Data** Review your hypothesis and the observations you recorded in Data Table 2. Use your observations to confirm or reject your hypothesis.

   Students' observations will probably indicate that the skin color of the anole did not change in response to

   the color of the construction paper.

   _____

10. **Inferring** The anole has the ability to lose its tail and then regenerate a new one. How is this a useful adaptation for the anole?

If the anole is grabbed by a predator, it can lose its tail and escape. Later the anole will grow a new tail.

11. **Observing** Name three adaptations that anoles have for living on land.

Answers may include tough, thick skin, nonwebbed feet, lungs, protective coloration, eyelids, nostrils, and teeth.

Going Further

Obtain a liquid-crystal temperature strip. Under the supervision of your teacher, hold the strip against the skin of a live anole. Record the surface temperature of the anole. Place the anole in the sun for 5 minutes and check the temperature again. Carry out the same procedure with a small mammal such as a gerbil or hamster and compare the results.

Chapter 32   Mammals

Comparing Primates

You may want to refer students to Section 32–3 in the textbook for a discussion of primates.
Time required: 30 minutes

Introduction

In *The Descent of Man*, the English naturalist Charles Darwin formulated the hypothesis that humans and other primates have a common ancestor. All scientific hypotheses, including this one, are tested by observations. For example, observations of fossils lend support to Darwin's hypothesis of human origins.

Darwin observed that despite common ancestry, human beings and other primates differ in many important ways. Although all primates have opposable thumbs, the human hand is capable of more refined and exact movements than those of other primates. The human braincase, or cranium, has more volume than those of other primates. Human beings are bipedal, or able to walk on two limbs. Other primates use all four limbs for locomotion. Being bipedal frees the arms and hands for other tasks, such as toolmaking. Darwin regarded these human traits as adaptations, resulting from natural selection. The adaptations of other primates, he suggested, evolved differently.

In this investigation, you will examine the skeletal features of different primates in order to understand the evolutionary relationships among them.

Problem

How can skeletal evidence be used to understand the evolutionary relationships of primates?

Pre-Lab Discussion

Read through the entire investigation. Then, work with a partner to answer the following questions.

1. What hypothesis did Charles Darwin formulate about evolutionary relationships between humans and other primates?

   Human beings and other primates have a common ancestor.
   _____

2. What characteristics of primates will be examined in this investigation?

   Jaw size, jaw angle, teeth, and skeletons.
   _____

3. How do the hand and cranium of humans differ from those of other primates? Suggest what behaviors these traits might allow.

   The human hand is capable of more refined and exact movements than those of other primates,
   _____
   allowing use of tools. The cranium has more volume than those of other primates, which enables
   _____
   more advanced thinking, language, and written communication.
   _____
   _____

4. What does it mean to be bipedal and how might it benefit a primate?

Being bipedal means having the ability to walk on two limbs instead of using all four limbs for locomotion.

This would free up the arms and hands for a multitude of uses.

5. What determines the characteristics of organisms like those examined in this investigation?

The physical characteristics of organisms are determined by genes.

Materials *(per student)*

metric ruler
protractor

Procedure

1. In Figure 1 measure the length in millimeters of lines *ab* and *bc,* the lower jaw of each primate. Record these lengths in Data Table 1 on page 234. Record the product of these lengths in Data Table 1.

2. Use a protractor to measure the angle *xy* in each primate skull in Figure 1. Record your observations in Data Table 1.

Stress that the methods used here are not those used by anthropologists and paleontologists in comparing the bones of primates. These measurements serve only to show students relative differences in primate anatomy.

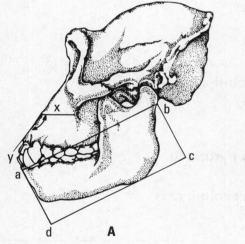 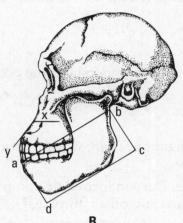 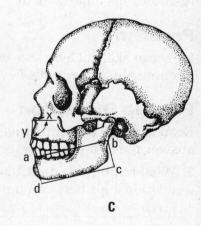

Primate Skulls

Figure 1

3. Examine the teeth of each of the three primates in Figure 2 on page 233.

4. Count the number of incisors, canines, premolars, and molars of each primate jaw in Figure 2. Record your observations in the appropriate columns in Data Table 2 on page 234.

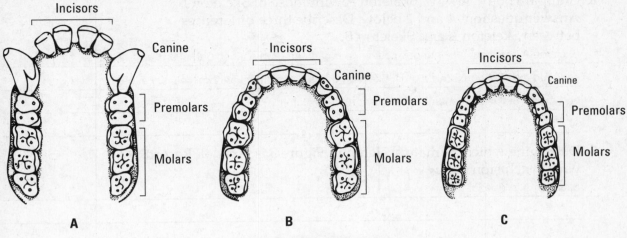

Teeth of Three Primates

Figure 2

5. Examine the two skeletons in Figure 3.

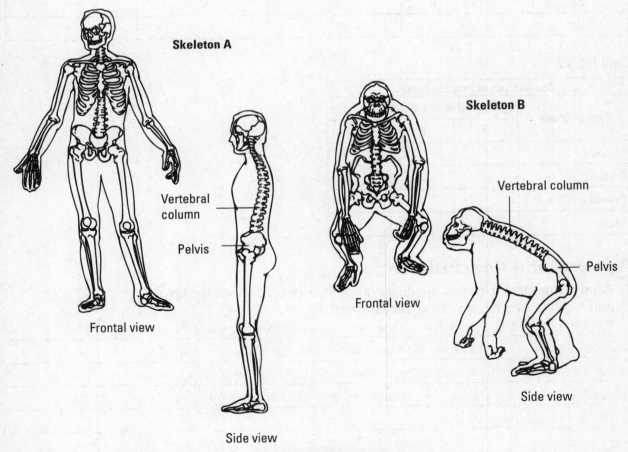

Two Primate Skeletons

Figure 3

6. Compare both views of Skeleton A with those of Skeleton B. Answer questions 1 and 2 below. Describe three differences between Skeleton A and Skeleton B.

Skeleton A has a curved vertebral column, a broad and bowl-shaped pelvis, and a skull that is

centered over the vertebral column. Skeleton B has a straighter vertebral column, a longer pelvis,

and a skull that is not centered over the vertebral column.

7. Determine which primate skeleton in Figure 3 is bipedal. Record your conclusion below.

Skeleton A is bipedal.

Data Table 1

Skull	Length of Lower Jaw (mm) *(ab)*	Depth of Lower Jaw (mm) *(bc)*	Area of Lower Jaw (mm²) *(ab × bc)*	Angle of Jaw
Comparison of Three Primate Skulls				
A	40	17	680	118°
B	28	13	364	118°
C	20	7	140	90°

Data Table 2

Type of Teeth	Number of Teeth		
Comparison of Primate Teeth			
	A	B	C
Incisors	4	4	4
Canines	2	2	2
Premolars	4	4	4
Molars	6	6	6

Analysis and Conclusions

1. **Analyzing Data** Discuss the observations you made about the jaws and teeth of primates in Data Tables 1 and 2.

The jaw of Skull A had the largest length, depth, and area (680 mm²); the jaw of Skull C had the smallest

length, depth, and area (140 mm²); and the jaw of Skull B was intermediate between A and C (area was

364 mm²). All three primates have 4 incisors, 2 canines, 4 premolars, and 6 molars. However, primate A has

very large canines and incisors, while those of primate C are much smaller, and those of primate B are

intermediate between A and C.

2. Analyzing Data Discuss the observations you made about the two
primate skeletons shown in Figure 3.

Skeleton A has a curved vertebral column, a broad and bowl-shaped pelvis, and a skull that is centered over

the vertebral column. Skeleton B has a straighter vertebral column, a longer pelvis, and a skull that is not

centered over the vertebral column.

3. Drawing Conclusions Based upon your observations of Figures 1
and 2, identify primates A to C as gorilla, chimpanzee, or human.
Explain your answers.

Primate A is a gorilla (smallest brain; largest jaw, incisors and canines). Primate B is a chimpanzee.

Primate C is a human (largest brain; smallest jaw, incisors and canines).

4. Drawing Conclusions Based upon the skulls and teeth, which two
primates are most different from one another? Does one primate
seem intermediate between the other two?

The gorilla and the human seem most different. The chimpanzee is intermediate between the gorilla and

the human.

5. Drawing Conclusions Which of the two types of primates shown
in Figure 3 is human? What conclusion can be made about its mode
of locomotion and what would be the benefits of this mode?

Primate A is a human. It is bipedal, the benefits of which include having free use of hands and a better ability

to see its environment.

6. Inferring Based on teeth structure, tell how the diet of primate A
might differ from that of primate C.

The large canine teeth of primate A are adapted for cutting and slashing tough materials. The teeth of

primate C are smaller, so it probably is adapted to a softer and more varied diet.

7. Evaluating Do you think the observations you made in this
investigation support Darwin's hypothesis? Explain why or why not.

The observations support his hypothesis. The three different primates have similarities indicating that they

had a common ancestor. Differences also exist that indicate that natural selection has been at work and each

primate has become better adapted for a particular habitat and lifestyle.

Going Further

Visit a local zoo to observe the behavior of gorillas, chimpanzees,
baboons, and other primates. Observe the ways in which the animals
communicate and interact with one another. What similarities and
differences do you observe between the behaviors of the primates you
studied and those of human beings? Use a notebook to record your
observations.

Chapter 33   Comparing Chordates

Observing Vertebrate Skeletons

You may want to refer students to Section 33–3 in the textbook before performing this investigation.
Time required: 45 minutes

Introduction

One characteristic common to all vertebrates is the presence of a skeleton. The endoskeleton provides support, protects the internal organs, and is a site for the attachment of muscles. In jawless fishes— lampreys and hagfishes—and in sharks and rays, the endoskeleton is made of cartilage. Other vertebrates have endoskeletons of bone with small amounts of cartilage present.

Similar skeletal features reveal important evolutionary links among vertebrates. Structures such as bones that have a common origin but different function are called homologous structures.

In this investigation, you will compare the skeletons of several different vertebrates and look for evidence of homologous structures. You will also classify unknown bone specimens based on their similarities to and differences from known vertebrates.

Problem

What homologous structures can be identified in vertebrate skeletons?

Pre-Lab Discussion

Read the entire investigation. Then, work with a partner to answer the following questions.

1. What will you be comparing in this investigation?

   The skeletons of a human, a frog, a crocodile, a pigeon, a cat, and an unknown animal.

2. Which labels on the human skeleton show specific groups of bones?

   Skull, pectoral girdle, pelvic girdle, hand, and foot are all groups of bones.

3. How will you label the bones in Figure 3?

   By finding a corresponding bone on the human skeleton and noting the name.

4. How will you begin to identify your mystery bones?

   Note the general size and shape, then compare it to the different skeletons.

5. Are you certain that your mystery bones will be from an animal whose skeleton is pictured in this lab?

   No, the bones may be from a completely different animal.

Materials *(per group)*

set of "mystery" bones

If actual skeletons or models are available, they should be used in conjunction with this investigation.
The "mystery" bones can be made by boiling a chicken and removing the meat from the bones. For a more challenging problem, you can obtain pig, lamb, or cattle bones from a butcher or grocery store; cook the bones to destroy any pathogens. Each group should be given several bones from the same type of animal to identify.

Procedure

1. Carefully examine the labeled human skeleton in Figure 1. The human skeleton contains more than 200 bones. Become familiar with the names and structures of the bones in Figure 1.

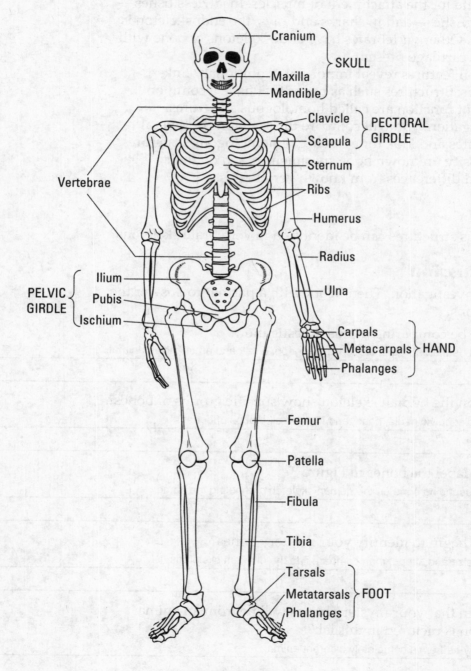

Cranium

Maxilla

Mandible

SKULL

Clavicle

Scapula

PECTORAL GIRDLE

Sternum

Ribs

Humerus

Radius

Ulna

Carpals

Metacarpals

Phalanges

HAND

Vertebrae

Ilium

Pubis

Ischium

PELVIC GIRDLE

Femur

Patella

Fibula

Tibia

Tarsals

Metatarsals

Phalanges

FOOT

Human Skeleton

Figure 1

2. Look at the frog skeleton in Figure 2. As you examine the skeleton, compare it to the human skeleton in Figure 1. Label the bones of the frog skeleton using the names from Figure 1.

3. Repeat step 2 with the skeletons of the crocodile, pigeon, and cat in Figures 3, 4, and 5.

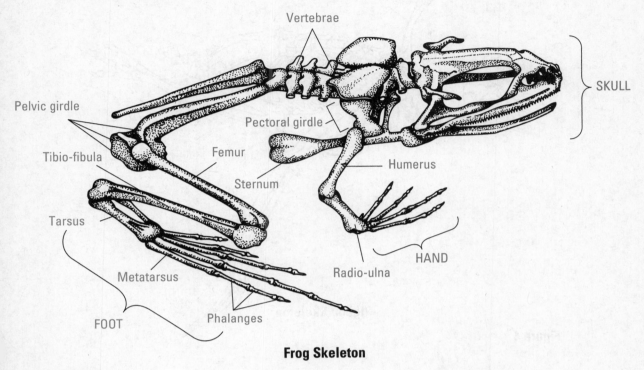

Frog Skeleton

Figure 2

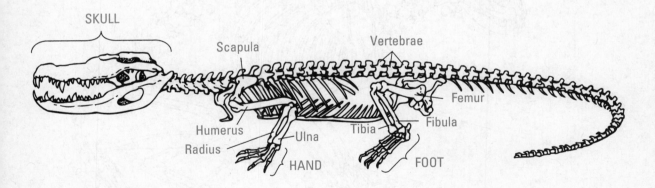

Crocodile Skeleton

Figure 3

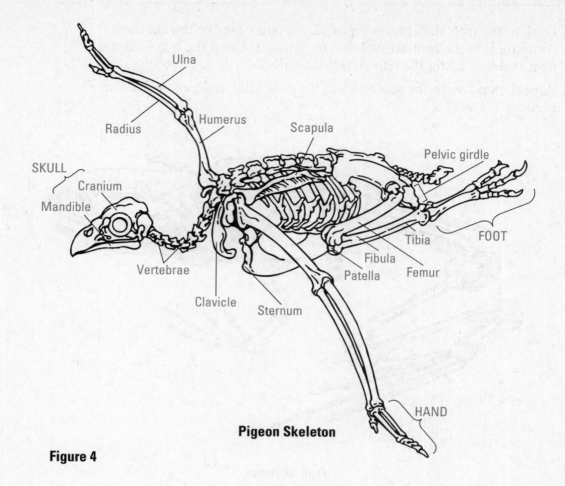

Pigeon Skeleton

Figure 4

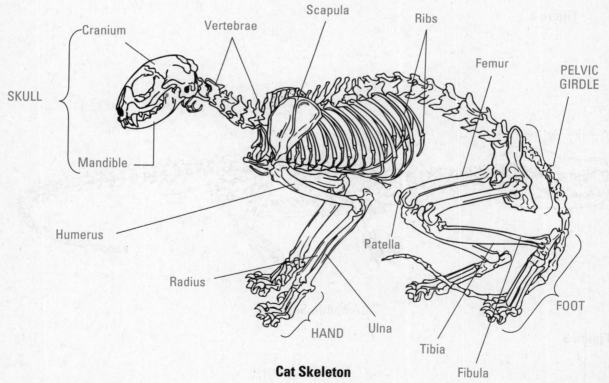

Cat Skeleton

Figure 5

4. Obtain a set of "mystery" bones from your teacher. Try to identify the bones by comparing them to the bones of each skeleton observed in this investigation.

Analysis and Conclusions

1. Comparing and Contrasting What are three characteristics that all of the skeletons share?

Answers may include a bony skeleton, four limbs, a skull, presence of vertebrae in the backbone,

jaws, and an internal skeleton.

2. Comparing and Contrasting What are three differences that exist among the skeletons?

Answers may include number of bones, presence of a tail, shape of bones, overall size, and type

of teeth.

3. Comparing and Contrasting How are the vertebral columns of the skeletons similar? How are they different?

All of the skeletons have vertebral columns that consist of a series of individual vertebrae in a chain.

The vertebral columns have different numbers and sizes of vertebrae.

4. Comparing and Contrasting How are the hindlimbs similar? How are they different?

Each of the skeletons has one bone (femur) in the upper portion of the leg. Each of the skeletons has

a different number of bones in the lower portion of the leg, the ankle, and the foot.

5. Comparing and Contrasting How do the foot bones of the frog, the crocodile, and the cat differ from one another?

The frog has long feet for swimming; the cat has elongated metatarsals

and claws; the crocodile has a relatively small foot.

6. Observing Describe the "mystery" bones in your collection.

Answers should mention the sizes and shapes of the bones.

7. Classifying To what parts of the skeleton do your "mystery" bones belong?

Answers will depend on the materials provided.

8. **Inferring** How do the functions of the forelimbs differ among the five vertebrates you have examined?

The forelimbs of humans are used for grasping objects, the forelimbs of frogs are used in landing after

a jump, the forelimbs of pigeons are used for flying, and the forelimbs of crocodiles and cats are used

for walking.

9. **Analyzing Data** What type of evidence indicates that the human hand, pigeon wing, and cat paw are homologous structures?

These structures contain bones of similar shape, number, and arrangement.

10. **Drawing Conclusions** To what type of animal do you think your "mystery" bones belong? On what evidence do you base your conclusion?

Answers will vary according to the set of bones examined by the students.

11. **Drawing Conclusions** Are bones that are similar in structure always similar in function? Give an example to defend your answer.

No. While the forearms of cats and humans are similar in structure, the cat generally uses its forearms for

walking, and the human uses its forearms for grasping objects.

12. **Drawing Conclusions** What evidence have you obtained in this investigation to support the theory that vertebrates evolved from a common ancestor?

All of the vertebrates examined in this investigation had homologous structures within their skeletons.

13. **Drawing Conclusions** Which of the skeletons is most closely related to humans? What evidence supports your answer?

The cat is most closely related to humans. Both are mammals, both have similar vertebral columns, both have

similar forearms and hindlimbs, and the human hand is similar to the cat's paw.

Going Further

Using reference materials, find examples of other vertebrate skeletons. How are these skeletons similar to and different from those you have studied in this investigation? How are the skeletons of these other vertebrates adapted to the environments in which they live?

Observing Animal Behavior

You may want to refer students to Chapter 34 in the textbook for a discussion of animal behavior. Time required: 45 minutes

Introduction

The way in which an organism responds to its environment is called behavior. Behaviors can be classified as either inborn or learned. Inborn behavior is also referred to as involuntary, innate, or instinctive behavior. Inborn behaviors are predictable, automatic responses to physical or psychological stimuli. The simplest inborn behaviors are known as reflexes. Some reflexes coordinate internal body processes, such as the slowing or quickening of the heartbeat. Other reflexes protect the organism. For example, when a cat is frightened by another animal, it will arch its back and fluff up its fur. This response makes the cat appear larger and may scare away the other animal.

Learned behavior is also referred to as acquired, voluntary, or conditioned behavior. This type of behavior depends on memory, repetition, and experience. Learning gives animals flexibility in the way they respond to situations, allowing them to deal with uncertainty and change. Although it's common to discuss behaviors in terms of being either inborn or learned, most behaviors result from a combination of both innate ability and learning.

In this investigation, you will be observing both inborn and learned behaviors of a small mammal—a rodent.

Problem

What is a behavior? How do inborn and learned behaviors differ?

Pre-Lab Discussion

Read the entire investigation. Then, work with a partner to answer the following questions.

1. List at least three stimuli you expect the rodent to respond to in each part of the investigation.

   Stimuli include the following: Part A—students around its cage, another animal of the same species,

   a confining container (the flower pot); Part B—food, sides of the maze, classroom sounds, etc.

   _____

2. Predict how the two rodents will react when placed in a box together.

   Students might predict that one or both animals will be aggressive or submissive or show territoriality

   or flight behaviors.

3. In Part A, what is the purpose of placing the flower pot inside a larger box before placing the rodent in it?

   Students might suggest that the outside container will prevent the rodent from fully escaping and running

   around the room or will insulate the rodent from extraneous stimuli in the classroom.

   _____

4. Do you think the amount of time it takes the rodent to complete the maze in Part B will increase or decrease over the five trials? Explain your answer.

Students may predict that the rodent will become faster at completing the maze with practice. Other students

may predict that the rodent will lose interest in the food or tire of running the maze, increasing the amount of

time it takes to complete the maze.

5. What types of behavior—inborn or learned—do you think Parts A and B of the Procedure are intended to reveal? Explain your answers.

Students may say that Part A is intended to reveal inborn behaviors because the rodents are put in situations

they are likely to encounter outside the laboratory. Part B is intended to show learning as the rodent encounters

the maze over several trials.

Materials *(per group)*

rodent

rodent food

See p. 245 for instructions for constructing a maze.

thick leather gloves

small animal cage or cardboard box

clay flower pot, 10 cm high

box or other large container

animal maze

clock or watch with second hand

Mice, rats, hamsters, gerbils, and guinea pigs are small and can be handled easily. Any of these animals can be purchased from local pet stores or science suppliers. Do not allow students to bring rodents from home. Be aware that hantavirus pulmonary syndrome (HPS), a potentially deadly respiratory disease, is associated with viral pathogens present in the feces of some rodents. *Do not use rodents that were captured in the wild, their offspring, or any animals that have come in contact with wild rodents.* Local or state health departments can advise you of the relative danger of exposure to rodent-associated pathogens, and should be able to suggest measures to reduce risk when handling rodents.

You will need at least two groups of animals of the same species that have not been raised in the same cage. Allow students to work only with healthy animals that have been living in cages with clean bedding and proper nourishment. Do not have students who are afraid of the animals handle them. Remove any animals that are agitated or aggressive.

Caution students to wear thick leather gloves whenever handling a rodent. Tell students if rodents are handled gently and calmly, they are much less likely to become frightened or excited.

Safety

Put on a laboratory apron, safety goggles, and thick leather gloves. Be careful to avoid breakage when working with the clay flower pot. Follow your teacher's directions and all appropriate safety procedures when handling live animals. Wash your hands thoroughly after carrying out this investigation. Note all safety alert symbols next to the steps in the Procedure and review the meanings of each symbol by referring to Safety Symbols on page 8.

Procedure

Part A. Observing a Rodent in Different Environments

1. Obtain a rodent in a container from your teacher. Observe the physical characteristics of your rodent. **CAUTION:** *Put on a laboratory apron, safety goggles, and thick leather gloves before handling the rodent. Follow your teacher's directions and all appropriate safety procedures while working with the rodent.*

2. Observe any behavioral responses of the rodent as it moves around its cage or box. Record your observations in Data Table 1 on p. 246.

3. Working with another group of students, carefully pick up your rodent and place it in the box of another rodent of the same species. Observe the two rodents' behaviors as they interact with each other. Record your observations in Data Table 1. **CAUTION:** *Handle the animals carefully and gently, without frightening them. Mice and rats may be picked up gently by their tails. Do not pick up gerbils or hamsters by their tails because the tips of their tails will break off. Separate the animals immediately if one attacks the other.*

4. Return your rodent to its cage or box and allow it to readjust to its surroundings for several minutes.

5. Place an empty clay flower pot in a larger box or other container. Gently pick up your rodent and place it in the clay flower pot with slanted sides, as shown in Figure 1. Observe the rodent as it explores the flower pot, and record your observations in Data Table 1. Record the time it takes the rodent to explore the flower pot, seek a way out and escape. Record the number of times it attempts to escape before succeeding. **CAUTION:** *The clay pot can break and cut you. Handle it carefully and notify your teacher immediately of any breakages. Do not clean up broken pots unless your teacher instructs you to do so.*

Rodent

Flower pot

Figure 1

Simple mazes can be constructed out of balsa wood or sturdy cardboard boxes. Care should be taken to construct a maze that is challenging to the rodent but that can be completed within a reasonable amount of time. You may have to experiment with several different designs to find one that is appropriate for your needs. The wood-shop teacher in your school may be able to assist you in the construction of mazes.

6. Return the rodent to its original cage or box and allow it to readjust to its surroundings for several minutes before beginning Part B.

Part B. Observing a Rodent's Run Through a Maze

1. Obtain a maze from your teacher. Place a piece of rodent food at the end of the maze. Carefully place the rodent at the beginning of the maze, as shown in Figure 2.

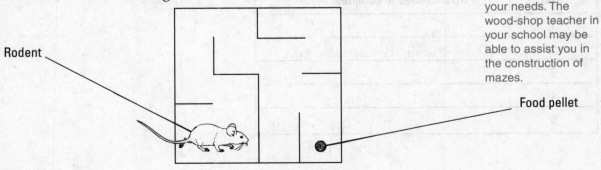

Rodent

Food pellet

Figure 2   **Top View of Animal Maze**

2. In Data Table 2, record the time it takes the rodent to successfully complete the maze the first time.

3. Repeat steps 1 and 2 four more times and record the times in Data Table 2.

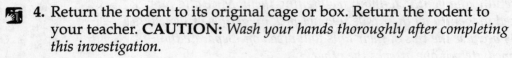 4. Return the rodent to its original cage or box. Return the rodent to your teacher. **CAUTION:** *Wash your hands thoroughly after completing this investigation.*

Data Table 1

Type of Environment	Animal Behaviors
Alone in a large area	
In an area with another member of the same species	Answers will depend on rodent's behavior.
Alone in small, confining area	

Data Table 2

Trial	Time Needed to Complete Maze
1	
2	Answers will depend on rodent's behavior.
3	
4	
5	

Analysis and Conclusions

1. **Observing** In what ways did your rodent's behavior change when it came in contact with another rodent after having been alone?

Answers will depend on student observations. Possible answers include that the animal ran into the corner,

attacked the other animal, cowered and shivered, etc.

2. **Inferring** Why might an animal's behavior change when it comes in contact with another animal of its own species?

The animal may become frightened, excited, or aggressive when it is in contact with another member of its

species. Behaviors of groups of animals are often different from the behaviors shown by individual animals.

3. **Observing** In what ways did your rodent's behavior change when it was placed in a small, confining place?

Answers will depend on student observations. It is likely that the animal tried to escape from the flower pot.

4. **Inferring** Why might an animal respond differently to a small confining area than to a large nonconfining area?

The animal may feel threatened, physically uncomfortable, or claustrophobic in its new smaller environment.

Many species of animals will try to escape when placed in a smaller environment.

5. **Comparing and Contrasting** How did the time it took the rodent to run the maze the first time compare with the time it took the rodent to run it the fifth time? Why might a change in time have occurred?

Students should notice a decrease in the time it takes the rodent to run the maze the fifth time in comparison

with the first time. Through repeated performance and trial-and-error, the rodent learned how to successfully

maneuver through the maze.

6. **Classifying** How would you classify the behaviors you recorded in each data table—as inborn or learned? Explain your classifications.

Answers will depend on student observations and interpretations. Students may say that the behaviors they

recorded show a combination of both inborn and learned characteristics. The observations recorded on Data

Table 1 probably include some inborn behaviors. Data Table 2 describes the rodent's repeated runs through

the same maze. The run time should decrease over the five trials, showing that the rodent learned to run the

maze with experience.

Going Further

Due to the incredible variety of physical and behavioral adaptations they possess, insects have been successful in inhabiting even the harshest and remotest places on Earth. To observe the complex behaviors of ants, obtain an ant farm from a hobby shop or biological supply company. Follow the manufacturer's instructions for establishing the ant colony and providing food and water for the ants. Using a hand lens, observe the ants twice a week for one month. Use a notebook to record any social behaviors you observe among members of the ant colony. **CAUTION:** *Do not handle the insects. Follow your teacher's directions and all appropriate safety procedures when working with live animals. If the ant farm is made of breakable materials, take care to avoid breakage.*

Do not allow students to handle the ants. Ant stings can cause serious injury to individuals who are allergic to them.

Observing Nervous Responses

You may want to refer students to Section 35–3 in the textbook for a review of reflex and voluntary reactions before performing this lab.
Time required: 30 minutes

Introduction

The nervous system is a series of conducting tissues that carries impulses to all parts of the body. Your nervous system initiates many types of reflex actions. When you touch a hot object, you immediately pull your hand away. You might be aware of this reflex action occurring, but you are unable to stop or control it.

How do reflex actions occur? When your hand touches a hot object, for example, heat receptors in the skin send an impulse to the muscles of the arm to contract. The impulse travels along the sensory neurons, to the spinal cord, across a synapse, and stimulates a motor neuron. The impulse leaves the spinal cord, passes back to the same nerve, and back to the arm muscles, causing them to contract and pull your hand away. This pathway is called the reflex arc. Because the reflex arc involves only the spinal cord and not the brain, a reflex action occurs in a matter of a fraction of a second. you are not able to control a reflex—it happens automatically.

In a nonreflex response, an impulse must travel to the brain. The brain interprets the stimulus and initiates an appropriate response. In this case, the time it takes to respond is measurably longer than the time required for a reflex arc. A person's reaction time can be measured by how quickly he or she can perceive a stimulus and then react to it. Driving a car and playing tennis are examples of activities in which reaction time is very important.

In this investigation, you will observe two reflex actions and measure your reaction time.

Problem

Can you control reflex actions? How can you measure reaction time?

Pre-Lab Discussion

Read the entire investigation. Then, work with a partner to answer the following questions.

1. What data will you record in Data Table 2?

   The distance the meterstick falls before it is grabbed.

2. What is another name for an involuntary or automatic response to a stimulus?

   A reflex.

3. What caution should you observe for shining the light?

   Do not shine the light directly in the eye.

4. Why do you put your elbow on the table when you are catching the meter stick?

This helps keep the arm steady and prevents it from dropping too low, thus giving a false reading.

5. In Part A, why do you use an eyepatch instead of just closing your eye?

The eye patch will allow less light to reach the eye.

Materials *(per group)*

pen light

eye patch or eye cover

meter stick

A flashlight may be used instead of a pen light, as long as the light is not too bright. Students should be reminded never to stare directly into the light for a long period of time.

If an eye patch is not available, a clean, white handkerchief may be used. Fold the handkerchief to fit over the eye. Use masking tape to hold it in place.

Safety 🔾

This experiment involves physical contact. Avoid this experiment if a problem with the knee, eye, or hand exists. Note the safety alert symbol next to step 3 in the Procedure and review the meaning of the symbol by referring to Safety Symbols on page 8.

Procedure

Part A. Reflexes

1. Sit on a chair or stool.

2. Cross your left leg over your right.

🔾 3. Have a member of your group tap your knee firmly, slightly below the knee cap, with the side of his or her hand, as shown in Figure 1. **CAUTION:** *Be sure the knee is not hit hard. A firm, quick tap is sufficient. Avoid this experiment if a physical problem in the knee exists.* Record your observations.

Figure 1

4. Repeat steps 1 to 3. This time, try to stop your knee from jerking. Record your observations.

5. Reverse roles and repeat steps 1 to 4.

6. Sit on a chair or stool.

7. Close one eye and cover it with the eye patch. Keep the other eye open.

8. Have a group member shine the pen light close to the open eye for about 10 seconds. **CAUTION:** *Do not shine light directly into the eye.*

9. Quickly remove the patch from the other eye.

10. Have a group member observe what happens to the pupils of both the eye exposed to light and the eye that remained in darkness. Record the observations in Data Table 1.

Data Table 1

Stimulus	Observations
Light	Pupil contracted (became smaller).
Dark	Pupil dilated (became wider)

11. Reversing your roles, repeat steps 6 to 10.

Part B. Reaction Time

1. Rest your elbow on a table and extend your arm over its side as shown in Figure 2.

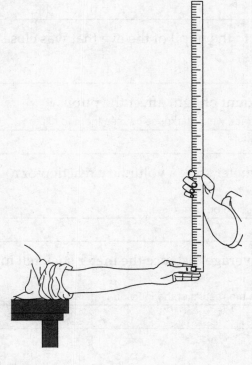

Figure 2

2. Have a group member hold a meter stick in the air, with the 0-cm line between the thumb and index finger of your extended hand.

3. Have the group member drop the meter stick without advance notice. Try to catch it between your thumb and index finger as quickly as possible.

4. In Data Table 2, record in centimeters the position of your thumb and index finger. This is the distance the meter stick fell before you caught it.

5. Repeat steps 2 to 4 three times.

Data Table 2

Trial	Distance (cm)
1	
2	
3	
4	

Analysis and Conclusions

1. **Observing** What happened to your knee when it was tapped?

The reflex action caused the leg to move forward.

2. **Inferring** Could you prevent the knee jerk or the pupil contraction? Explain your answer.

The reactions could not be prevented because they are reflex responses.

3. **Observing** What happened to the pupil of the eye that was close to the light?

The pupil contracted.

4. **Inferring** How does the amount of light affect the pupils?

Bright light causes the pupils to contract, while darkness causes them to dilate.

5. **Classifying** Is catching the meter stick a voluntary reaction or a reflex? Explain your answer.

It is a voluntary reaction, because it could be controlled.

6. **Calculating** What was the average distance the meter stick fell in your four trials?

The average distance will depend on the results of the individual trials.

7. **Comparing and Contrasting** In catching the meter stick, were your reactions faster or slower than those of your classmates? How do you know?

The reaction time was faster (slower) than classmates' because the meter stick didn't fall as far (fell farther) than classmates'.

8. **Classifying** From your observations, how would you classify the knee-jerk and the pupillary response? Explain your reason.

Both are reflex responses because they were automatic.

9. **Drawing Conclusions** Suggest some possible ways that reflex arcs could be advantageous to a species.

They enable an organism to escape danger rapidly by producing an immediate resonse. They also reduce the potential severity of injuries by producing specific and appropriate responses to pain.

Going Further

Do the senses of sight, smell, hearing, taste, and touch also affect our reflex actions? Why does your mouth water when you are hungry and see a picture of a delicious meal? Ivan Pavlov, a Russian biologist, carried out many experiments on conditioned reflexes. What are conditioned reflexes? How are stimulus and response related? Use resources in your school library or on the Internet to find out more about conditioned reflexes. Share your findings with the class.

Observing Bone Composition and Structure

You may want to refer students to Section 36–1 in the textbook for a discussion of the structure of bones.
Time required: 50 minutes plus a 5-minute observation period after 3 days

Introduction

Human bone contains living tissue and nonliving materials. The living tissue includes bone cells, blood vessels, fat cells, nerve cells, and cartilage cells. The nonliving materials include water, extra cells, protein, and minerals, such as calcium and phosphorus. In fact, bones are hard and strong because they contain a great amount of calcium. Bone is composed of compact bone and spongy bone. Unlike compact bone, which is very hard and dense, spongy bone is soft and has many spaces in it.

In this investigation, you will examine the internal structure of compact bone. You will also determine the percentage of water in bone and observe how calcium gives strength to bone.

Problem

What is the internal composition and structure of bone?

Pre-Lab Discussion

Read the entire investigation. Then, work with a partner to answer the following questions.

1. What is the purpose of heating the bone in Part A?

Heating the bone causes water in the bone to evaporate, so that the bone's water content can be measured.

2. Why do you find the mass of the bone before you heat it?

By finding the mass before and after water in the bone is evaporated, you can deduce the percentage of water

in the bone.

3. Predict what will happen to the bone after it soaks in hydrochloric acid for several days.

Students may predict that soaking the bone in the acid breaks down the calcium and other minerals in the bone.

4. Predict the properties of a bone that is low in calcium.

Predictions include that the bone will be spongy, flexible, brittle, and more easily broken.

Materials *(per group)*

prepared slide of compact bone
  with Haversian system [1]
compound light microscope
2 uncooked pork or beef bones [2]
triple-beam balance
felt-tip marker
heat-resistant gloves
heat-resistant pad
large metal cookie sheet or cooking tray

parafilm or glass plate
100 mL of 20% hydrochloric
  acid solution [3]
250-mL beaker [4]
oven [5]
tongs
paper towels
100-mL graduated cylinder
masking tape
nitrile gloves

[1] Prepared slides are available from a biological supply house.
[2] Fresh bones are available from a local butcher or grocery store. The bones should be fresh to ensure that they contain water.
[3] To make 1 L of 20% hydrochloric acid solution, put on safety goggles, a lab apron, and nitrile gloves. Slowly and carefully add 200 mL concentrated hydrochloric acid to 800 mL distilled water. Stir constantly while mixing. Read all the information on chemical safety from the Materials Safety Data Sheet that accompanies the hydrochloric acid.
[4] Provide plastic wrap, parafilm, or a glass plate as a cover for the beaker.
[5] Use the oven in the cafeteria kitchen or the home economics classroom.

Safety

Put on a laboratory apron, safety goggles, and nitrile gloves. Be careful to avoid breakage when working with glassware. Observe proper laboratory procedures when using electrical equipment. Use extreme care when working with heated equipment and materials to avoid burns. Always use special caution when working with laboratory chemicals, as they may irritate the skin or stain skin or clothing. Never touch or taste any chemical unless intructed to do so. Always handle the microscope with extreme care. You are responsible for its proper care and use. Use caution when handling glass slides, as they can break easily and cut you. Note all safety alert symbols next to the steps in the Procedure and review the meanings of each symbol by referring to Safety Symbols on page 8.

Procedure

Part A. Calculating the Percentage of Water in a Bone

1. Put on your laboratory apron. Place a small piece of paper towel on the pan of a triple-beam balance. Move the rider on the front beam of the balance until the pointer of the balance points to zero. Find the mass of the paper towel to the nearest tenth of a gram.

2. Place the uncooked bone on the balance and find the mass of the bone and paper towel to the nearest tenth of a gram. To determine the mass of the bone, subtract the mass of the paper towel from the mass of the bone and paper towel. Record this information in Data Table 1.

3. Using the marker, write the last name of one of your group members on the surface of the bone.

4. Place the bone, along with bones of the other groups, on a large metal cooking tray. Place the cooking tray in an oven that has been preheated to 149°C (300°F) for 25 minutes. **CAUTION:** *Wear heat-resistant gloves when handling hot materials. Place the tray in the oven carefully to avoid burns.*

5. **CAUTION:** *To avoid burns, use heat-resistant gloves to remove the hot tray from the oven slowly and carefully.* Using heat-resistant gloves, remove the tray from the oven and place it on a heat-resistant pad to cool.

6. After the bone has cooled for 10 minutes, place it on the piece of paper towel on the triple-beam balance and again determine its mass to the nearest tenth of a gram. Record this information in Data Table 1.

Data Table 1

Object	Mass Before Heating (g)	Mass After Heating (g)
Bone		

Percentage of water in bone _____Answers should be approximately 10–15%_____

7. The loss in mass of the bone is due primarily to the evaporation of water and to some oxidation of the minerals in the bone. Calculate the percentage of water in the bone by using the following formula:

$$\frac{\text{mass before heating/mass after heating}}{\text{mass before heating}} \times 100 = \text{percentage of water}$$

8. Record the percentage of water in the bone below Data Table 1.

9. Follow your teacher's instructions for proper disposal of the bone. Wash your hands thoroughly after completing Part A of this investigation.

Part B. Observing Bone Cells
Students should perform Part B of the investigation while waiting for their bones to heat.

1. Observe a prepared slide of compact bone under the low-power objective of a microscope. Notice the circular-patterned units in the cross section of the bone. Each of these circular units is a Haversian system. **CAUTION:** *Microscope slides have sharp edges and can break. Always handle the microscope with extreme care. Do not use electrical equipment near water or with wet hands. Never use direct sunlight as the light source for a microscope.*

2. Switch to high-power to observe the structures that make up each Haversian system. **CAUTION:** *When switching to the high-power objective, always look at the objective from the side of the microscope so that the objective does not hit or damage the slide.*

3. Focus on a group of concentric circles. The central, hollow core of these circles is called the Haversian canal. The Haversian canal contains nerves and blood vessels. The rings around the Haversian canal are called lamellae (singular, lamella). The small dark cavities between adjacent lamellae are called lacunae (singular, lacuna). Lacunae appear as long, dark areas between lamellae.

4. Within each Haversian system, the lacunae are interconnected by small, branching canals called canaliculi (singular, canaliculus). Canaliculi appear as thin, dark lines that resemble the spokes of a wheel. Fluids pass from one part of the bone to another through the canaliculi.

5. Look for darkly stained bodies within the lacunae. These are the osteocytes, or living bone cells. See Figure 1. Notice that osteocytes have fine branches that extend into the canaliculi. The osteocytes are responsible for controlling the life functions of the bone.

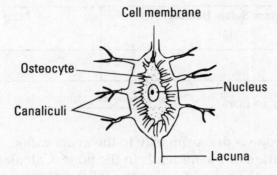

Figure 1

6. In the space provided below, draw a section of bone tissue as seen through the high-power objective of the microscope. Label the following parts of the Haversian system: Haversian canal, lamella, lacuna, canaliculus, and osteocyte. Record the magnification of the microscope.

Students should complete steps 1–3 in Part C while waiting for their bones to heat

Magnification _____

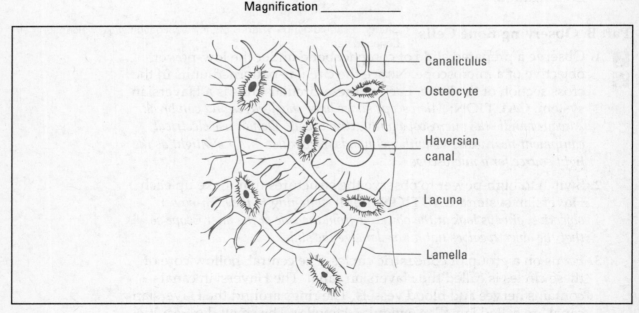

Haversian System of a Human Bone

Part C. Determining the Role of Calcium in a Bone

1. Obtain another uncooked bone. Observe the flexibility of the bone by trying to bend and twist it. Record your observations in Data Table 2.

Data Table 2

Object	Description of Flexibility
Bone before being soaked in acid	The bone is hard, rigid, and inflexible. It cannot be bent.
Bone after being soaked in acid	The bone is soft and easy to twist and bend.

You may want to have students line the beaker with gauze because the parts of the bone that touch the glass will not decalcify. Students should add enough hydrochloric acid solution to cover the bone entirely.

2. Place the bone in a 250-mL beaker. Use masking tape to label the beaker with the name of one member of your group.

3. Put on your safety goggles and nitrile gloves. Carefully add 100 mL of a 20% hydrochloric acid solution to the beaker. **CAUTION:** *Hydrochloric acid can burn the skin or clothing. If any acid spills on your skin or clothing, wash the affected area with water immediately. Notify your teacher.*

4. Cover the beaker with parafilm or a glass plate. Then label the beaker and place it in a ventilated hood for 3–7 days until the bone becomes spongy. **CAUTION:** *Avoid inhaling the fumes of the acid.*

5. Using tongs, carefully remove the bone from the acid. Rinse the bone under running tap water to remove any acid solution.

6. Dry the bone with a paper towel. Again test the flexibility of the bone. Record your observations in Data Table 2. **CAUTION:** *Do not touch the bone with your bare hands. Wear protective gloves while handling the bone.*

7. Follow your teacher's instructions for the proper disposal of the bone and the acid solution. Wash your hands thoroughly after completing this investigation.

Analysis and Conclusions

1. **Analyzing Data** Is the percentage of water loss in your group's bone exactly the same as that of other groups? If not, why might the percentages vary?

Students should find that their percentages are not exactly the same. Some bones may contain more water than others.

2. **Inferring** Why is water a necessary substance in a bone?

Water is necessary to carry materials into and out of the living bone cells. Without water the bone cells would die.

3. **Comparing and Contrasting** Many people incorrectly think of bone as nonliving tissue. How is a bone similar to other living tissues?

Both bones and other tissues are made up of cells that have specialized functions within the organism in

which they are found. Bone cells have nuclei and cell membranes, as do other types of animal cells.

4. **Drawing Conclusions** What materials are removed from a bone when it is soaked in a hydrochloric acid solution for several days? What evidence do you have to support your answer?

Calcium and other minerals are removed from a bone. The absence of calcium causes bone to lose

its rigid structure.

Going Further

Use reference materials to research the degenerative bone disease known as osteoporosis. What is the cause of this disease? What are its symptoms? What age group does it normally affect? What preventive measures can be taken to prevent osteoporosis?

Measuring Lung Capacity

You may want to refer students to Section 37–3 in the textbook for a discussion of the mechanics of breathing.
Time required: 40 minutes

Introduction

The amount of air that you move in and out of your lungs depends on how quickly you are breathing. The amount of air that is moved in and out of the lungs when a person is breathing normally is called the tidal volume. This amount of air provides enough oxygen for the body when the person is resting. It is possible to inhale more deeply and exhale more forcefully than usual. The maximum amount of air moved in and out of the lungs when the deepest possible inspiration is followed by the strongest possible expiration is called the vital capacity.

In this investigation, you will determine the tidal volume and vital capacity of your lungs.

Problem

How are the tidal volume and vital capacity of the human lungs measured?

Pre-Lab Discussion

Read the entire investigation. Then, work with a partner to answer the following questions.

1. Why is it important to measure tidal volume and tidal capacity more than once and then calculate means for these measurements?

   Calculating the mean for several trials should help to compensate for small measurement errors and other

   sources of uncertainty.

2. What would you conclude if the balloon were smaller during your vital capacity measurement than during your tidal volume measurement?

   This result would suggest an error in conducting the experiment.

3. List some possible sources of error that could occur during this experiment.

   Sources of error could include using balloons of different original sizes or of different elastic strengths,

   over-inhaling or -exhaling during the tidal volume measurement, under-inhaling or -exhaling during the

   vital capacity measurement, errors of mathematics or of interpreting graphs, and so on.

4. How do you expect your estimated vital capacity to compare to your measured vital capacity? Explain your answer.

   Student predictions may reflect their knowledge of the effects of aerobic training on vital capacity and whether

   or not they perceive themselves as well-trained.

5. Why might a doctor want to determine the tidal volume or vital capacity of a patient?

Vital capacity could be monitored to determine the physiological effects of exercise on the body. A low tidal

volume or vital capacity might alert the doctor to the presence of a respiratory illness such as asthma,

pneumonia, or emphysema.

Materials *(per pair)*

2 round balloons (1 for each student in the pair)
metric ruler
meter stick
bathroom scale (1 per class is adequate)   metric if possible

Safety ⚄

Do not participate in this investigation if you are ill or if you have any breathing difficulties. You will be exercising during this investigation. If at any time you feel faint or dizzy, sit down and immediately call your teacher. Note the safety alert symbol next in the Procedure and review the meaning of the symbol by referring to Safety Symbols on page 8.

Allow students to participate in this investigation on a voluntary basis. Students with chronic or acute respiratory illnesses should not participate. You may wish to consult the school nurse for information about students who should not be allowed to conduct this investigation.

Procedure

Part A. Measuring Tidal Volume

1. Stretch a round balloon lengthwise several times.

2. Inhale normally and then exhale normally into the balloon. **Note:** *Do not force your breathing.*

3. Immediately pinch the end of the balloon shut so that no air escapes. Place the balloon on a flat surface. Have your partner use the metric ruler to measure the diameter of the balloon at its widest point, as shown in Figure 1. Record this measurement in Data Table 1 on page 264.

You may wish to tell students to pinch their nostrils shut while exhaling into the balloon to prevent air from escaping through the nose.

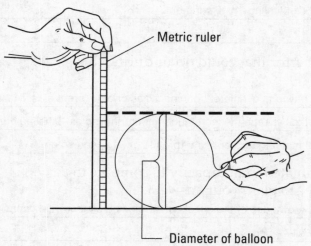

Metric ruler

Diameter of balloon

Figure 1

4. Deflate the balloon and repeat steps 2 and 3 two more times. Use your three measurements to calculate an average diameter. Record this number in Data Table 1.

Part B. Measuring Vital Capacity

1. After breathing normally, inhale as much air into your lungs as possible. Exhale as much air as you can from your lungs into the balloon.

2. Immediately pinch the end of the balloon shut so that no air escapes. Place the balloon on a flat surface. Have your partner use the metric ruler to measure the diameter of the balloon at its widest point. Record this measurement in Data Table 1.

3. Deflate the balloon and repeat steps 1 and 2 two more times. Use your three measurements to calculate a mean diameter. Record this number in Data Table 1.

4. Use Figure 2 to convert the balloon diameters in Data Table 1 into lung volumes. On the horizontal (x) axis, locate the diameter of the balloon in centimeters and follow the number up until it meets the curved line. Then move across in a straight line to the vertical (y) axis and approximate the lung volume. Record this number in Data Table 2. Repeat this procedure for all of the balloon diameters in Data Table 1.

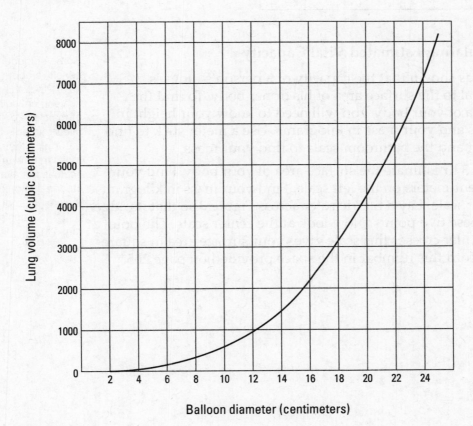

Figure 2

Data Table 1

	Balloon Diameter (cm)	
Trial	**Tidal Volume**	**Vital Capacity**
1		
2		
3		
Average		

Data Table 2

	Lung Volume (cm³)	
Trial	**Tidal Volume**	**Vital Capacity**
1		
2		
3		
Average		

Part C. Calculating Estimated Vital Capacity

1. Research has shown that the capacity of a person's lungs is proportional to the surface area of his or her body. To find the surface area of your body, you will need to know your height in centimeters and your mass in kilograms. Use a meter stick to find your height and the bathroom scale to find your mass.

2. Use Figure 3 to estimate the surface area of your body. Find your height in centimeters on the left scale. Find your mass in kilograms on the right scale. Lay a metric ruler across Figure 3 so that its edge connects these two points. Now look at the center scale. The point at which the ruler crosses this scale gives your surface area in square meters. Record this number in the space provided on page 265.

Some students are sensitive about their body size. Place the bathroom scale in an isolated part of the classroom, and allow students to determine their body mass in private. If a metric scale is not available, students should multiply the weight in pounds by 0.454 to calculate the mass in kg.

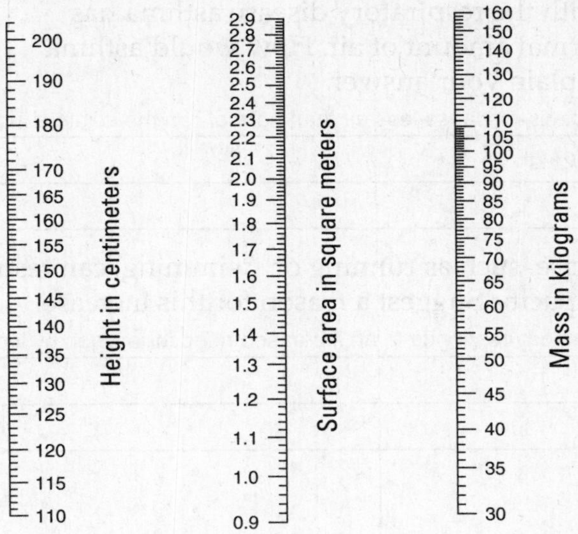

Figure 3

3. To calculate the estimated vital capacity of your lungs, multiply your surface area by the ratio of vital capacity to surface area. For females this ratio is 2000 mL per square meter. For males this ratio is 2500 mL per square meter. Record the estimated vital capacity of your lungs in the space provided below.

Body surface area (m²) _____

Vital capacity (cm³) _____

Analysis and Conclusions

1. **Analyzing Data** How do your tidal volume and vital capacity compare with those of other class members? Why might there be variation among different people?

   Answers will depend upon student data. Students may mention body size, respiratory health, aerobic training,

   or inaccuracy of measurement as reasons for variations.

2. **Evaluating** How does your estimated vital capacity compare to your measured vital capacity? Was your prediction in Pre-Lab Discussion question 4 confirmed?

   Answers will depend on student predictions. Some students who have undergone aerobic training may have

   expected their measured vital capacities to exceed their estimated vital capacities.

3. **Formulating Hypotheses** If a person forcibly exhales and then relaxes but does not deliberately inhale, air is taken into the lungs. Suggest a hypothesis to explain this phenomenon.

   Inspiration of air occurs passively when the pressure of air outside the body is significantly higher than that

   within the lungs.

4. Predicting A person with the respiratory disease asthma has difficulty exhaling a normal amount of air. How would asthma affect vital capacity? Explain your answer.

Asthma would reduce vital capacity because less air than normal can move into a lung that does not

empty normally.

5. Inferring Aerobic exercise, such as running or swimming, can result in an increase of vital capacity. Suggest a reason for this increase.

Students may suggest that the body responds to an increased need for oxygen by increasing the volume of

air it takes in with each breath.

Going Further

The vital capacity of the lungs is affected by the anatomical build of a person, the position of the person during the vital capacity measurement, and the stretching capability of the lungs and chest cavity. Measure the vital capacity of your lungs while sitting up and then while lying down. In each position, inhale as much air into your lungs as possible and exhale as much air as you can into a balloon. Measure the diameter of the balloon each time. Compare your vital capacity in each position. Suggest an explanation for any difference between the two volumes.

Students should find that vital capacity is greater when standing up. Some students may realize that the diaphragm tends to move downward in a standing posture, while when lying down, there is less downward force on the diaphragm, reducing the volume of the lungs.

Simulating Urinalysis

You may want to refer students to Section 38–3 in the textbook for a discussion of the function of the kidneys and other excretory structures.
Time required: 60 minutes

Introduction

All organisms produce wastes that must be removed. In humans, urine is the fluid produced by the kidneys as they remove waste chemicals from the blood. Urine is a watery fluid containing excess salts, nitrogenous wastes, and a variety of organic molecules. The concentration of each of these substances depends on a person's health and diet.

Physicians can evaluate the general health of an individual by testing the chemical composition of urine. Ions such as phosphate and chloride are normally found in urine, but glucose molecules are a symptom of diabetes. Albumin, a protein, is sometimes found in urine after heavy exercise, but the presence of albumin over an extended period can be a symptom of a kidney infection. The analysis of a urine sample is called urinalysis and includes a physical, chemical, and visual examination.

In this investigation you will be testing *artificial* urine samples for the presence of some commonly found chemicals in healthy patients and patients with certain diseases.

Make it clear that the samples students will analyze are artificial, so only a few of the chemicals normally found in urine will be present. None of the chemicals in the artificial urine can cause injury, but students should observe all the safety procedures appropriate to handling chemicals.

Problem

Which chemicals are found in the urine of a healthy person and which chemicals can be symptoms of disease?

Pre-Lab Discussion

Read the entire investigation. Then, work with a partner to answer the following questions.

Rinse all glassware with distilled water before use in this investigation.

1. In each analysis two samples are tested, one with the chemical and one without it. What is the purpose of testing a sample without the chemical?

   Any visual changes in the sample without the chemical are caused by the reagents, and do not indicate

   the presence of the chemical being tested. A visual change after addition of the reagents to the sample with

   the chemical is a positive test.

2. Which of the tests require heating of the reagent with the sample in a water bath?

   Only the test for glucose with Benedict's solution.

3. Which of the tests require heating of the sample before addition of any reagents?

   The tests for phosphate and albumin both require heating the sample.

4. What substance is detected by reaction with Benedict's solution?

   Benedict's solution is used to detect glucose.

5. When is the silver nitrate reagent used?

   Silver nitrate is used to test for chloride.

Materials *(per group)*

12 test tubes

glass-marking pencil

test-tube rack

test-tube holder

10-mL graduated cylinder

hot plate

Bunsen burner

400-mL beaker

matches

Benedict's solution [7]

silver nitrate solution [8]

Prepare 1 L of each urine sample as follows:

[1] Urine with glucose—add 10 drops yellow food coloring and 1 tablespoon glucose to 1 L distilled water.

[2] Urine with phosphate—add 10 drops yellow food coloring and 1 tablespoon sodium phosphate dibasic anhydride (Na_2PO_4) to 1 L distilled water.

10% acetic acid solution [9]

simulated urine samples:

with glucose [1]

without glucose [5]

with phosphate [2]

without phosphate [5]

with albumin [3]

without albumin [5]

with chloride [4]

without chloride [5]

unknown [6]

[3] Urine with albumin—add 10 drops yellow food coloring and 1 egg white to 1 L distilled water.

[4] Urine with chloride—add 10 drops yellow food coloring and 1 tablespoon sodium chloride (table salt) to 1 L distilled water.

[5] Urine without glucose, phosphate, albumin, or chloride can be made by adding 10 drops yellow food coloring to 1 L distilled water.

[6] To prepare the unknown urine samples, mix samples containing all, a few, one, or none of the previously tested substances. Number the samples and keep a record of their contents.

[7] To make Benedict's solution dissolve 173 g sodium citrate and 100 g sodium carbonate in 700 mL distilled water. Heat until chemicals are dissolved. Filter. Dissolve 17.3 g copper sulfate in 100 mL distilled water. Slowly add to the first solution, stirring constantly. Add distilled water to a total volume of 1 L. Benedict's solution can also be purchased premixed from a biological supply house.

[8] To make a silver nitrate solution, put on plastic gloves and add 2 g silver nitrate to 125 mL distilled water. Stir until dissolved. Pour into dropper bottles.

[9] To make a 10% acetic acid solution, put on nitrile gloves, safety goggles and a lab apron. Add 10 mL glacial acetic acid to 90 mL distilled water while stirring. Pour solution into dropper bottles.

Safety

Put on safety goggles and a laboratory apron. Observe proper laboratory procedures when using electrical equipment. Be careful using matches. Tie back loose hair and clothing when working with flames and do not reach over an open flame. Always use special caution when working with laboratory chemicals, as they may irritate the skin or stain skin or clothing. Never touch or taste any chemical unless instructed to do so. Wash your hands thoroughly after carrying out this lab. Note all safety alert symbols next to the steps in the Procedure and review the meaning of each symbol by referring to Safety Symbols on page 8.

Procedure

Part A. Test for Glucose

Commercial glucose testing papers can also be used for this part of the investigation. They are available at a local drugstore, and no heat is required for the test.

1. Put on your lab apron and safety goggles. Place two test tubes in a test-tube rack. With a glass-marking pencil, label one test tube "G" for glucose. Allow the other test tube to remain unlabeled as it will serve as the control.

2. Half fill the 400-mL beaker with water and place it on the hot plate to prepare a hot-water bath. **CAUTION:** *Use extreme care when working with hot water. Do not let the water splash onto your body.*

3. Put on your plastic gloves. Add 3 mL of Benedict's solution to each test tube. **CAUTION:** *Use extreme care when handling Benedict's solution to avoid staining of the skin and clothing.*

4. Add 3 mL of the simulated urine sample with glucose to the test tube labeled "G." Add 3 mL of the simulated urine sample without glucose to the unlabeled test tube. Note the appearance of the solution in each test tube. Record this information in Data Table 1.

Read all the information on chemical safety from any Materials Safety Data Sheet that accompanies a chemical.

5. Place both test tubes in the hot-water bath for 2 minutes.

6. After 2 minutes, remove the test tubes from the hot-water bath with a test-tube holder. Place the test tubes in the test-tube rack.
CAUTION: *Be careful when working with heated equipment or materials to avoid burns.* Note any color changes in the test tubes. Record your observations in Data Table 1.

Data Table 1

Substance	Appearance Before Heating	Appearance After Heating
Sample with glucose	Blue	Orange-red
Sample without glucose	Blue	Blue

Part B. Test for Chloride

1. Place two test tubes in a test-tube rack. With a glass-marking pencil, label one test tube "C" for chloride. Allow the other test tube to remain unlabeled as it will serve as the control.

2. Add 5 mL of the simulated urine sample with chloride to the test tube labeled "C." Add 5 mL of the urine sample without chloride to the unlabeled test tube. Note the appearance of the substance in each test tube. Record this information in Data Table 2.

3. Carefully add 3 drops of silver nitrate solution to each test tube.
CAUTION: *Use extreme care when working with silver nitrate solution to avoid staining of the skin and clothing.* Observe the top surface of the liquid in each test tube. Record its appearance in Data Table 2.

Data Table 2

Substance	Appearance Before Adding Silver Nitrate	Appearance After Adding Silver Nitrate
Sample with chloride	Clear yellow	White cloud forms
Sample without chloride	Clear yellow	Clear yellow

Part C. Test for Albumin

1. Place two test tubes in a test-tube rack. With a glass-marking pencil, label one test tube "A" for albumin. Allow the other test tube to remain unlabeled as it will serve as the control.

2. Half fill the test tube labeled "A" with the simulated urine sample with albumin. Half fill the unlabeled test tube with the simulated urine sample without albumin.

3. Using a test-tube holder, pass the top surface of each test tube over the flame of a Bunsen burner for 15 to 20 seconds, as shown in Figure 1.
CAUTION: *Secure all loose clothing and hair when using a Bunsen burner. When heating a test tube, always point it away from yourself and other students. Keep your hand to the side of the flame, never above it.* After heating each test tube, place it in a test-tube rack. Note the appearance of each substance. Record your observations in Data Table 3 on p. 270.

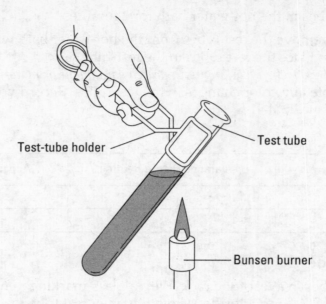

Test-tube holder

Test tube

Bunsen burner

Figure 1

4. Add 5 drops of acetic acid to each test tube. **CAUTION:** *Be careful when using an acid.* Note the appearance of each substance. Record your observations in Data Table 3.

Data Table 3

Substance	Appearance After Heating	Appearance After Adding Acetic Acid
Sample with albumin	White haze forms at top	White haze remains
Sample without albumin	Clear yellow	Clear yellow

Part D. Test for Phosphate

1. Place two test tubes in a test-tube rack. With a glass-marking pencil, label one test tube "P" for phosphate. Allow the other test tube to remain unlabeled as it will serve as the control.

2. Half fill the test tube labeled "P" with the simulated urine sample with phosphate. Half fill the unlabeled test tube with the simulated urine sample without phosphate.

3. Using a test-tube holder, pass the top surface of each test tube over the flame of a Bunsen burner for 15 to 20 seconds. **CAUTION:** *Secure all loose clothing and hair when using a Bunsen burner. When heating a test tube, always point it away from yourself and other students.* After heating each test tube, place it in a test-tube rack. Note the appearance of each substance. Record this information in Data Table 4.

4. Add 5 drops of acetic acid to each test tube. Record your observations in Data Table 4. **CAUTION:** *Be careful when using an acid.*

Data Table 4

Substance	Appearance After Heating	Appearance After Adding Acetic Acid
Sample with phosphate	White haze forms at top	White haze disappears
Sample without phosphate	Clear yellow	Clear yellow

Part E. Testing an Unknown Simulated Urine Sample

1. Obtain a sample of simulated urine marked "unknown." Record the identification number of the sample in Data Table 5.

2. Using four clean test tubes, perform the glucose, chloride, albumin, and phosphate tests on the unknown sample. Follow the Procedures in Parts A through D of this investigation.

3. Record your results in Data Table 5. Wash your hands with soap and water.

Data Table 5

Test	Composition of Unknown Simulated Urine Sample # _____
	Present or Absent?
Glucose	Answers will depend on unknown sample used
Chloride	
Albumin	
Phosphate	

Analysis and Conclusions

1. **Inferring** Should you always assume that a color change in the urine is a sign of an abnormal condition?

   No, sometimes foods such as beets contain a natural dye that changes the color of the urine to red or purple.

2. **Analyzing Data** Which of the four chemicals tested were found in the unknown sample you analyzed?

   The results will depend on the sample made by the instructor, so the answers will vary.

3. **Comparing and Contrasting** Which tests should be positive for a normal healthy person?

   Positive tests for chloride and phosphate are normal.

4. **Predicting** Would it be possible to estimate the amount of a chemical present in a sample based on the strength of the color change?

   Yes, a stronger color change usually indicates that more of the chemical is present.

Going Further

Athletes participating in collegiate competitions are routinely tested for drugs by urinalysis. Use the National Collegiate Athletic Association guidelines to determine which drugs they test for and investigate the tests and their reliability.

Chapter 39   Endocrine and Reproductive Systems

Comparing Ovaries and Testes

You may want to refer students to Section 39–3 in the textbook for a review of the male and female reproductive systems before performing this investigation.

Time required: 40 minutes

Introduction

Reproduction is the process by which offspring are produced. The most important function of reproduction is to continue the species. Reproduction may also serve to increase the number of individuals in a species.

Humans reproduce sexually. Gametes are produced in specialized sex organs, or gonads. The gonad of the human male is the testis (plural, testes). The two functions of this organ are the production of sperm cells, which are the male gametes, and the production of the male hormone testosterone. The gonad of the human female is the ovary. The two ovaries of the human female produce egg cells, which are the female gametes, and also secrete female sex hormones.

In this investigation, you will examine prepared slides of mammalian ovaries and testes. You will also investigate the process of egg and sperm production.

Problem

What structures are found in a mammalian ovary and testis? How are eggs and sperm produced?

Pre-Lab Discussion

Read the entire investigation. Then, work with a partner to answer the following questions.

1. In Part A, why should the cross section of the ovary be taken from a nonpregnant cat?

   A cross section of the ovary of a pregnant cat would not show a follicle or a discharged egg cell, and the

   corpus albicans would not be present.

2. Where would you look to find the female hormone estrogen?

   The estrogen would be found within a follicle.

3. What care should be taken when switching the microscope from the low power objective to the high power objective?

   You should watch from the side to see that the objective does not hit or damage the slide.

4. You may observe something stained red on the slide in Part B. What does the red stain most likely indicate?

   The red stain most likely identifies the cytoplasm of the cell.

5. What cells provide nutrients for developing sperm cells?
Sertoli cells provide nutrients.

Materials

compound light microscope

prepared slides of: Prepared slides are available from biological supply houses.

   cat ovary, transverse cross section

   rat testis, longitudinal cross section

   rat epididymis, transverse cross section

Safety 🔲🔲

Be careful to avoid breakage when working with glass. Always handle the microscope with extreme care. You are responsible for its proper care and use. If you are using a microscope with a lamp, follow all safety rules related to electrical equipment. Use caution when handling microscope slides, as they can break easily and cut you. Note the safety alert symbol in the Procedure and review the meaning of the symbol by referring to Safety Symbols on page 8.

Procedure

Part A. The Mammalian Ovary

 1. Obtain a stained slide of a transverse cross section of a mature ovary of a nonpregnant cat. **CAUTION:** *Be careful to handle the slides only by their sides to prevent smearing the sample.* Using the low-power objective of a microscope, focus on a part of the ovary where you can see both the outer edge and the interior of the ovary. The outermost layer of cells of the ovary consists of the germinal epithelium, a single layer of epithelial cells. Immediately below the germinal epithelium is the connective tissue called the stroma. Within the stroma you will observe numerous round structures of various sizes. These structures are the follicles, where the ovarian eggs develop and mature. In some of the follicles you can observe the developing egg, a large, circular cell with a darkly stained nucleus.

2. Examine different areas of the slide under low power to find follicles containing eggs in various stages of development. Using Figure 1 as a guide, trace the development of one developing egg cell. A developing egg is surrounded by a covering, or corona, of follicle cells. As the follicle matures, a cavity filled with the female hormone estrogen develops. Estrogen is essential to the growth and development of the maturing egg. The mature follicle gradually moves to the surface of the ovary, where it ruptures the surface and releases the egg into the Fallopian tube.

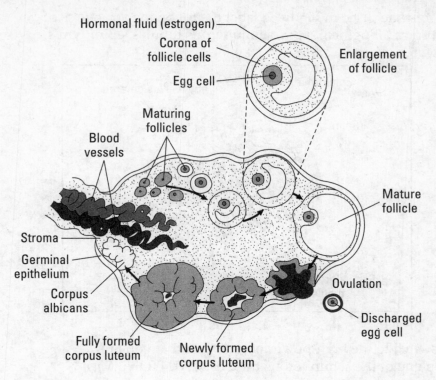

Figure 1

3. After a follicle ruptures and releases an egg from the ovary, the follicle undergoes a series of changes and becomes a structure called the corpus luteum. In this process, the follicle cells enlarge and a yellowish substance called lutein accumulates in their cytoplasm. The lutein cells secrete the hormones estrogen and progesterone, which are responsible for building up the lining of the uterus in preparation for pregnancy. Examine a corpus luteum on your slide. If pregnancy does not occur, the corpus luteum continues to grow for about 10 to 12 days and then shrinks, eventually becoming a small, white ovarian scar called a corpus albicans. Locate a corpus albicans on your slide.

Part B. The Mammalian Testis

1. Obtain a stained slide of the testis of a mature rat for examination under the low-power objective of a microscope. The thick outer covering of the testis is called the tunica albuginea. The testis is separated into several wedge-shaped compartments by partitions called septa (singular, *septum*). Examine the cluster of small circles within each compartment. These are the cut surfaces of the tiny, coiled seminiferous tubules, which are involved in the production of sperm. The seminiferous tubules lead into the epididymis, a long, narrow, flattened structure attached to the posterior surface of the testis. Sperm complete their maturation while passing through the epididymis. The lower portion of the epididymis uncoils and widens into a long duct called the vas deferens.

2. In the appropriate place in Figure 2, label the following structures of the testis: tunica albuginea, septa, seminiferous tubules, epididymis, and vas deferens.

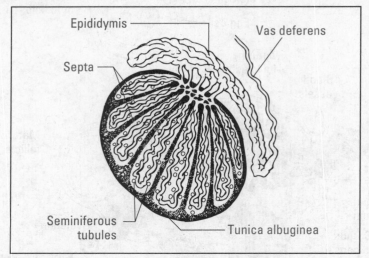

Epididymis

Vas deferens

Septa

Seminiferous tubules

Tunica albuginea

Figure 2   **Rat Testis**

3. Carefully switch to the high-power objective so that you are focusing on one of the seminiferous tubules. **CAUTION:** *When turning to the high-power objective, always look at the objective from the side of the microscope so that the objective does not hit or damage the slide.*

4. Notice that the walls of the seminiferous tubule consist of many layers of cells. The cytoplasm of these cells will most likely be stained red, and the chromosomes in the nuclei will most likely be stained blue. Closely examine these cells in order to trace the various stages of spermatogenesis, or sperm cell production. The cells nearest to the outer surface of the seminiferous tubule are called spermatogonia. These are the sperm-producing cells. The spermatogonia divide by mitosis. Half of the daughter cells remain as spermatogonia, while the other half undergo changes and become cells called primary spermatocytes. The primary spermatocytes make up the layer next to the spermatogonia. Observe the chromosome arrangement in the primary spermatocytes.

5. The diploid primary spermatocyte undergoes the first stage of meiosis, producing two haploid cells called secondary spermatocytes. The secondary spermatocytes are found in a layer next to the primary spermatocytes. The two secondary spermatocytes undergo the second meiotic division, producing four haploid spermatid cells. The spermatid cells make up the innermost layer of the seminiferous tubule. A spermatid cell develops into a sperm with an oval head and a long, whiplike tail.

6. Observe how the sperm cells are clustered around elongated cells that are evenly spaced around the circumference of the seminiferous tubule. These cells, called Sertoli cells, probably provide nutrients for the developing sperm cells. Observe how the sperm cells have their tails facing out into the central opening, or lumen, of the seminiferous tubule.

7. In the appropriate place in Figure 3, label the following parts of the seminiferous tubule: spermatogonia, primary spermatocytes, secondary spermatocytes, spermatids, sperm cells, Sertoli cells, and lumen.

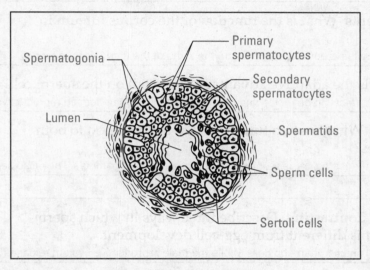

Figure 3   Rat Seminiferous Tubule

8. Obtain a prepared slide of a cross section of the epididymis of a mature rat. Observe the epididymis under low and high power. Note the sperm cells clustered within the lumen of the epididymis. Observe that the cells lining the lumen are lined with cilia. These cilia help propel the sperm cells through the epididymis. Observe the smooth muscle cells in the walls of the epididymis. As these muscles contract, the sperm cells are pushed through the epididymis, toward the vas deferens.

9. In the appropriate place in Figure 4, label the following parts of the epididymis: lumen, sperm cells, cilia, and smooth muscle cells.

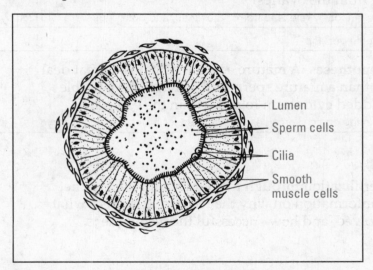

Figure 4   Rat Epididymis

Analysis and Conclusions

1. **Comparing and Contrasting** In what way are mature sperm and egg cells different from all other types of body cells?

   Body cells are diploid, sperm and egg cells are haploid.

2. **Applying Concepts** What is the function of the corpus luteum in the ovary?

   Hormones secreted by the corpus luteum prepare the lining of the uterus for pregnancy.

3. **Inferring** What is the adaptive advantage of the tail on the sperm cell?

   The tail allows the sperm cell to be motile and swim upward through the female reproductive system.

4. **Analyzing Data** What are two functions that are common to both ovaries and testes?

   Both the ovaries and the testes are responsible for the production of gametes. They also secrete

   important hormones.

5. **Comparing and Contrasting** Describe three ways in which sperm-cell development is different from egg-cell development.

   Sperm cells are much smaller than egg cells. While the male reproductive system releases countless sperm

   at one time, the female reproductive system releases only one egg. Egg production ceases at a certain point

   in a female's life, whereas males produce sperm throughout their lifetimes.

6. **Drawing Conclusions** The middle section of a sperm cell is packed with mitochondria. Use your knowledge of cell organelle function to determine the function the mitochondria serve in the sperm cell.

   Mitochondria are the "powerhouses" of the cell. They supply most of the energy for the cell. Sperm need large

   amounts of energy to swim to the egg. The presence of mitochondria in the middle section of the sperm provides

   the energy needed by the tail as the sperm swims.

7. **Predicting** What might happen if more than one egg were released at the same time from the ovaries?

   If two eggs were simultaneously released from the ovaries, and both eggs were fertilized by different sperm

   cells, two embryos would develop.

8. **Formulating Hypotheses** A mature egg cell contains a great deal more cytoplasm than a mature sperm cell. What is the possible function of the added cytoplasm found within the egg cell?

   The extra cytoplasm in the egg cell provides nourishment for the developing embryo.

Going Further

Research in vitro fertilization through the library and the Internet. Be sure to include information on why the technique is used, what procedures are involved, and how successful the technique is.

Detecting Viruses

You may want to refer students to Sections 40–1 and 19–3 in the textbook for a discussion of viruses.
Time required: Part A—50 minutes

Part B—50 minutes plus observation period after 24 and 48 hours

Part C—Time required will depend on student designs

Introduction

Some diseases that affect people are caused by viruses. Viruses also cause plant diseases and infect bacteria.

Lysis is an important tool used by virologists to detect the presence of viruses in a cell population. If a culture of bacteria is inoculated with bacteriophages, or viruses that infect bacteria, the lysis of the bacterial cells make the culture appear clear. This clear area is called a plaque. The clearer a phage-infected culture of bacteria is, the greater the number of phages present in the culture.

The culturing of bacteria and bacteriophages requires the use of aseptic, or sterile, techniques. Aseptic techniques prevent contamination of existing cultures by other microorganisms. The heat produced by autoclaving or passing certain materials through the flame of a Bunsen burner is sufficient to destroy microorganisms and keep the environment sterile.

In this investigation, you will inoculate a bacterial culture with a bacteriophage and observe the results. You will also design and carry out an experiment to test for the presence of the same bacteriophage in an unknown suspension.

Problem

How is the presence of bacteriophages in a culture of bacteria determined?

Pre-Lab Discussion

Read the entire investigation. Then, work with a partner to answer the following questions.

1. **Formulating Hypotheses** State a hypothesis that explains the relationship between the presence of bacteriophage and the condition of a bacterial culture.

If bacteriophage is present, it will impair the growth of the bacterial culture. Cloudy areas of bacterial growth

may become clear in appearance as bacterial lysis occurs.

2. **Controlling Variables** In the procedure performed in Parts A and B, what is the manipulated variable? What is the responding variable?

The manipulated variable is the concentration of bacteriophage. The responding variable is the reduction of

growth of a bacterial culture, as evidenced by the presence of plaques (or the relative lack of the turbidity that

indicates bacterial growth in the test tubes).

3. What will happen to the bacteriophage culture as it is transferred from one test tube to the next in Part A, step 12?

The bacteriophage culture will become more diluted upon each transfer.

4. Predicting What differences do you expect to see among the five bacteriophage-inoculated lines on the petri dish? Explain the reasons for these differences.

Lines 1 through 4 probably will show evidence of bacteriophage in the form of reduced bacterial growth

and plaques. Line 1 should show the greatest effect, because it contains the largest concentration of

phage. Line 4 should show the least effect, because it contains the lowest concentration of phage.

5. Controlling Variables What is the control in this experiment? How do you expect the responding variable to behave in the control?

Test tube number 5, which is not inoculated with phage, serves as the control. Students should expect the

inoculation line from test tube 5 to show no evidence of bacterial lysis.

Suggested Materials *(per group)*

Bunsen burner

culture of T-4 bacteriophage   Available from a biological supply house.

inoculating loop

12 sterile test tubes containing nutrient broth   Dissolve 3 g beef extract and 5 g peptone in 1 L distilled water. Pour 1 mL broth into each test tube, and sterilize test tubes in an autoclave or pressure cooker set at 15 pounds pressure for 15 minutes.

glass-marking pencil

test-tube rack

nutrient agar plate [1]

culture of *Escherichia coli* B [2]

sterile cotton swab

incubator

test tube containing unknown suspension [3]

Request additional materials from your teacher if you think you will need them to carry out your experiment.

[1] Add 3 g beef extract, 5 g peptone, and 15 g agar to 1 L distilled water. Heat the mixture until the agar dissolves. Pour the agar into petri dishes, and sterilize them in an autoclave or pressure cooker set at 15 pounds pressure for 15 minutes.

[2] Available from a biological supply house.

[3] You may wish to prepare more than one unknown type. Unknown suspensions might include one with no phage and others at the four dilution levels produced by Part A of the student's investigation.

Safety

If your immune system has been weakened, you should not be present when this experiment is being performed. Put on safety goggles, a laboratory apron, and plastic gloves. Be careful to avoid breakage when working with glassware. Always use special caution when working with bacterial cultures. Follow your teacher's directions and all appropriate safety procedures when handling and disposing of live microorganisms. Tie back loose hair and clothing when working with flames. Do not reach over an open flame. Wash your hands with soap and warm water after carrying out this investigation. Note all safety alert symbols next to the steps in Design Your Experiment and review the meanings of each symbol by referring to Safety Symbols on page 8.

Students who are immunosuppressed should not be required to perform this activity.

Design Your Experiment

If you wish students to perform the first investigation in Going Further, have students save test tubes 4 and 5. A microbiological filter will also be needed to perform the investigation.

Part A. Preparing a Bacteriophage Culture

1. Put on your lab apron and safety goggles. Obtain a culture of T-4 bacteriophage from your teacher. **CAUTION:** *Be very careful when working with microorganisms.*

2. Sterilize the inoculating loop by passing it through a Bunsen burner flame as shown in part A of Figure 1. Allow the loop to remain in the flame until the entire length of the wire has turned red. **CAUTION:** *When using a Bunsen burner, wear safety goggles and be sure that hair and loose clothing do not come into contact with the flame. Do not touch the end of the inoculating loop that is placed in the flame or allow it to come into contact with any flammable objects.*

3. While holding the sterile inoculating loop in one hand, pick up in the other hand the test tube containing the T-4 bacteriophage culture and one sterile test tube containing the nutrient broth.

4. Remove the cotton plugs from each test tube by grasping the plugs between the fingers of the hand holding the loop. This technique is shown in part B of Figure 1.

5. Sterilize the mouths of the test tubes by quickly passing them through the flame two or three times as shown in part C of Figure 1.

6. Carefully insert the inoculating loop into the test tube containing the T-4 bacteriophage culture and remove one loopful of culture. **CAUTION:** *Allow the inoculating loop to cool before inserting it into the test tube.*

7. Transfer this loopful of T-4 bacteriophage culture to the test tube containing the nutrient broth.

8. Before replacing the cotton plugs on the two test tubes, sterilize the mouths of the test tubes as you did in step 5. Also, resterilize the inoculating loop. Be sure to replace each plug in the correct test tube.

9. Mix the contents of the test tube containing the nutrient broth and bacteriophage culture by rotating the tube rapidly between your hands. With the glass-marking pencil, label this tube "Stock Phage Culture."

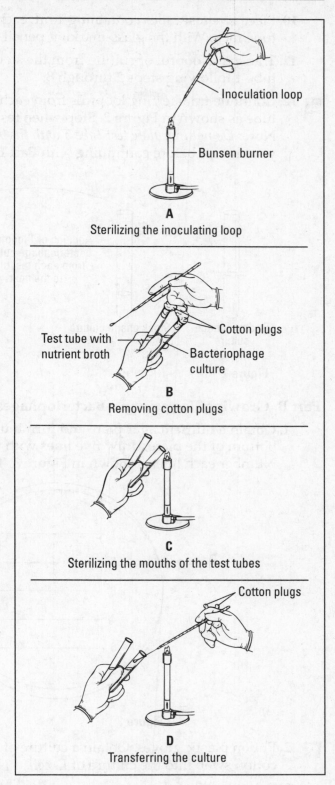

A
Sterilizing the inoculating loop

Inoculation loop

Bunsen burner

B
Removing cotton plugs

Test tube with nutrient broth

Cotton plugs

Bacteriophage culture

C
Sterilizing the mouths of the test tubes

D
Transferring the culture

Cotton plugs

Figure 1

10. Place five test tubes containing 1 mL each of nutrient broth in a test-tube rack. With the glass-marking pencil, label them 1 through 5.

11. Transfer a loopful of culture from the stock phage culture to test tube 1 following steps 2 through 8.

12. Continue transferring loopfuls from each test tube to the next test tube as shown in Figure 2. Stop when test tube 4 is inoculated. **Note:** *Do not inoculate test tube 5 with the bacteriophage culture.* Wash your hands before continuing with Part B.

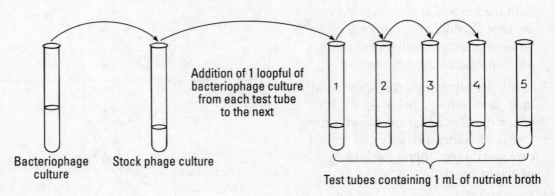

Bacteriophage culture

Stock phage culture

Addition of 1 loopful of bacteriophage culture from each test tube to the next

Test tubes containing 1 mL of nutrient broth

Figure 2

Part B. Growing Bacteria and Bacteriophages on Agar

You may wish to have some or all of the groups use one nutrient agar plate for each of the five streaks.

1. Obtain a nutrient agar plate and turn it upside down. Across the bottom of the plate, draw five lines with the glass-marking pencil. Number each line as shown in Figure 3. Turn the petri dish upright.

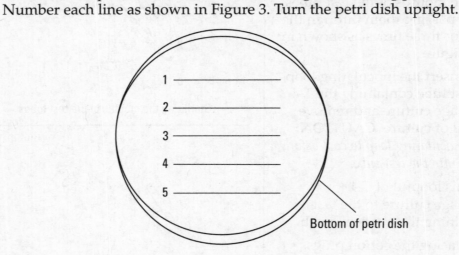

Bottom of petri dish

Figure 3

2. Put on plastic gloves. Obtain a culture of *E. coli*. Dip the sterile cotton swab into the culture of *E. coli*.

3. Raise the lid of the petri dish slightly and swab the entire surface of the agar plate with the cotton swab. Try to cover the surface of the agar plate at uniformly as possible.

4. Using the sterile techniques described in steps 2 through 8 of Part A, remove a loopful of material from test tube 1 and streak this on the surface of the nutrient agar plate along line 1. Replace the cotton plug.

5. Follow the same procedure for each of the remaining four test tubes, including test tube 5. Be sure to streak one loopful along the line that corresponds to the test tube number. **Note:** *Be sure to sterilize the loop after each streaking.*

6. After completing the streaking of the bacteriophage dilutions onto the nutrient agar plate, inoculate test tubes 1 through 5 with a loopful of *E. coli* B culture. Be sure to follow the sterilization procedures for each inoculation. Mix the contents of each tube well by rapid rotation.

7. Incubate the plate and broth cultures in the incubator at 35° to 37°C.

8. Examine the plate and test tubes after 24 and 48 hours. In Figure 4, sketch what you observe on the agar plate after 24 and 48 hours.

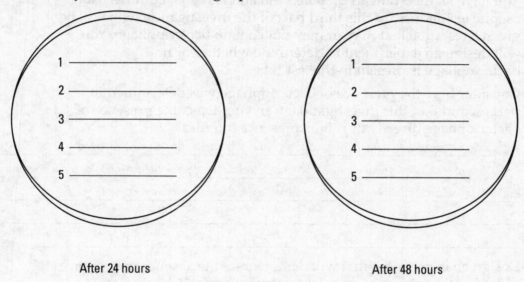

After 24 hours   After 48 hours

Growth of Bacteria on Agar Plate

Figure 4

9. In the Data Table, record the results of your observations after 48 hours. In the first column, use a range of + to indicate minimum plaque formation to + + + + to indicate maximum plaque formation on the agar plate. In the second column, use a range of + for slightly cloudy to + + + + for maximum cloudiness in the test tubes.

10. Return the agar plate and test tubes to your teacher for proper disposal. **CAUTION:** *Wash your hands thoroughly with soap and water and wipe the tabletop where you worked with 70% alcohol before leaving the laboratory.*

Data Table

Test Tube	Plaque formation (clearing on streaks)	Growth of E. coli (cloudiness in test tubes)
1		
2		
3	Answers will depend on student observations.	
4		
5		

Part C. Your Own Experiment

1. You have learned how to prepare viral and bacterial cultures using aseptic techniques. In this third part of the investigation, you will be given a test tube that may or may not contain bacteriophage. You will design an experiment to determine whether or not bacteriophage is present in the test tube.

2. Consider how the presence of bacteriophage was determined in parts A and B of this investigation. Can you detect the presence of bacteriophage directly or is it its presence inferred?

   If bacteriophage was present in the bacterial cultures, bacterial growth was reduced and plaques, or clear

   areas where lysis of bacterial cells has occurred. We cannot detect the presence of bacteriophage directly;

   rather, it is inferred from the effects we observe in the bacterial cultures.

3. Design an experiment that will demonstrate the absence or presence of T-4 bacteriophage in an unknown suspension. Begin by formulating a hypothesis. Describe the results you expect to see if your hypothesis is supported. Describe the experimental results you expect to see if your hypothesis is *not* supported.

   Hypothesis

   Answers will depend on student hypotheses. Acceptable examples include "A bacteriophage will

   destroy cultured bacteria that are subject to being infected by it." Students may have difficulty formulating

   their hypotheses. Encourage them to recall the hypothesis associated with Parts A and B. Remind them

   that they saw that the absence or presence of bacteriophage was demonstrated by effects on a bacterial

   culture.

   Prediction

   Answers will depend on student hypotheses. An example is "If the unknown suspension contains

   bacteriophage specific for *E. coli*, a bacterial culture inoculated by the suspension will show plaques."

⚠ **4.** In the lines below, write down your experimental plan for submission to your teacher. Note your manipulated, responding, and control variables. List the materials you will use and any safety precautions you should follow. Write the procedure you will use as numbered steps. Submit your experimental plan to your teacher for approval. When your teacher approves your plan, carry out your experiment. Record your data in an appropriate format on a separate sheet of paper.

Students' experimental plans may differ. However, they should demonstrate the presence or absence of bacteriophage in the unknown suspension by exposing a bacterial culture to the suspension and observing the results. For example, a petri dish broadly inoculated with *E. coli* could then be inoculated with a streak of the unknown and a streak of sterile broth, and the effect on the bacterial culture of the two variables compared. Accept any logical research design, but encourage students to perform the simplest experiment possible that achieves the desired end.

Manipulated variable

Answers will depend on student hypotheses. An example is the dilution of the unknown suspension.

Responding variable

Answers will depend on student hypotheses. An example is the presence of plaques in the culture inoculated with the unknown suspension.

Controlled variables

Answers will depend upon student hypothesis. Examples include the volume of inoculum applied and the time and temperature of incubation.

Materials

Answers will depend on students proposed procedures.

Safety Precautions

Student-cited safety precautions should be much the same as for Parts A and B of the investigation.

For example: 🧫🧴🧤🥽🔬🔥🗑️♨️⚠

Procedure

Answers will depend on student hypotheses. For example, students could broadly inoculate a nutrient agar plate with *E. coli* and then inoculate a control streak of sterile broth and an experimental streak of the unknown solution.

Analysis and Conclusions

1. **Designing Experiments** What were the manipulated and responding variables in your experiment, and how did you evaluate (or quantify) them?

   An example of a manipulated variable is the presence of the unknown suspension. An example of a responding

   variable is the presence of plaques in the area inoculated with the unknown suspension. Some students may

   have quantified the relative concentration of the phage in the unknown suspension using the $+++$ system

   introduced in Part B of the investigation.

2. **Controlling Variables** What was a controlled variable in your experiment?

   An example of a controlled variable is the inoculation of the agar plates with the bacterial culture.

3. **Observing** Summarize the results of your experiment.

   Answers will depend on student experiments. For example, students given a sterile unknown suspension

   should see no evidence of bacterial lysis.

4. **Analyzing Data** Do your results support your hypothesis or contradict it?

   Answers will depend on the results of student experiments. For example, if students hypothesized correctly

   that the unknown contained phage, students should see evidence of bacterial death, which will support their

   hypothesis.

5. **Drawing Conclusions** How strongly do your results support your conclusion? Explain your answer.

   Answers will depend upon student predictions and results. Unknown suspensions with high concentrations of

   phage likely will produce very obvious plaques.

Going Further

To determine whether viruses are filterable, obtain a microbiological filter from your teacher and filter the contents of test tube 4. Using the inoculating loop and aseptic techniques, inoculate test tube 5 with the filtered material and incubate the test tube at 35° to 37°C for 24 hours. What do you observe in test tube 5? What conclusions can you make?

Students should observe evidence of bacterial lysis in test tube 5. Students should conclude that the virus passed through the pores of a microbiological filter—one that traps even small prokaryotic cells.